POST-ACCIDENT PROCEDURES
FOR CHEMICALS AND PROPELLANTS

POST-ACCIDENT PROCEDURES FOR CHEMICALS AND PROPELLANTS

by

Deborah K. Shaver and Robert L. Berkowitz

Systems Technology Laboratory, Inc.
Arlington, Virginia

np NOYES PUBLICATIONS
Park Ridge, New Jersey, USA

7227 - 7580

CHEMISTRY

Copyright © 1984 Noyes Publications
Library of Congress Catalog Card Number: 84-4123
ISBN: 0-8155-0986-3
ISSN: 0090-516X
Pollution Technology Review No. 109
Printed in the United States

Published in the United States of America by
Noyes Publications.
Mill Road, Park Ridge, New Jersey 07656

10 9 8 7 6 5 4 3 2 1

Library of Congress Cataloging in Publication Data

Shaver, Deborah K.
    Post-accident procedures for chemicals and propellants.

    (Pollution technology review, ISSN 0090-516X ; no. 109)
    Bibliography: p.
    Includes index.
    1. Hazardous substances--Transportation--Accidents.
I. Berkowitz, Robert L. II. Title. III. Series.
T55.3.H3S48 1984 363.1'79 84-4123
ISBN 0-8155-0986-3

FOREWORD

This book presents guidelines for responding to hazardous materials transportation accidents. Nationwide concern about the control and management of hazardous materials makes this study both timely and relevant. This state of the art assessment was prepared to develop technology which will minimize the hazards and environmental damage from transportation accidents or other spills of 28 large volume, widely-used industrial chemicals and propellants. The book is unique in that all response activities requiring attention from decision makers have been combined into a single coherent, comprehensive user's manual.

Specific data are presented on these hazardous materials, and guidelines are given for post-accident handling procedures, such as reporting an accident; initiating the response communications network; first on-scene responders; assessing the accident scene; determining the magnitude of the accident and estimating the danger areas from vapor dispersion; containment; vapor suppression; handling leaks; selection of personnel, equipment and materials; firefighting; evacuation; cargo transfer, wreckage removal and cleanup/disposal activities. Pertinent legislation and regulations are also reviewed.

The book is divided into five sections, each corresponding to a separate area of accident management—from precautionary guidelines to reporting accidents, to assessing the magnitude of the problem, to management and containment. Appendices provide information on chemical and physical properties, on-line information retrieval systems, information sources, locations of regional U.S. Coast Guard and EPA offices and hazardous waste disposal sites.

The information in the book is from *Guidelines Manual—Post Accident Procedures for Chemicals and Propellants,* prepared by Deborah K. Shaver and Robert L. Berkowitz of Systems Technology Laboratory, Inc. for the U.S. Air Force Rocket Propulsion Laboratory and the U.S. Department of Transportation Federal Railroad Administration, January 1983.

The table of contents is organized in such a way as to serve as a subject index and provides easy access to the information contained in the book. A glossary and a list of acronyms are also included.

Advanced composition and production methods developed by Noyes Publications are employed to bring this durably bound book to you in a minimum of time. Special techniques are used to close the gap between "manuscript" and "completed book." In order to keep the price of the book to a reasonable level, it has been partially reproduced by photo-offset directly from the original report and the cost saving passed on to the reader. Due to this method of publishing, certain portions of the book may be less legible than desired.

NOTICE

CONTENTS AND SUBJECT INDEX

EXECUTIVE SUMMARY AND INTRODUCTION

This Final Technical Report was prepared for the United States Air Force and the Federal Railroad Administration for Phase I of the "Post-Accident Procedures for Chemicals and Propellants" program conducted under interagency agreement AR-9157. The overall objective of the project is to perform a state-of-the-art assessment to develop technology which will minimize hazards and environmental damage from transportation accidents or other spills of 28 chemicals and propellants. This research was conducted by Systems Technology Laboratory of Arlington, Virginia under USAF contract F04611-80-C-0046. The project involved six tasks which were performed between August 1980 and August 1982.

This report has been structured into five sections with each section corresponding to a separate area of accident management. Section 1 (General Guidelines) includes information on precautionary guidelines; technical assistance and information; protective clothing, gear and equipment; wreckage removal contractors; and product transfer, cleanup/disposal contractors. Section 2 (Initial Response Guidelines and Hazardous Chemical Data) describes guidelines for reporting an accident; initiating the response communications network; first on-scene responders; and hazardous chemical data. Section 3 (Hazards Assessment Guidelines) contains information for assessing the accident scene, determining the magnitude of the accident and estimating the danger areas from downwind vapor cloud dispersion. Section 4 (Hazards Mitigation Guidelines) identifies guidelines on containment; vapor suppression; handling leaks; selection of personnel, equipment and materials; erecting barriers; firefighting and evacuation. Section 5 (Cargo Transfer, Wreckage Removal, Cleanup and Disposal Guidelines) discusses guidelines concerning cargo transfer, wreckage removal and cleanup/disposal activities.

There are currently several accident response/handling manuals and training courses available, however, not one addresses all phases of accident managment. Manuals such as the USCG Chemical Hazards Response Information Systems, DOT Emergency Response Guidebook, EPA Manual for the Control of Hazardous Materials Spills and AAR Emergency Handling of Hazardous Materials in Surface Transportation do provide response guidelines for several hazardous materials, but fail to supply adequate information to integrate all the accident response and handling phases into a coherent, comprehensive accident management guide. This guidelines manual, however, attempts to integrate all response activities requiring attention by decision-makers into one user's manual. The manual includes specific data on 28 hazardous materials and guidelines to post-accident handling procedures such as hazards mitigation, cargo transfer, wreckage removal and cleanup/disposal; however, this document covers only those 28 specific hazardous materials.

A brief review of appropriate legislation covering both the transportation of hazardous materials and environmental protection considerations shows a recognition of the overlap and convergence of transportation and environmental protection concerns beginning with the Toxic Substances Control Act of 1976, followed by the Resource Conservation and Recovery Act of 1976, the Clean Water Act of 1977 and finally the Superfund Act (CERCLA) of 1980. These laws recognize the necessity of integrating environmental cleanup/disposal into the emergency response efforts undertaken when transportation emergencies involving hazardous materials occur.

These public laws provide specific spill notification requirements, define governmental response responsibilities, set up civil and criminal penalties for violations, and require adequate cleanup to protect the public and the environment. The following paragraphs describe the nature of these legislative acts.

Resource Conservation and Recovery Act (RCRA) - Enactment of the Resource Conservation and Recovery Act established for the first time control for the generation, transportation, and disposal of hazardous wastes. While RCRA provided the tools to track and regulate the handling of such substances, it did not deal with existing hazardous sites which had become troublesome as a result of past improper disposal practices. These sites, as well as accidents in the handling or transportation of hazardous substances, can present emergency situations requiring an immediate cleanup or removal.

Clean Water Act (CWA) - Federal authority found in Section 311 of the Clean Water Act has existed for many years to respond to releases of oil and hazardous substances into the nation's navigable waters. This authority is assigned to the Environmental Protection Agency and the United States Coast Guard. The Clean Water Act also established a fund to finance these responses (Section 311(k) of P.L. 95-12); however, it provided only limited

1

authority and limited funds to tackle the variety of problems caused by release of hazardous substances into land, ground water and air.

To provide a more effective and comprehensive response to the foregoing problems, Congress in 1980 enacted the Comprehensive Environmental Response Compensation and Liability Act. Popularly referred to as the "Superfund," CERCLA and Section 311 of the Clean Water Act permit the Federal government to work with state and local government to provide an immediate and comprehensive response to accidental releases of hazardous substances.

Comprehensive Environmental Response Compensation and Liability Act (CERCLA) - Superfund authorizes the Federal Government to respond directly to releases (or threatened releases) of hazardous substances, pollutants or contaminants that may endanger public health or welfare. Superfund cleanups, financed by a trust fund which will grow to $1.6 billion by 1985, are 86 percent financed by taxes on the manufacture or import of certain chemicals and petroleum, the remainder coming from general revenues. The Hazardous Substances Response Fund is established by Section 221 of P.L. 96-510 (CERCLA). This fund is reimbursable; the government generally can take legal action to recover its cleanup costs from those subsequently identified as responsible for the release. Anyone liable for a release who fails to take ordered actions is (under specified conditions) liable for punitive damages equal to three times the government's response costs. Liability under Superfund is that which is defined in Section 311 of the Federal Water Pollution Control Act (or Clean Water Act).

1. GENERAL GUIDELINES

When a hazardous materials (HM) transportation accident occurs, several groups will be required to respond on-scene. These include, at a minimum, fire, police and medical services. However, prior to the occurrence of a hazardous materials transportation accident in a community, local decision-makers should familiarize themselves with the following information so they will be capable of handling the emergency in a timely manner assuring community environmental and personal safety:

● Pre-accident precautions such as training, contingency pre-planning, communications and decision-making responsibility, designation and resource allocation;

● Availability of and access to technical assistance;

● Protective clothing, gear, breathing apparatus, detectors and monitoring equipment availability and uses;

● Specialized treatment chemicals, sorbents, equipment resources availability and uses (e.g., analytical and heavy equipment);

● Wreckage removal contractors; and

● Product transfer, cleanup/disposal contractors and special industry teams.

This volume discusses these factors and provides general guidelines for their implementation and use.

1.1. TRAINING

There are a number of training courses available which are taught by government, industry, educational institutes and consulting organizations aimed specifically at responders to hazardous materials incidents. These courses vary from formal academic class sessions to slide-tape presentations, with an instructor's guide and student workbook, to the home-study (correspondence) course. The slide-tape courses run from five to twenty hours of class time. They may or may not be modular (i.e., deal with topical areas such as hazardous materials identification, decision-making and seeking technical assistance).

Hazardous materials training courses stress planning but also present some basic information concerning the nature of hazardous materials; how to identify spilled/ leaking material;

where to find technical help; danger assessment; decision-making; and to a certain extent some general procedures for on-scene actions such as controlling access to the area, evacuation, surveillance of vapor clouds, firefighting, rescue and communications. In some instances, there is hands-on training such as use of polyurethane foam for sealing holes in drums or diking liquid pools, applying metal patches to tank car holes by means of bolts or stopping leaks with wooden plugs. These are useful techniques, but have limited application in specific situations. Heavy reliance must still be placed on the specialists from the various disciplines involved. These specialists operate and make decisions based predominately on their own experience and knowledge and, with few exceptions, perform tasks without the benefit of written procedures, particularly with respect to cargo transfer, wreckage removal, and cleanup/disposal. Although these courses give some attention to restoring the scene to normal, there is a lack of procedural training in these four activities.

There are many training aids available in addition to the courses themselves. Examples are nomographs, slide rules, pocket manuals, checklists, brochures, guides, films, video tapes, slide-tape presentations, reference books, data bases, resource lists and charts (see Reference 1 and Appendix D). The U.S. Department of Transportation Materials Transportation Bureau provides, free-of-charge, quantities of a number of hazardous materials training aids to emergency service organizations. Others may be purchased from the Government or private companies. Rail carriers, in conjunction with the Chemical Manufacturers Association, are putting on hazardous materials transportation emergency training courses in communities where chemical shippers are located or through which rail lines run.

The U.S. Department of Transportation, Research and Special Programs Administration, Materials Transportation Bureau has compiled a list of 342 organizations offering training courses on hazardous materials transportation. This list can be obtained by contacting the Material Transportation Bureau's Information Services Division at (202) 426-2301.

Regardless of the type of activity -- immediate response, hazards mitigation, cargo transfer, wreckage removal, and cleanup/disposal or the specialist discipline involved -- training must assure that procedures are understood

3

and utilized to accomplish the following four items:

1. Provide communications training

2. Evaluate/assess the situation, hazards and actions (Refer to Appendix K)

3. Make decisions

4. Take appropriate actions

These are discussed in the following paragraphs.

1.1.1 Communications Training

An incident must be recognized and promptly reported to the proper authority. It is essential that specific information about the accident be provided in this report so that the response network may be activated and those involved can have a reasonable idea of the nature of the accident and hazardous materials involved. Training in how, when, what and to whom to report a hazardous materials accident is the first criterion. It involves the ordinary citizen, who by chance may be present at an accident scene, as well as those who might become involved as professionals. Communications within a particular response discipline, between groups and with the on-scene coordinator (OSC) are complex but vital. Therefore, training is required in the proper use of communications equipment. Also, the assignment of proper frequencies and responsibility for coordination of communications must be clearly identified in the emergency action plan. The persons responsible for coordinating communications need training:

- To understand the interface between different communication modes, frequencies and equipment;

- To understand, interpret and relay facts and requests being made by or sent to the numerous groups and individual specialists involved in the emergency;

- To recognize and expedite priority communications;

- To deal effectively with the news media, by providing appropriate factual information and by utilizing the news media as a means of mitigating hazards to the public such as preventing panic and providing proper instructions or warnings; and

- To utilize communications to coordinate effectively the many activities taking place on-scene and as backup, so that such activities do not interfere with or jeopardize safety of each group and that resources are used most effectively.

The various response groups and individual specialists need communications training in order to learn proper procedures for maintaining constant contact within their particular groups so that everyone is always accounted for, prompt escape action may be taken if the need arises, and the OSC can be provided with the latest facts on conditions, progress, problems and needs.

The public needs training in such areas as simple self-protection actions (i.e., stuffing towels in cracks of windows or doors) in the event of a hazardous materials spill; getting upwind and keeping away from the scene; obeying evacuation orders; and, as previously mentioned, reporting an incident.

The news media can be a real help or can compound the problem. Making the news media aware of and, where possible, a participant in hazardous materials spill response training, can make it a strong positive force in a real emergency. Training courses need to contain a portion showing how the news media can assist in the event of an accident. News media representatives should be included in the preparation of the community's HM emergency response plan and in available training courses.

All persons who will be concerned with a spill must have further training in evaluation/assessment methods, decision-making, the procedures required in their specific activities and awareness of how their actions impact others.

1.1.2 Training for Decision-Makers

It is imperative that training be designed to meet the needs of all decision-makers. Depending upon the individual responsibilities and the particular types of activities involved, training can range from checkoff lists to computer-simulated decision-making methods. Essential to all decision-making is consideration of the situation or problem, the alternative courses of action, how the action will be accomplished, when and by whom, and what will be the expected impact or results of each. Evaluation and assessment of the situation are the key factors upon which sound decisions are based. Therefore, a detailed discussion of training requirements for decision-makers in evaluation and assessment is presented.

A chemical, propellant or other hazardous materials transportation accident requires initial and continued assessment of the situation and evaluation of the requirements and effectiveness of corrective actions. Essentially, these involve obtaining facts and analyzing them. Training is vital to assure that those involved with the emergency know what information is necessary, how it may be obtained and how to analyze it for determining the existing hazards, potential dangers, what damage has been sustained, the magnitude of the spill, who and what are exposed, what resources exist and how they can be used most effectively, what additional resources are required, and the effectiveness of corrective actions. Such training should involve how to:

- Identify at a distance any HM involved or that have been released;

- Determine the integrity of the HM containers;

- Establish the danger perimeter;

- Predict the downwind toxic or flammable vapor concentration versus distance as well as cloud size and travel rate;

- Use resources most effectively;

- Determine the applicability and effectiveness of corrective actions;

- Use remote sensing/detection/analytical equipment;

- Interpret data;

- Spot changing conditions which pose additional dangers;

- Assess risks;

- Determine hazards; and

- Monitor the scene for toxic or flammable vapor levels and for evidence of personnel exposure.

Such training includes teaching formalized methodologies where appropriate (i.e., risk/ hazards analysis).

1.1.3 Response Activities Training

Training is required to assure effective and safe performance of all the on-scene and support activities in handling hazardous materials transportation spills. This third aspect of training deals with the actual field operations and what type of procedural training is appropriate to each of the

specialized groups and individual experts involved. This training involves ways to select, use and identify the limitations of equipment and materials (i.e., use only transfer equipment which is compatible with the particular hazardous material or use gravity flow, pressure flow or pumping for cargo transfer). Training can help railroad crew members and truck drivers:

- Understand the HM aboard, their hazards and the precautionary procedures they can use in the event of an accident;

- Assist them in seeking response help;

- Convey HM information to response personnel; and

- Otherwise cooperate with authorities on-scene.

There are continued hazards at chemical and propellant spill scenes and the degree or nature may change. Training for on-scene personnel needs to include guidelines for recognizing the actual and potential hazards and the eventuality of a significant change. Their training needs to assure that each person understands not only how to perform his own task efficiently, but to recognize the absolute necessity for safety and accomplishing the task without jeopardizing the safety of others at the scene or creating problems for them, while at the same time protecting the environment and property. Training on the selection and use of proper protective clothing, breathing apparatus, gear, tools, equipment and materials is vital to personnel safety and the successful handling of the spill. Training is needed in the techniques, limitations and safety precautions for cargo transfer, wreckage removal, and cleanup/disposal operations. Hazards mitigation involves any means for reducing or eliminating the hazard or threat, so it involves the full spectrum of on-scene activities. Training needs to concentrate on the use of common sense coupled with good information and sound technical analysis.

1.2 PLANNING

This section describes components and mechanisms for developing and utilizing hazardous materials transportation accident contingency plans at the community, industrial, state and Federal level. The reason for including planning in a document concerned with post-accident guidelines is the fact that basic guidelines must exist beforehand. After the accident it is too late to develop guidelines. Post-accident guidelines should simply involve doing what had been planned and subtly modifying the planned guidelines to fit the specific case.

1.2.1 Community Emergency Response Planning

An analysis of hazardous materials transportation accidents[1][42] showed that municipalities having pre-established contingency plans for handling hazardous materials transportation accidents were better prepared for handling the hazardous environment when an accident occurred than those areas that had not pre-planned. However, many localities have not prepared or are not aware of existing hazardous materials transportation accident contingency plans. This fact is exemplified by such transportation accidents as Beattyville, KY and Youngstown, FL. In fact, communities which have contingency plans usually have a large community-oriented chemical manufacturer in the area or have previously had a major transportation accident.

It is recommended that a viable community contingency plan for hazardous materials transportation accidents be developed for every locality and that this plan contain the following information:

- Hazardous materials shipping routes and volumes through community;

- Community transportation network in terms of possible evacuation routes and also access by emergency services;

- Location of specialized personnel, materials, and equipment in community or nearest location adequate to handle hazardous materials emergencies;

- Appropriate segments of the emergency response community, with clearly defined individual roles, responsibilities and statutory authorities;

- Methods for accessing relevant technical assistance sources; and

- Designated communications network (radio frequency, network channel, siren) to alert the public and to handle communications between the Communications Command Center (CCC), the accident site and other off-scene support organizations.

These topics are discussed in subsequent paragraphs of this section. At least two states, California and Virginia, have conducted studies to assess the magnitude and volume of hazardous materials traveling along various segments of the state's transportation network. However, because local emergency responders (i.e., fire, police, medical) are the first groups on-scene, it is anticipated that an inventory of hazardous materials traffic will be conducted on the local level. The city or regional planning office might be the logical organization to be charged with performing this duty and possibly some other duties associated with municipal contingency pre-planning. Statutes may dictate some other agency. The important idea is to have some organization responsible.

It is recommended that an inventory of the community's transportation network be conducted. Also, physical/chemical data should be compiled for the hazardous commodities being transported through a community. Appendix A presents physical/chemical properties for the 28 chemicals/propellants which are addressed by this manual. Based on current emergency response practice, this information should be carried in the cars of each emergency service "chief" (i.e., designated on-scene coordinator or his representative). The types of commodity information which the "chief" should carry include specific gravity, vapor density, explosive limits, toxicity levels and fire-fighting/first-aid information.

A catalog of appropriate segments of the response community and their responsibilities and authority should also include an inventory of specialized hazardous materials response teams in, or available to, the community including local emergency services (fire, police, medical), industrial teams, trade association teams and Federal, state and local government personnel. The type of information which should be collected for each specialized responding personnel/organization should include the following:

- Name and address of key persons/contacts;

- 24-hour emergency phone numbers;

- Toll-free telephone numbers, if available; and

- What resources they can provide.

Other personnel or organizational information which should be cross and sub-indexed includes:

- Response speciality (e.g., fire-fighting, wreck handling, cleanup/disposal);

- Specific commodity expertise; and

- Availability of specialized equipment and materials.

The inventory of specialized equipment and materials suitable for hazardous materials traveling through a community should identify:

- Materials and equipment needed for each hazardous material being shipped; and

- Location and availability of materials and equipment at public facilities and commercial/industrial facilities.

Technical assistance may be obtained in several ways (See Section 1.5). The Chemical Transportation Emergency Center (CHEMTREC 800/424-9300) which is operated on a 24-hour, 7-day-a-week basis by the Chemical Manufacturers Association, can provide some "cookbook" initial response actions for an identified HM and get the shipper in direct contact with the emergency scene. If the HM happens to be one for which a segment of the chemical industry has developed special response teams (e.g., the CHLOREP teams of the chlorine industry through the Chlorine Institute), CHEMTREC alerts such groups. The shippers/chemical manufacturers are the most knowledgeable about the HM they produce/handle and are in the best position to provide technical assistance at the accident scene. CHEMTREC information per se is "cookbook" for specific commodities and no judgments or recommendations are offered.

The National Response Center (NRC), operated by the U.S. Coast Guard (800/424-8802) in conjunction with EPA in handling water spills of hazardous substances, likewise is operated around-the-clock and has a direct telephone tie-in with CHEMTREC through a written agreement.

Memorandum of Understanding

The U.S. Coast Guard (USCG) and EPA have joint regional response teams, with designated on-scene coordinators (OSC), which are dispatched to the scene if either EPA or the Coast Guard deems it necessary. These teams can provide technical advice and/or actually conduct cleanup/disposal operations, if necessary. In addition, the NRC and other agencies have various computer programs to predict the dispersion of spilled HM (currently this is essentially confined to water spills). The computerized data system makes available more detailed technical information than CHEMTREC can provide. EPA and the Coast Guard also have technical experts who may be contacted for technical advice.

There are several cleanup/disposal contractors who specialize in handling and advising cleanup and disposal operations at HM spills. Some shippers utilize such contractors when they do not have in-house specialized teams. However, carriers rarely have such capability and would have to rely on a contractor. Normally, the shipper and carrier agree how the matter will be handled, so it does not become a problem.

A number of shippers provide a company toll free 800 emergency number on shipping papers and sometimes on the tank cars or cargo tanks.

Without adequate, fully-coordinated communications, it is impossible to successfully handle a HM transportation emergency. The communications network must enable those groups at the scene to communicate within their respective disciplines, between disciplines and with the OSC. Additionally, the OSC must have direct contact with all the off-scene support activities (e.g., aerial surveillance, weather service, and hospitals) and shipper, carrier, local, state and Federal officials and response centers (e.g., NRC and CHEMTREC) and the news media.

Most of the emergency services organizations have communications systems. The important concept is tieing all communication into a centralized communications center. A system of priorities must be established as to what transmission to the centralized communications center takes precedence. If possible, assignment of specific frequencies to the various groups is recommended. "Ham" operators, particularly, may be a valuable resource. The CB system might be of value under special circumstances.

Smith[2] uses a different set of parameters for a community contingency plan. He lists several specific items for some of the topical areas previously mentioned. All of these are valid and should be in the plan; however, the scope is not complete. He indicates that every local community contingency plan should include:

- A statement of purpose and scope;

- Enabling acts and authority;

- Identification and function of the officials involved (in the sheriff's office, fire department, civil defense organization, state police, EMTs, and social service organizations);

- An evacuation plan with predesignated shelters and logistical support;

- Identification of radio and TV stations that will continually inform the public during the initial trauma (these stations should be publicized periodically as a public service);

- Identification of the predesignated local on-scene coordinator (LOSC) by name and/or position;

- A mechanism for updating;

- A document showing how the local plan interfaces with the federal and state plans;

- Identification of a liaison official to work with the state and federal on-scene coordinators;

- Continually updated phone numbers (home and business) of key officials;

- A check-in location where key officials can be located or tracked once they have appeared on-scene; and

- A method of identifying and accounting for anyone who may have authority to go beyond the roadblock. This can be preplanned by reviewing the state and federal plans and can be coordinated during the spill response with the federal OSC and the state OSC.

1.2.2 Industrial Emergency Response Planning

Many industrial organizations which produce, consume or transport hazardous chemicals have developed contingency plans. In fact, several of the trade associations which represent these industrial organizations have developed specialized response teams, such as in the chlorine industry. According to Smith[2], the advent of industrial contingency plans has provided more competent response on the part of industry and development of innovative cleanup technologies.

Trade organizations such as the Chemical Manufacturers Association (CMA) and American Society for Testing and Materials (ASTM) should continue to develop improved information, specialized equipment and procedures to handle HM emergencies and to provide technical assistance, so that communities may develop effective contingency plans for general or specific HM accidents from both near- and long-term aspects.

1.2.3 State Emergency Response Planning

40 CFR, Part 109, "A Guide for State Contingency Plans[3]", published by EPA in the early 1970's requires that each state develop an emergency/disaster plan which is as stringent as federal contingency planning laws. As a result of this enactment, all states are required to have some form of emergency disaster contingency plan. However, few deal specifically with the potential of a hazardous materials transportation accident. Based on the frequency and severity of hazardous materials transportation accidents occurring, and the inability of local emergency services in many localities to handle the emergency situation adequately, it is recommended that a specialized contingency plan be developed which addresses only hazardous materials transportation accidents. As recommended by Smith and others[2][5][42], this plan should include the following elements:

- A statement of purpose and scope;

- Enabling laws;

- Identification of authorities involved;

- A mechanism for updating;

- An activity scenario (short but specific) for each element of state government involved;

- A merging doctrine, showing how the plan interfaces practically with federal and local plans;

- The predesignated state on-scene coordinator (SOSC) identified by name and/or position;

- Identification of a liaison official to work with the federal OSC and the SOSC;

- The state's 24-hour reporting number (maintaining this phone is absolutely critical);

- A current list of key state and local phone numbers;

- Provisions for local contingency plans by district, region, country, and/or key cities;

- Brevity (the federal plan should be no more than 50 to 75 pages long, excluding state plans and annexes. A good state plan should be 20 to 30 pages long, excluding annexes); and

- A designated place where key officials can be found or at least where they check in upon arrival.

1.2.4 Federal Emergency Response Planning

The Federal contingency plan is based upon "The National Oil and Hazardous Substances Pollution Contingency Plan[4] (40 CFR Section 1510). This plan designates a group of Federal government organizations to serve on a Regional Response Team (RRT). The purpose of this team is to facilitate the participation of several Federal, state, and local government officials for responding on-scene to a polluting or hazardous materials release. The plan predesignates a presiding officer and lists the various government organizations with legal authority to participate as members of this team. It identifies an on-scene coordinator (OSC) at the Federal level and outlines basic ground rules for the mitigation of damage from the spill. It is designed specifically for HM spills in water; however, the concept and organizational structure is also adaptable to land accidents.

This plan establishes a National Response Team (NRT) located in Washington, D.C. This group provides national policy guidance and works continually with the Council on Environmental Quality (CEQ) in updating the 1510 plan. The NRT monitors significant accidents involving spills of oil and hazardous substances and is capable, on request of the RRT, to resolve major issues. Should an event become so large or so sociologically or technically complex based on the RRT's capabilities, the NRT could become actively involved. The NRT is co-chaired by EPA and the U.S. Coast Guard. Its members are high-level officials of the following federal agencies: EPA, the Department of Transportation (DOT) represented by the U.S. Coast Guard, Department of Defense (DOD), Department of Commerce (DOC) represented by the National Oceanographic and Atmospheric Administration (NOAA), the Federal Emergency Management Agency (FEMA), the Department of Agriculture (USDA), Department of Justice (DOJ), Department of Health and Human Services (HHS), Department of Labor (DOL), Department of Energy (DOE), Department of State (DOS), and the Department of Interior (DOI). The National Transportation Safety Board (NTSB) is a liaison member. Members are added as national interests change in the HM accident picture.

1.3 COMMUNICATIONS

An integral component of every community's contingency plan for hazardous materials transportation accidents should be guidelines for intra- and inter-organizational communications at an accident scene. Having means for timely establishment of a communications link saves valuable time for the on-scene coordinator and other response personnel for mitigating the hazards associated with an accident. Section 2.2 (Initiating the Response Communications Network) discusses these requirements in detail.

1.4 DECISION-MAKING

Decisions are made by people, and methodologies are tools which can be used to help organize and present information to assist the decision-makers in this task. Decisions are made at every level by every person responding to or coming upon a transportation accident involving hazardous materials. The decision may be as simple as turning a car around and heading the other direction, if one spots what appears to be a train wreck five miles across the valley. Decisions must be made as to whether the wreckage can be safely approached or not. Typical decisions include what types of response equipment and personnel need to be deployed; whether or not to order an evacuation, what area should be evacuated and when; should an attempt be made to stop the leak, do nothing, or further open a damaged container to dispose of its contents; whether or not to transfer hazardous cargo or attempt to move, upright or rerail overturned cars or tank trucks containing hazardous materials; and what should be the order for performing these activities. The railroad crew must decide if the engine and remaining cars should be moved away from the wreckage. A decision must be made each time personnel, equipment or materials are deployed on-scene. Appropriate cleanup procedures must be chosen. Someone must decide if residual material is to be neutralized, burned, vented, recovered on-site or disposed of off-site, as well as what methods to use. Again it must be emphasized that for every action that is taken a decision must be made. It is imperative that decision-makers be properly trained, so that decisions such as these will be made with a high level of technical expertise and safeguard for personal safety.

At most accidents, the decision-maker (i.e., on-scene coordinator) is typically the local fire chief. When the accident is of such magnitude that local emergency services do not have the personnel, equipment or material resources required to mitigate the hazards or if a water pollution threat exists on-scene, the on-scene coordinator is typically a designated USCG or EPA representative. Section 2.6 discusses the responsibilities of an on-scene coordinator in detail.

The on-scene coordinator has a wide range of tools for mitigating the hazards at his disposal. These tools include several spill response manuals (i.e., EPA[5], DOT[6], USCG[7] and AAR[8]) which provide initial response actions, access to CHEMTREC and USCG National Response Center (Section 1.5), flow charts which illustrate the sequence of actions to be performed based on the specific accident conditions and checklists of action items. These tools as well as other methods are discussed in Section 2.1.

The importance of training for decision-makers is discussed in Section 1.1.2.

1.5   TECHNICAL   ASSISTANCE   AND INFORMATION

Several information retrieval systems are available for obtaining chemical data which would be useful to on-scene response personnel to mitigate the hazards associated with a HM transportation accident. This section discusses the information contained in these systems, mode of operation as well as means of access. Appendix B is a listing of applicable retrieval systems, type of organization providing the service information and type of on-site response assistance which can be obtained. Appendix C is a list of on-line information retrieval services which provide information in the form of an annotated bibliography or listing of applicable topic references. Access to an on-line retrieval system would be beneficial to on-site responders due to the system's quick response time.

Also included as Appendix D is a sample listing of reference texts, guides and handbooks containing information on the thermophysical/chemical properties of hazardous materials. Information on sources of technical assistance and information are based on a

discussion given in EPA "Manual for Sources of the Control of Hazardous Material Spills: Volume 1 - Spill Assessment and Water Treatment Techniques (EPA-600/2-77-227)[5].

1.5.1   EPA Oil and Hazardous Materials Technical Assistance Data System (OHMTADS)

The OHMTADS computerized information retrieval service includes more than 850 oil and hazardous substances on file. OHMTADS is an on-line system which can assist on-scene responders in identifying a hazardous material from limited on-site information such as material color, smell, etc. There are 123 parameters of each OHMTADS file which includes a varied description of physical, chemical, biological, toxicological, transportation and commercial data. Of the file parameters, 95 of the 123 segment headers are also file search components.

This system enables the identification of unidentified pollutants through the use of a random access feature. This is accomplished by the input of physical or chemical characteristics of the material(s) involved allowing the input of each key word to be automatically processed into an inverted index file, thus becoming a search component of the data base. The system utilizes Boolean logic to generate a list of the probable materials involved based on the input characteristics provided. These materials are then displayed on the user's CPU. To assist in identification, the 95 search components can take an interactive mode which prompts the user to input additional material or accident data until the material's identity may be confirmed.

The oil and hazardous materials spill coordinator at the EPA Regional office (Regional Response Center) provides access to OHMTADS or an on-line computer search can be performed through the University of Indiana.

1.5.2   U.S. Coast Guard Chemical Hazards Response Information System (CHRIS)

This system is comprised of four user manuals, a regional contingency plan, a hazards assessment computer system (HACS) and an organizational entity at the Coast Guard Station. The four manuals are:

- Vol. 1. CG-446-1 - Condensed Guide to Chemical Hazards. Provides vital information on hazardous chemicals that are shipped in large quantity by marine transportation.

- Vol. 2. CG-446-2 - Hazardous Chemical Data Manual. Contains similar information to Vol. 1 as well as data in terms of the chemical, physical, and toxicological properties of hazardous chemicals.

- Vol. 3 CG-446-3 - Hazard Assessment Handbook. Contains methods for determining the source strength of spilled hazardous chemicals as well as procedures for estimating the toxic, flammable and explosive hazards for the materials contained in the HACS system.

- Vol. 4 CG-446-4 - Response Methods Handbook. Provides information on techniques for handling spills of the materials in CHRIS. The Appendix to CG-446-4 lists manufacturers of equipment that could be used in the event of a spill.

CHRIS was established as a result of the development of the National Contingency Plan.

HACS, the computerized counterpart of CHRIS Volume 3, provides detailed hazard assessment information. CHRIS Volume 3 identifies methods for hand calculating the spill situation. The Coast Guard recommends that HACS be used because it provides sophisticated, rapid and more accurate evaluation of the spill situation than by the manual method. HACS has been designed for estimating release information of spills into water.

Volume 1, Condensed Guide to Chemical Hazards, has been designed primarily for use by port security personnel and others who may be first to arrive at the scene of a spill. When a chemical's identity is known, basic spill information on the chemical can easily be obtained. This volume is designed to provide essential guidance to decision-makers concerning immediate steps necessary to insure protection to life, property and the environment. In conjunction with CHRIS Volume 3, Volume 1 can be used to assess the possible hazardous effects of a spill. CHRIS Volumes 2, 3, and 4 are designed for use by the On-Scene Coordinator's (OSC) office, the Regional and National Response Centers and Coast Guard Stations. HACS is also designed for use by OSC personnel.

HACS, Volume 2 and Volume 3 should be used together. A hazard assessment code for each chemical is stated in Volume 2, Hazardous Chemical Data, and this code can be used in Volume 3, Hazard Assessment Handbook, to select appropriate calculation methods for hazard mitigation assessment. This provides the user with approximate evaporation source-strength data for hazardous chemicals under various conditions. Methods are also available for approximating the concentration of hazardous chemicals in both water and air as a function of time and distance from the spill. The computerized counterpart of CHRIS Volume 3, HACS, makes detailed hazard evaluations easily obtainable. The HACS system has been designed basically for use by OSC personnel through the NRC at Coast Guard Headquarters. When using the HACS system, the following information should be provided, when available, to the NRC:

- Material discharged;

- Quantity spilled;

- Quantity originally in tank;

- Location of spill;

- Time of occurrence;

- Tank dimensions;

- Other cargos or nearby chemicals;

- Hole diameter;

- River depth;

- River width;

- Stream velocity;

- Temperature (air);

- Temperature (water); and

- Cloud cover (percent).

In the event that Coast Guard personnel require additional information, a call back number should be given to NRC personnel.

CHRIS Volume 4, Response Methods Handbook, provides descriptive and technical information on methods of spill containment, mainly for oil spills. Volume 4 is designed basically for use by Coast Guard OSC personnel who have had previous training in hazard response.

Coast Guard Regional Offices have CHRIS Manuals available for use in the event of an emergency (see Appendix E) (Appendix E also includes a listing of EPA Regional offices and appropriate State Agencies to contact in the event of a spill). The HACS can be accessed for emergencies directly through the Department of Transportation National Response Center, USCG Regional Response Center or Coast Guard District Office.

1.5.3 U.S. Coast Guard National Strike Force Description

The Coast Guard's National Strike Force (NSF) is part of the National Contingency Plan established under the authority of the Federal Water Pollution Control Act Amendments of 1972, Section 311[1]. As needed and specified in the National Contingency Plan, equipment and trained personnel are provided to aid the on-scene coordinator during Phase III (containment and countermeasures), Phase IV (cleanup, mitigation and disposal) and Phase V (Documentation and Cost Recovery). The East, West, and Gulf Coasts each have a Coast Guard Strike Team. Each team is comprised of about 19 personnel with three or four officers and can effectively respond to a pollution incident in its area with at least four persons responding within two hours and at full strength in 12 hours. The strike team supplies communicatibn support, assistance and advice on ship salvage, diving and removal procedures. The following equipment, basically designed for air transport, is available:

- Air Deliverable Antipollution Transfer System (ADAPTS), consists of a pumping system to off-load stricken cargo vessels;

- Yokohama fenders, used for side protection during vessel-to-vessel cargo transfer;

- High-seas containment barrier; and

- High-seas skimmer.

On-scene coordinators anywhere in the U.S. can request the services of the National Strike Force by contacting the National Response Center 24-hour emergency telephone number (800/424-8802). Specific details and any pertinent information should be given regarding the emergency condition.

1.5.4 Chemical Transportation Emergency Center (CHEMTREC)

CHEMTREC (service of Chemical Manufacturers Association) operates at an office in Washington, D.C. maintaining an emergency 24-hour telephone number (800/424-9300 or 202/483-7616 in Washington, D.C.) for emergencies involving the transportation of chemicals. CHEMTREC's initial response is to contact the shipper of the chemical, obtain necessary information as well as assistance and follow-up. If the chemical can be identified, CHEMTREC will then assist by providing "cookbook" cautionary measures that can be exercised at the spill site. The CHEMTREC system is not computerized but it contains over 3,600 items considered by manufacturers to be their primary items of shipment.

CHEMTREC's emergency telephone number is extensively distributed throughout the chemical industry as well as to emergency services, chemical distributers, and can generally be found on shipping documents. When CHEMTREC receives an emergency call, its personnel will obtain as much data from the caller as can be provided, making a written and recorded record of the information received. CHEMTREC personnel will then relay to the site available precautionary information, on the chemicals reported, as previously supplied by chemical producers (e.g., toxic, fire and explosion hazards). The shipper of the chemical will then be notified and will be responsible for further actions regarding additional assistance, including making contact with the caller.

The primary purpose of CHEMTREC is as a medium for putting the caller and chemical shipper and/or chemical manufacturer into contact with each other when an accident occurs because the chemical manufacturers will have the necessary data concerning the properties of their products. CHEMTREC is also available as a contact point for such organizations as the Chlorine Institute (chlorine spills), the National Agricultural Chemicals Association (spills of pesticides), the Fertilizer Institute (ammonia spills) and the Department of Energy (radioactive materials).

CHEMTREC may be accessed by using an emergency telephone number. When contacting CHEMTREC, as much of the following information as possible should be provided:

- Name of caller and call back number;

- Location of problem;

- Shipper or manufacturer;

- Container type;

- Rail car or truck number;

- Carrier name;

- Consignee; and

- Local conditions.

1.5.5 Chlorine Emergency Plan (CHLOREP)

Chlorine emergencies can be handled by procedures outlined in the Chlorine Emergency Plan, developed by chlorine manufacturers in the U.S. and Canada through the Chlorine Institute. The plan (CHLOREP) provides for the manufacturer closest to the emergency site to provide technical assistance, regardless of whose product is involved.

The CHLOREP system operates through CHEMTREC. When an emergency call is placed, CHEMTREC contacts the individual suggested by the mutual aid plan. The individual then gets in touch with the spill site to make a decision as to the necessity of dispatching a technical team to provide assistance. Each manufacturer contributing to this service has experienced crews and adequate equipment available to respond to an emergency.

CHLOREP may be accessed through CHEMTREC's 24-hour emergency number.

1.5.6 Additional Sources of Material Information

There are many handbooks and reference texts which may prove helpful in the event of a hazardous materials spill. Any person or organization who may be confronted with a HM spill emergency should have access to the commonly used references. The USCG Regional Response Center (RRC) maintains a hazardous materials reference library. At a minimum, the references listed in Appendix D should be acquired. Each community should establish a central location where all the necessary documents may be maintained. These may be found at the USCG RRC.

In developing community emergency response plans for hazardous materials transportation emergencies, local decision-makers should provide the telephone numbers of the information assistance systems identified and develop an accident site data sheet which keys needed data for operation of many of these systems.

1.6 PROTECTIVE CLOTHING, GEAR AND EQUIPMENT AVAILABILITY AND USES

When entering a hazardous environment, appropriate protective clothing, gear, breathing apparatus and equipment must be used. This section does not discuss the specific items required for working in hazardous environments for each chemical/ propellant dealt with in this manual, but does identify the types which should be available on-scene and their uses. A commodity-specific listing of protective clothing, breathing apparatus, gear and equipment to be used for the hazardous materials addressed by this manual is presented in Table 5-2 of Section 5.

In terms of personal protection, emergency services should have available protective clothing, acid suits, chemical/gas suits, cooling systems (heat exchangers) and fire entry suits for use by responding personnel. In terms of breathing equipment these same services should have the following equipment available for use: breathing apparatuses, regulated manifold air supply systems and assorted cannister masks and cartridges.

Several commercial manufacturers/ suppliers produce this type of equipment. A sample listing of a few manufacturers/suppliers is given in Table 1-1. Table 1-1 is not an endorsement of any of these items or manufacturers and the types of personal protective clothing, equipment and gear which they supply. Chemical manufacturers, the U.S. General Services Administration catalogues, telephone yellow pages, EPA and USCG Regional Offices are other sources for this type of information.

Local emergency services should obtain the obvious personal protective clothing, equipment and gear required for handling the types of hazardous commodities being transported through or consumed in a community. Clothing, equipment and gear should be thoroughly inspected and tested periodically to assure that it will provide the required level of personal safety. Protective clothing, equipment, breathing apparatus or gear which does not meet these strict safety standards should be either discarded or repaired. Once repaired, inspection and testing should be conducted to assure that the repair was adequate. Penalties should be imposed on individuals/organizations which do not abide by these guidelines and who subject personnel to unnecessary hazards due to negligence in enforcing these requirements. These items are expensive and the various segments of the emergency response community have much to gain by pooling resources.

1.7 SPECIALIZED TREATMENT CHEMICALS, EQUIPMENT, RESOURCES AVAILABILITY AND USES

Specialized treatment chemicals, equipment and resources are needed at a hazardous materials transportation accident. This section does not directly discuss the treatment chemicals, equipment or resources which can be used to mitigate the hazards associated with the chemicals/propellants examined in the manual, but identifies treatment chemicals, sorbents and analytical and heavy equipment which can be utilized. A

TABLE 1-1. PARTIAL LISTING OF PROTECTIVE CLOTHING,
BREATHING APPARATUS, GEAR AND EQUIPMENT

Item	Manufacturer	Location
Portable Resuscitation Units	Robert Shaw	Anaheim, CA
Gas/Vapor Respirators	3M Company	St. Paul, MN
Breathing Apparatuses (15-60 minute capacity)		
Gas Mask (30 minute capacity)		
Organic Vapor Respirator		
Acid Gas Respirator		
Gloves		
- neoprene (corrosives)		
- nitrite (aromatic, petroleum and solvents)	Lab Safety Supply	Janesville, WI
- polyethylene		
- PVA coated		
(organic solvents, aromatics, ketones and chlorinated solvents)		
Face Shields		
Safety Caps		
Splash Suits		
First Aid Kits		
Breathing Apparatus	Mine Safety Appliances (MSA)	Pittsburgh, PA
Acid Suits		
Cooling Systems (heat and exchangers)		
Regulated Manifold Air Supply System		
Bullhorns		
Road Blocks		
Absorbents (e.g., sawdust, fly ash, cotton, straw)		
Gelling Agents (e.g., wax, soap)		
Shovels		
Signs		
Rope		
Portable Generator and Lights		
Foams		
Portable and Mobile Radios		
Videotape Recorder, Camera		

Source: Equipment Manufacturer's catalogs/pamphlets.

detailed discussion of commodity-specific information is given in Section 5.3.8.

1.7.1 Treatment Chemicals and Methods

According to Smith[2], several treatment chemicals and methods exist for mitigating the hazards associated with a spill.

"The decision for use of specific treatment chemicals and methods will be dependent on such factors as existing legal limits for materials in the environment (RCRA, state and local laws, water quality limits), private property and riparian water rights, nature of the contaminant, cost considerations, safety and public health considerations, physical limitations, testing, quarantine and residual disposal constraints."

Once the treatment considerations have been analyzed based on the accident conditions and the aforementioned factors, it is then possible to select the appropriate treatment method. Table 1-2 lists treatment methods for handling spills of hazardous materials.

TABLE 1-2. HAZARDOUS MATERIALS TREATMENT METHODS

- Carbon absorption
- pH adjustment
- Air stripping and aeration
- Precipitation
- Neutralization
- Biological
- Destruction
- Solution/Dilution
- Mixing
- Land spraying

Source: Al J. Smith, Jr., Managing Hazardous Substances Accidents, McGraw-Hill, Inc. 1981.

A discussion of each of these methods and their potential applicability to the chemicals/propellants addressed by this manual are given in Section 5. It needs to be emphasized that only compatible treatment chemicals should be used with the spilled material because mixing incompatible materials may result in worsening the situation. Local contingency plans should identify the location and availability of chemicals for treating any hazardous material which flows through a community. Some common spill control materials available are acid and caustic neutralizing agents, diatomaceous earth, vermiculite,

activated carbon and various commercial absorbents.

1.7.2 Sorbent Materials

Use of sorbent materials to soak up and contain spilled hazardous materials during initial response, product transfer, and cleanup/disposal operations at the accident site is common practice. Typical sorbent devices include spill control pillows, which absorb 98% of their capacity (e.g., of oil) in 30 seconds (a number of these can be combined to form a dike), spill squeegee and absorbent paper. It is recommended that a stockpile of such materials be kept by the local community at all times. However, if this is not feasible, the community should identify the location where these supplies can be obtained in a timely fashion, establish cooperative agreements with local chemical manufacturers who would have a supply in-house or obtain these materials from the product transfer, cleanup/disposal contractor directly. A detailed discussion of these materials is given in Section 5. This technique is not recommended for oxidizing materials like nitrogen tetroxide.

1.7.3 Analytical and Heavy Equipment

In addition to the tools needed as indicated in Table 1-1, analytical and heavy equipment are a necessity at hazardous materials transportation accidents. Analytical monitoring devices serve such functions as identifying hazardous materials on-site and providing continuous monitoring for toxic, flammable and explosive vapors during all phases of accident response. Heavy equipment is used in initial response, wreckage removal, and cleanup/disposal operations. Table 1-3 is a partial listing of analytical detection/testing and heavy equipment that communities should have available for use in the event of a hazardous materials transportation accident. An in-depth discussion of the equipment identified in Table 1-3, which may be used for the hazardous materials addressed by this manual, is given in Section 3. In the event of a hazardous materials transportation emergency, communities should seek to have most of this equipment available for their use. Heavy equipment can usually be obtained through the state or local Department of Highways and Transportation or through a local construction contractor. Analytical detection/testing equipment may be purchased exclusively for the use of a city's emergency services, borrowed from a community chemical manufacturer or chemical laboratory, obtained from a region's state emergency preparedness/civil defense office or acquired for use from a nearby military installation. Fire departments have flammable vapor detectors. It is recomended that communities obtain and pool as much of this equipment as possible. However, when a locality can not fund such purchasing it is recommended that agreements be pre-established with state preparedness/ civil defense and military installations for their use and any technical assistance in their operation, as needed.

TABLE 1-3. ANALYTICAL
AND HEAVY EQUIPMENT

Analytical Detection/Testing Equipment

● Gas detector

● Combustible gas/oxygen detector

● Oxygen deficiency monitor

● Electrical safety hazard analyzer

● Radiation/contamination survey meters

● Infrared radiometer

● Explosimeter

● Mass spectrometer

● Colorimetric tubes

Heavy Equipment

● Bulldozer

● Crane

● Backhoe

● Highloader

● Dump trucks

1.8 WRECKAGE REMOVAL CONTRACTORS

When a transportation accident occurs and the services of a wreckage removal contractor are required on-scene, the choice of a wreckage removal contractor will depend upon the transportation mode involved in the accident, accident severity in terms of structural damage to equipment, proximity of accident site to contractor's facility, and contractor's available resources. This manual is concerned with wreckage removal contractors who will respond to rail and highway hazardous materials transportation accidents only. Most often, and it is sound safety practice that, these contractors will not respond on-scene until all toxic, flammable and explosive vapor related to hazardous

materials have been dissipated from the accident site, and the area is considered to be a safe working environment. When wreckage removal contractors are required at rail transportation accidents, special heavy equipment is needed. Two organizations which have historically provided on-site wreckage removal activities to rail transportation accidents are:

● Isringhausen, Railroad Specialists, Inc.
One Industrial Drive
Jerseyville, Illinois 62052
(618) 498-6441

● Hulcher Emergency Services, Inc.
Box 191
Virden, Illinois 62690
(217) 965-3361   .
(800) 252-3371 in Illinois
(800) 637-5471 outside Illinois

Wreckage removal contractors responding to highway vehicles accidents are typically the local towing or wreckage services. A listing of these organizations can be found in the local telephone directory yellow pages. Unfortunately, their response capabilities are less sophisticated than the groups which respond to railroad accidents. Local contingency plans should have these telephone numbers available for use in the event of an accident and only those considered to be qualified and reliable should be listed.

Accident severity influences the level of sophistication required for equipment to be brought on-scene. Proximity of the accident site to the contractor's location influences response time and availability of personnel, equipment and materials. State and local emergency response plans should have pre-identified wreckage removal firms which are capable of responding to transportation accidents that occur in a specific area. A detailed discussion of the guidelines to be followed during wreckage removal operations is given in Section 5.2.

The personnel, equipment and material resources available to the wreckage removal contractor at the time of the accident may influence the choice of a firm to perform the wreckage removal operations. This can be illustrated by a situation where a wreckage removal contractor's facility is located one mile from a railroad accident, but due to their inability to provide heavy lifting equipment to the scene, it is concluded that this firm does not have long-term on-scene response capabilities. Since heavy equipment would be needed in this instance, a wreckage removal contractor having heavy equipment would have to be contacted, even if this firm's facility is located 500 miles from the accident scene. Of course, response time will be increased significantly, but this should not create a big problem because wreckage removal should not begin until the situation is stabilized. The on-scene coordinator should not automatically discount the value of a wreckage removal contractor who does not have the heavy equipment because this firm may be able to assist in the short-term until the more distant wreckage removal contractor can arrive on-scene.

Acquiring a wreckage removal contractor is just one of the many decisions which the on-scene coordinator must make regarding the use of outside technical experts.

1.9 PRODUCT TRANSFER, CLEANUP AND DISPOSAL CONTRACTORS

At most hazardous materials transportation accidents, the services of product transfer, and cleanup/disposal personnel are required. This section provides a number, but not necessarily complete listing of contractors involved in these activities. An in-depth discussion of the guidelines to be used on-scene by these organizations is given in Section 5. In many cases, the shipper or association to which the shipper belongs, may provide such specialized service. The carrier should involve the shipper in the selection of a product transfer, and cleanup/disposal contractor.

It is intended that the information in this section be used by the on-scene coordinator and other officials as a guide for determining the appropriate contractor to hire based on proximity to accident site; availability of personnel, materials and resources; cost considerations; and the advice and consent of the shipper and carrier. The community contingency plan should identify product transfer, and cleanup/disposal contractors who are capable of meeting the locality's requirements based on the hazardous materials being transported in the area.

Table 1-4 has been prepared to show a representative listing of cleanup and disposal contractors, their office locations, mode of transportation used for response and emergency response access numbers. These contractors are regionally and, in some instances, nationally recognized experts in handling hazardous materials.

For on-site product transfer and cleanup/disposal operations, the following information is supplied for the on-scene coordinator and others who must make decisions regarding these activities:

● Waste disposal sites capable of handling the materials addressed by this manual as well as state solid waste management agencies (Appendix F);

● Shipping containers required for transport of each chemical/propellant; and

● Applicable Federal Regulations pertinent to the transport of these commodities (Appendix M).

Local decision-makers should familiarize themselves with this information, so that, when local contingency plans are developed, data on the location and capabilities of local waste disposal facilities and availability of required shipping disposal containers based on the community's hazardous materials transportation needs will have been identified. By so doing it is anticipated that product transfer/cleanup/disposal activities may be performed at the greatest level of cost-effectiveness and personal safety. Typical equipment that would be available to cleanup/disposal contractors is given in Appendix N.

TABLE 1-4.   CLEANUP AND DISPOSAL CONTRACTORS*

Contractor	Office Locations	Mode of Transportation Used for Response	Emergency Response Access Number
OH Materials, Inc.	Findlay, OH Atlanta, GA Ottawa, IL St. Marks, FL	Air	(800) 537-9540**
IT Corporation	Wilmington, CA Martinez, CA Benica, CA Rio Vista, CA Kelsyville, CA Imperial County, CA Milpitas, CA Baton Rouge, LA Concord, CA Knoxville, TN Taft, CA Bakersfield, CA San Diego, CA Arlington, VA Long Beach, CA	Highway	(800) 262-1900** in California (213) 830-1720** outside California
Industrial Marine Service, Inc.	Norfolk, VA	Highway	(804) 543-5718
Rollins Environmental Services, Inc.	Bridgeport, NJ	Highway	(800) 232-6530 in New Jersey (800) 257-5543 outside New Jersey (609) 467-3100**
	Baton Rouge, LA Deer Park, TX		(504) 778-1234** (713) 479-6001**
Great Lakes Environmental Services, Inc.	Roseville, MI	Highway	(313) 758-0400** (800) 482-4483 in Michigan (800) 462-1968 outside Michigan
Energy Systems, Co.	El Dorado, AR	N/A	(501) 863-7173** (501) 375-8444
H&H Ship Service, Co.	San Francisco, CA	N/A	(415) 543-4835**
Crosby & Overton, Inc.	Long Beach, CA	N/A	(213) 432-5447** (213) 432-5445**
National Industrial & Environmental Services	Wichita, KS	N/A	(316) 744-1286 (316) 261-9230 (after 5 p.m.)

----

*   Source: 1982 Hazardous Materials Spills Conference.

**   24-Hour number.

TABLE 1-4 (cont'd)

Contractor	Office Locations	Mode of Transportation Used for Response	Emergency Response Access Number
Ryckman's Emergency Action & Consulting Team (REACT)	St. Louis, MO	Air Highway	(314) 569-0991** (800) 325-1398** outside Missouri
Chemical Waste Management	Oak Brook, IL	N/A	(312) 841-8600**
Ecology and Environmental, Inc.	Buffalo, NY	N/A	(716) 631-9530**[1]
J&L Industries, Inc.	Baltimore, MD	N/A	(301) 488-0800** inside Maryland (800) 638-9116** outside Maryland
Geo Detox, Inc.	Houston, TX	N/A	(713) 530-7870**
Marine Pollution Control	Detroit, MI	N/A	(313) 849-2333** (800) 521-8232 outside Michigan
Roberts Environmental Services	Eugene, OR	N/A	(503) 688-4531**
SCA Chemical Disposal Services	Brookline, MA	N/A	(617) 247-4001**
Western Environmental Services	Portland, OR Richmond, CA	N/A	(800) 547-0792** (415) 234-7400**

** 24-hour number.

1. Will start operating from February 1, 1983.

2. INITIAL RESPONSE GUIDELINES
AND HAZARDOUS CHEMICAL DATA

This section describes initial response guidelines for reporting the accident, initiating the response communications network, identifying hazardous materials, on-scene coordination, obtaining and relaying accident site information, assessing on-site resources availability, on-site decision-making, evacuation, news media interface, command post operations and status reporting for continual assessment.

2.1 REPORTING THE ACCIDENT

The objective of this section is to provide guidelines for reporting hazardous materials transportation accidents. Depending upon the particular accident circumstances, the reporting of the accident may be performed by anyone (e.g., a member of the civilian population, rail crew, truck driver or on-duty/off-duty member of the local emergency services).

When an accident does occur, Figure 2-1 shows the notification sequence for each of these groups from initial notification to dispatch of response units to the scene. It must be emphasized that the reporting of the accident in all instances should occur in a timely manner. If not incapacitated, the designated member of the rail crew or the truck driver should immediately notify their carrier's dispatcher/local authorities and provide accident facts as is found on the shipping documents (e.g., waybill, manifest, or bill of lading). This contact may be either by two-way radio, telegraph or telephone, whichever is available and fastest. An example of a carrier waybill is shown in Figure 2-2. Besides providing this basic information, the designated member of the rail crew, truck driver or whoever reports the accident, should provide the following information so that the person receiving the report may alert the appropriate response elements and provide the information necessary for preliminary assessment of the accident environment and resources required for mitigating its hazards:

- Precise accident location;

- Hazardous materials being transported;

- Quantity of material released;

- Injuries or fatalities;

- Number and type of cars damaged; and

- Accident site conditions, including

meteorological, topographic, demographic and hydrogeologic.

When members of the train crew or the truck driver are killed or incapacitated during the accide ., obviously they will not be able to notify their carrier's dispatcher or anyone else that an accident has occurred. When this is the case, initial accident notification is usually made by someone who happens to be nearby and sees or hears the accident. Civilian members of the community should immediately advise a local emergency response dispatcher (i.e., fire, police, medical) that an accident has occurred. Even though several individuals may contact the same dispatcher about the incident, this causes no problem. The important point is that no time is wasted, because this immediate notification can allow the local emergency services to respond on-scene promptly. The first few minutes are vital for successful response. This contact is usually by telephone, and the telephone numbers of the local emergency services are located in the front pages of the local telephone directory. Each citizen, who observes an accident should contact the local dispatcher instead of assuming that someone else will notify the appropriate official or agency. Although notification of the accident by the citizen to the local dispatcher is usually by telephone, sometimes an accident occurs in a remote area where there is no telephone service available. When this is the case, citizens band ("CB") radio, emergency channel nine (9) should be used for contacting the local emergency services. There may even be a "Ham" operator nearby. Prior to leaving the accident scene and seeking emergency assistance if radio communications are not available, the citizen should quickly assess the accident situation noting precise location, fires, injuries or fatalities, etc. Members of the civilian population should render medical assistance to those injured only to the point that they are trained and qualified to perform, without unduly exposing themselves.

In a few instances, a hazardous materials transportation accident may first be encountered by an off-duty or on-duty member of the local emergency services. This was the case at hazardous materials transportation accidents in Brooklyn, NY, in 1970, Youngstown, FL, in 1978, and Crestview, FL in 1979. When a member of the emergency services observes the occurrence of a hazardous materials transportation accident they should immediately notify their local emergency services dispatcher according to normal practice.

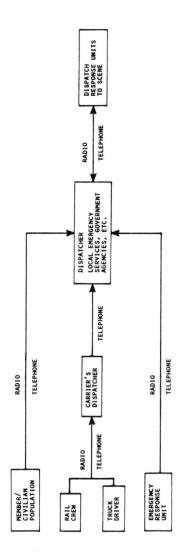

FIGURE 2-1.   INITIAL NOTIFICATION SEQUENCE FROM NOTIFICATION
TO DISPATCH OF RESCUE UNITS TO SCENE

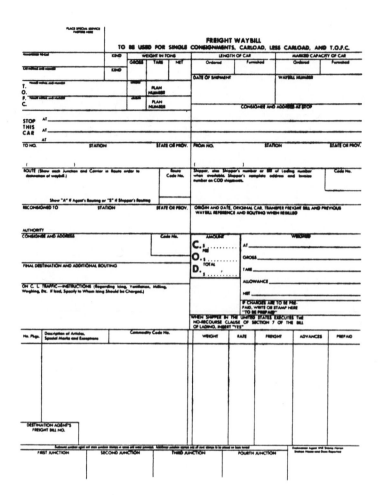

FIGURE 2-2.   CARRIER WAYBILL

Prior to notifying the dispatcher of the accident, a preliminary on-site assessment should be performed noting such on-site information as those described for the rail crew, truck driver and civilian community. After the local emergency services dispatcher is notified of the accident and its on-site conditions, the "alerting" member of the service should remain on-scene to provide emergency assistance as needed until additional response units arrive.

The rail or highway carrier's dispatcher is responsible for contacting the local emergency services as well as Federal, state and local officials and agencies when an accident occurs. This contact is usually performed by telephone. There was a problem of railroad dispatcher offices not being required to be manned 24-hours a day, 7-days a week, even though hazardous materials traffic was moving through a dispatcher's region. As a result of a serious hazardous materials accident at Youngstown FL in 1978, a dispatcher's station must now be manned on a 24-hour basis[9], mitigating this potential problem as it had been prior to 1978. The local emergency response communications coordinator should promptly notify all concerned organizations and not assume that the carrier's dispatcher has done so. This will assure that proper authorities have been notified.

The conductor should have a pre-designated listing of officials with telephone numbers to be contacted in the event of an accident. These lists should be developed through a cooperative effort between rail/highway carriers transporting the hazardous materials and those jurisdictions through which the materials are being shipped. Figure 2-3 identifies a few of the appropriate officials/agencies to be contacted initially. It is also the responsibility of these dispatchers to notify units to respond on-scene as required. Once the accident has been reported, it is imperative that the community's HM emergency response communications network be activated immediately.

A discussion of the required agencies to be notified in the case of an accident is given in Section 1.5 (Technical Assistance and Information).

2.2 INITIATING THE RESPONSE COMMUNICATIONS NETWORK

Once on-scene, one of the first actions to be performed by the local emergency response services is the establishment of the on-scene response communications network. The communications control may be a mobile unit or a fixed installation (e.g., police headquarters). A properly operated communications system is an essential tool at the accident site. However, a communications network that is over-utilized (e.g., everyone on the same frequency) or unstructured could be detrimental to any operation. Unfortunately, the latter occurs frequently at transportation accidents. Within a few minutes after an accident, many types of emergency and work crews begin arriving at the scene. There must be coordination among responding fire and police departments, and spectators also must be dealt with. As the number of people increase at the scene, communications become an extremely important tool for coordinating efforts to mitigate the potential danger of hazardous materials releases. Typically, this is the point where communications between groups begin to break down. There are too many independent groups operating at the scene with no overall communications network to knit them into a cohesive work force. This situation is undesirable for personal safety and response effectiveness.

There are two basic communication problems to and from an accident site. First, there is the problem of communication between individuals and/or groups of people at the site and communications with organizations not located at the accident. Secondly, a need exists to assure that field personnel have the most current methodology available for accident mitigation.

At a crash site, the radio communication equipment will typically belong to five different groups:

1. Fire department;

2. Police department;

3. Emergency medical groups;

4. Carrier; or

5. Civil defense.

Frequently these groups will not be able to communicate directly with one another by radio because they do not have a common frequency. A solution would be to establish a Communications Command Center (CCC). If located at the scene it should be under the control of the on-scene coordinator. If not at the accident site then a primary, priority link between the CCC and the OSC is imperative as is the need for the CCC to

Agency		Comments

1. Name:
    Address:
 	
    Contact:
    Tel. No.:
	National Response Center
	Headquarters, U.S. Coast Guard
	Washington,D.C.
	NRC Duty Officer
	800/424-8802 (24-hr)	

2. Name:
 	
    Address:
 	
    Contact:
    Tel. No.:
	U.S. EPA Regional Office
	Region No. _____
	_____
	_____
	_____
	_____
		
		(day)
		(night)

3. Name:
 	
    Address:
 	
    Contact:
    Tel. No.
	U.S. Coast Guard District Office
	District No. _____
	_____
	_____
	_____
	_____
		
		(day)
		(night)

4. State Agencies:
    Address:
 	
    Contact:
    Tel. No.:
	_____
	_____
	_____
	_____
	_____
		
		(day)
		(night)

FIGURE 2-3. INITIAL NOTIFICATION LIST FOR HAZARDOUS MATERIALS SPILLS

be operated by those trained in communications. Figure 2-4 shows the on-site CCC communications system interfacing.

The CCC has the potential of solving many of the problems that are inherent in present wreck-clearing and other operations. The CCC should be responsible for coordinating all communications between each of the rescue groups at the accident including carrier personnel. The CCC would allow for easy transfer of command to more experienced personnel as they arrive on-site. The CCC would also be responsible for making and maintaining contact with the National Response Center (NRC) and all other necessary away-from-the-scene organizations. This contact to the NRC is telephonic, toll free, and operating 24-hours daily. The CCC would pass real-time data on the conditions at the crash site to the NRC, which would return to the CCC information concerning the mitigation options available, given the hazardous materials involved. The NRC should also be able to make recommendations on alternative techniques for changing conditions at the crash site.

The CCC could furnish the NRC accurate on-scene meteorological conditions, especially wind speed, ambient temperature and precipitation/condensation information and receive estimated downwind HM vapor dispersion distances. The latter would enable the OSC to order timely evacuations to protect crews and civilian population in proximity to the accident.

To make the Communications Command Center effective there must be designated radio frequency channels assigned that will be used nationally for emergency operations. The transceivers to be used by field personnel must be portable and may be designed to transmit or receive only from the CCC. Ideally the CCC should be mobile and not be more than one mile from the accident site. Permanent centers also have advantages. The CCC should have redundant transceivers capable of transmitting and receiving all of the designated radio frequencies. A receiver scanner could be used to monitor the active channels. The operator could select the channels to be used based on the particular needs at the moment. The assignment of frequencies should be spelled out in the community HM emergency response plan.

The CCC must also be capable of relaying information to the NRC. The mechanism to implement this would be to use either a radio link or lay a wire to an acoustic coupler attached to a telephone receiver. This link must be able to transmit voice and data. The data would be transmitted over the telephone using a modem. Vapor concentration, temperature and wind speed and direction data would be transmitted to the NRC. The data should be collected from weather monitoring stations strategically placed around the accident site. The sensor stations would transfer their data to the CCC via cable or via small battery-operated transmitters. If transmitters are used, they could all be assigned the same transmission frequency. The weather sensor stations would initiate their data transmissions at random. The probability of two or more sensor stations transmitting simultaneously would be minimized. The CCC would decode the data and determine if the data were contaminated by two or more channels transmitting concurrently. When data proves to be valid, the CCC would forward it to NRC. If the data are not valid, it would be ignored and another transmission from the weather station would be requested. Until such sophistication becomes commonplace, telephones between the CCC and NRC may be used. The use of on-scene communications to the NRC via radio or video satellite signals would be a major forward step.

Data could also be transmitted by NRC to the CCC. This data could be in conjunction with voice communication and would consist of information concerning the mitigation of the hazards. Located in the CCC would be a line printer which can reproduce the data transmitted from the NRC into hard copy. The line printer should be capable of making additional copies, which could be forwarded to the field crews to minimize misunderstood verbal communication. The hard copy may also serve as reference material. This would minimize the need to carry manuals that cover all types of possible chemical hazard information.

Another function of the CCC, as directed by the OSC could provide factual information to the news media concerning the accident, evacuation possibilities and precautionary steps which the public can perform for self-protection. The CCC should also serve as the information clearinghouse for the accident site with all questions being directed to an official spokesman (the OSC or designee). It is recommended that the official spokesman hold periodic press conferences to keep the news media appraised of the accident situation and provide opportunity for questions. It is hoped that by providing this service the news media would be able to inform the public accurately about the accident status, any hazardous conditions and personal protection required. Members

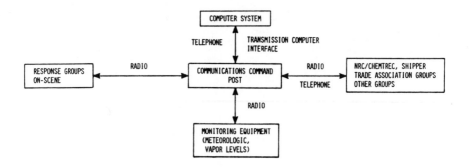

FIGURE 2-4.   ON-SITE CCC COMMUNICATIONS SYSTEM INTERFACE

of the emergency response community should not be asked to answer questions from the news media except at press conferences. Questions should be directed to the CCC, which will advise the OSC. The OSC's official spokesperson will serve as the direct news media interface. That person should also be the interface between the OSC and CCC.

Basic to the establishment of a CCC is the availability of communications equipment for field use. Transceivers for field use should be portable, be able to transmit and to receive from CCC and the necessary inter- and intradisciplinary on-scene groups, and be easily maintained. The capability to produce hard copy recordings for the former would be advantageous.

The cost considerations in terms of required system components are approximately $1,500. It is believed that such a micro-computerized communications system could be transported by mobile response van or other vehicle to the CCC location and that most localities would be able to allocate the purchase cost of materials from their budget. It need not be emphasized that a cost-benefit relationship exists between the purchase cost of equipment and those costs incurred as a result of a severe hazardous materials transportation accident. Being able to speed up communications by a few minutes could prevent a catastrophe and the equipment costs could be easily realized. However, using such a system would require that individuals are properly trained in its use, the system is available for use when an accident occurs, and that the system is durable, well-maintained and accessible to the site.

If the system exists to provide hard copy data output from the CCC to the accident site, it could be used to supplement verbal instructions given by the OSC to designated officials on-site. It is the responsibility of every community to establish designated responsibilities for hazardous materials transportation accident response, so that communications may be quickly established and that a coordinated response effort be conducted.

2.3 FIRST ON-SCENE RESPONDERS

First on-scene responders to a hazardous materials transportation accident include such emergency service organizations as fire, police and medical. A listing of the activities which each of these emergency service organizations normally performs on-scene are given in the following sections.

Activities of the Fire Service

When a call about a hazardous materials accident is received, the following list are activities that the fire service might be called upon to perform on-scene:

1. Activate a communications network;

2. Contact local authorities, USCG/NRC, CHEMTREC, shipper, carrier, DOD, DOT, hospitals and public health officials, state officials, news media and others indicated in the emergency response plan;

3. Obtain technical information about the hazardous materials being transported, its potential dangers (i.e., flammable, toxic, explosive, etc.) and monitor the area for dangerous levels;

4. Provide factual information about the accident status;

5. Advise news media of the status of the situation through the OSC/CCC;

6. Provide two-way radio links to groups involved in response activities;

7. Act in the capacity of the on-scene coordinator;

8. Obtain and utilize meteorological information for firefighting strategy;

9. Perform search and rescue operations;

10. Assist with evacuations;

11. Identify presence of vapor cloud and its direction;

12. Decide what personnel should be present during specific operations;

13. Establish command post;

14. Seek train crew or truck driver for waybill or bill of lading;

15. Decide whether to perform firefighting activities such as extinguishing fires, suppressing vapors, containing runoff to prevent contamination to waterways, closing valves of damaged tank to stop release; and

16. Keep any sources of ignition away from transfer operations, cool container if needed, place protective barriers and stand by on alert in case of an unforeseen event.

Activities of Law Enforcement Personnel

Law enforcement personnel should perform the following activities at hazardous materials accidents:

1. Receive notification of the accident;

2. Make contact with local fire department, carrier dispatcher, shipper and other local officials;

3. Provide communications backup;

4. Determine alternative traffic routes around hazard area;

5. Assess and implement measures needed to secure the area allowing only authorized response individuals into the area and keeping unauthorized personnel out;

6. Establish and monitor roadblocks and other barriers;

7. Assist with evacuation of residents;

8. Assist with removal of fatalities, injuries and exposures;

9. Assume control, if authorized, of community plan; and

10. Re-establish normal traffic flow after accident is considered stabilized.

Activities of Emergency Medical Services

Communication capabilities of emergency medical services should provide receiving information on hazardous materials and exposures and relaying this information to other responding units and provide secondary communication support.

These services must have procedures to give first-aid to victims and to transport them to hospitals. Also, emergency medical personnel should:

1. Have the training and equipment needed for transporting injured persons out of remote areas or rugged terrain;

2. Assist in evacuation; and

3. Assist in personnel decontamination.

Duties for members of the medical services other than emergency medical services should include the following:

1. Establishing communications with mobile emergency units and hospitals;

2. Obtaining information on the numbers and types of injuries, fatalities and exposures;

3. Determining the types of hazardous materials involved;

4. Contacting needed medical specialists;

5. Assessing the adequacy of the facility to treat victims;

6. Determining what if any, additional help or facilities will be needed;

7. Deciding what facilities are capable of handling victims with specific injuries or exposures; and

8. Contacting hospital personnel so they can prepare for the arrival of the injured victims.

2.4 BASIC CONSIDERATIONS FOR INITIAL RESPONDERS

First on-scene responders to a hazardous materials transportation accident are required to make many decisions about the hazards of the accident and their capability for handling them based on the availability of personnel, equipment, materials, and other resources. Figure 2-5 is an example of a decision matrix for firefighters. A detailed discussion in terms of hazardous materials identification is given in Section 3.2. Once the hazardous material has been identified then appropriate actions may be taken. Basic decisions such as whether or not to attempt to fight a fire should be made at this point. Basic considerations include the availability of water, anticipated effectiveness, and its compatibility with the released material. Local jurisdictions should have an inventory of available materials, equipment and trained personnel for handling the hazards associated with the hazardous commodities being transported through their jurisdiction. Such an inventory of commodity flow through a locality should also be produced. Once the inventory of personnel, equipment and materials has been compiled, these data should be available to the OSC on-site. The storage of these data could be at the State capital, county seat or any central location and be accessed through telephone link to the accident site, the OSC or CCC. The inventory would serve as a real-time decision-making tool for the OSC. Adjacent communities should have access to each others inventory of personnel, equipment, materials, and other resources as a backup.

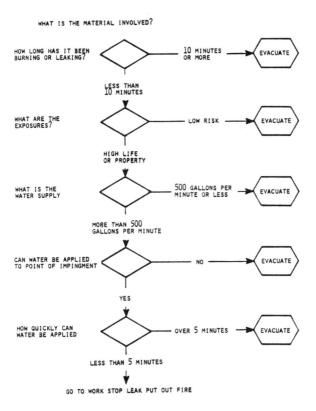

WHAT IS THE MATERIAL INVOLVED?

HOW LONG HAS IT BEEN BURNING OR LEAKING? — 10 MINUTES OR MORE → EVACUATE

LESS THAN 10 MINUTES

WHAT ARE THE EXPOSURES? — LOW RISK → EVACUATE

HIGH LIFE OR PROPERTY

WHAT IS THE WATER SUPPLY — 500 GALLONS PER MINUTE OR LESS → EVACUATE

MORE THAN 500 GALLONS PER MINUTE

CAN WATER BE APPLIED TO POINT OF IMPINGMENT — NO → EVACUATE

YES

HOW QUICKLY CAN WATER BE APPLIED — OVER 5 MINUTES → EVACUATE

LESS THAN 5 MINUTES

GO TO WORK STOP LEAK PUT OUT FIRE

FIGURE 2-5.   SAMPLE DECISION MATRIX FOR FIREFIGHTERS

The Department of Transportation, Environmental Protection Agency, U.S. Coast Guard and Association of American Railroads contain initial response procedures for each of the 28 chemicals and propellants in this document. Appendices G, H, I and J summarize these respective guidelines for first on-scene responders.

2.5 IDENTIFYING HAZARDOUS MATERIALS

The following section briefly describes methods for on-scene identification of hazardous materials. Current state-of-the-art for on-scene identification of hazardous materials involves sensing techniques, visual methods and external communications systems. Sensing techniques include monitoring equipment such as vapor detection devices, radiation absorption units and GC/MS. Visual methods include: waybills, consists, bills of lading, and other shipping documentation; DOT placards; UN and STCC numbers; specific service stenciling (e.g., chlorine, LPG and anhydrous ammonia) and tank car and vehicle markings. External communications systems include telephonic means (e.g., NRC and CHEMTREC) and computerized data hookup (e.g., OHMTADS). A detailed discussion for identifying hazardous materials on-scene is given in Section 3.2. Initial responders should familiarize themselves with these methods so that sound analysis of chemical information may be obtained and relayed to appropriate officials in a timely manner thus maximizing personnel safety and the public welfare.

2.6 ON-SCENE COORDINATION

The on-scene coordinator is the person in charge of operations at the accident site. By having this authority, the OSC must utilize the services of both technical and non-technical personnel in the fields of emergency response, wreckage removal, product transfer, cleanup and disposal operations and mesh these in with the needs of public officials and the public. To be an effective on-scene coordinator, an individual must have training and first hand experience in such areas and management as: hazardous materials identification; communications; protective clothing, gear, breathing apparatus and equipment; specialized chemical treatment; equipment (e.g., detection, containment, analytical and heavy); wreckage removal, product transfer, cleanup and disposal operations and contractors; regulations; evacuation; sources of hazardous material physical and chemical information; and vapor dispersion. A

detailed discussion of training requirements is given in Section 1.1.

At hazardous materials transportation accidents in which a water pollution threat is not possible or when the local community has personnel, equipment and materials available to mitigate the hazards, the on-scene coordinator is frequently the local fire chief. State contingency plans should identify a designated official or his representative as the on-scene coordinator, if the community does not have a viable plan with a designated OSC or the situation is beyond the capability of the community to deal with. When a potential water pollution threat exists or when a local community does not have sufficient personnel, equipment and materials to mitigate the materials hazards, the on-scene coordinator is either the USCG representative (threat to coastal and navigable waterways) or the EPA representative (threat to inland waters, groundwater). The identification of the appropriate representative to respond is designated through the NRC under the aegis of the National Contingency Plan. Once on-site, the federal on-scene coordinator supercedes the responsibility of the local coordinator, if the OSC has the authority or is requested by local authorities to do so. To assure that the identity of the on-scene coordinator is clearly defined the following guidelines should be followed:

- On-scene coordinator be located at command post; and

- Name and access number to OSC be given to each "service" chief.

When spills of chemicals or propellants occur on DOD facilities and vapors pose an off-site threat, the on-base emergency coordinator should work closely with the USCG or EPA representative. Because DOD is a participating member of the National Contingency Plan, matters of this type should be handled in a similar manner to other serious threats and in accordance with the authority and responsibilities found in the 1510 Plan.

The command post should be an off-site mobile facility in which the on-scene coordinator and technical representatives make decisions in terms of accident mitigation. This response unit should have the capabilities of serving as the Communications Command Center, if possible, and be equipped with other specialized equipment and materials needed at most hazardous materials accidents.

It is recommended that every locality have ready a mobile command post and, based upon the types and volumes of commodity flow through a community, be equipped with basic material and equipment resources described in Section 1.7. Having a computer terminal, at the county seat or other central location, which provides access to chemical and hazards information should enable the OSC to obtain real-time data for use on-site. The command post should be located upwind at sufficient distance from the accident site so personnel are not exposed to flammable or toxic vapors.

A detailed discussion of the communication link requirements on-site is given in Section 2.2.

2.7 OBTAINING ACCIDENT INFORMATION

When responding to the scene of a hazardous materials transportation emergency, initial on-scene responders should assess the accident site conditions so that appropriate personnel, equipment and materials may be alerted/deployed to the scene. In addition to information about the nature of the accident, HM involved, location and any obvious hazards, the responders should identify environmental, meteorological, topographic and demographic conditions.

Environmental conditions, such as presence of water bodies, soil composition, type of vegetation, aquatic and terrestrial animals are needed to determine control strategy. Much of this information may be obtained from a responders general knowledge of an area or from U.S. Geological Survey base maps and aerial photographs.

If possible, meteorological data should be collected at the accident site, but if an accident occurs in a remote area or rugged terrain, deploying mobile meteorological monitoring equipment may be unrealistic. However, when the topography is rather flat, mobile meteorological monitoring equipment should be placed at the accident site, with resultant data being continually or frequently forwarded to the CCC and to the NRC if the latter is involved.

Local meteorological forecasts, expected to impact an accident area, will always be important, especially when the accident is of such magnitude that the response operations will take several days. When required, forecasted meteorological information may be obtained through contact with a local weather service, the National Weather Service, National Oceanographic and Atmospheric Administration (NOAA) or a

nearby military base. Emergency response plans should have a provision which has arranged for an interface mechanism with these groups to obtain the necessary weather information.

The types of data, which should be collected either by the mobile equipment or through the weather service, include ambient temperature (vertical profiles, if possible, wind speed and direction, atmospheric pressure presence or absence of temperature inversion, any storm activity and location of nearest cold front (precipitation or condensation activity).

Devices, for the collection of meteorological or other data (e.g., vapor concentration) or for detection purposes, should meet the following requirements:

- Be able to function over a wide range of temperatures;

- Be able to withstand shock and hostile environments;

- Be easily maintained with replaceable parts;

- Require only simple input and output, used with a minimum of training;

- Have non-sparking components (be approved for operation in the presence of the vapors that may be present);

- Provide real-time monitoring capabilities;

- Be portable, easily carried;

- Have a long-lived, rechargeable power source;

- Provide a written record of the data; and

- Be cost-effective.

Meteorological and other types of monitoring devices should be conducted continuously throughout the entire period of the accident until the final cleanup/disposal have been completed. In conjunction with on-scene monitoring, any released material should be tracked by radar/aeriel surveillance methods.

Based on meteorological conditions and the toxic and flammable vapor hazards associated with the released material, decisions may be made concerning; (1) whether the hazardous condition has been stabilized enough to allow work in the area, and (2) whether downwind population should be evacuated and to what distance. These decisions are critical in cases where the released material presents toxic or flammable vapor hazards. A commercial source of meteorological monitoring equipment is Forestry Suppliers, Inc. of Jackson, MS (1-800-647-5368).

Topographic conditions should be noted by initial emergency responders because landforms can act as barriers or "funnels" for the hazardous materials (liquid or vapor) when spilled. For example, if a dense gas is released (most of the chemicals and propellants in this manual behave in this fashion), it tends to hug the ground, spread and seek low areas. If a population center is located in a valley and the spill occurs on a ridge, it may be necessary to evacuate the low lying area even though the area may be upwind.

Demographic data such as population density (persons/mi^2) and transportation infrastructure will influence the level of evacuation required and the evacuation routes which may be taken.

Once an initial on-site assessment is made (e.g., location, nature, HM involved, environmental, meteorological, topographic and demographic data), this information should be relayed to the CCC and in turn to the services dispatcher so personnel, equipment and materials may be deployed to the scene, applicable vapor dispersion models exercised, evacuation conducted, access to the accident site controlled and other decisions made by the on-scene coordinator.

2.8 HAZARD ASSESSMENT

Continuous hazard assessment should be conducted by the responders to enable operational decisions for mitigating the accident situation and, thus, returning to a normal state. The hazard assessment activities which should be performed by initial on-scene responders include the following:

- Determining whether hazardous materials have been released;

- Identifying hazardous materials released;

- Determining the location, terrain, nature and extent of released chemical or propellant;

- Determining who and what are at risk;

- Determining if there are fatalities, injuries, exposures and whether rescue is feasible;

- Ascertaining the extent of damage; and

- Determining sources and nature of any fires.

Section 3 presents detailed hazard assessment guidelines and their relationship to initial on-scene responders.

2.9 RELAYING ACCIDENT INFORMATION

Initial on-scene responders should be familiar with ways to relay on-site accident information. This necessity may be accomplished through training (Section 1.1) and actual experience in accessing accidents and using communications equipment (Section 2.2). The types of accident information which should be relayed to the service dispatcher includes hazardous materials identification (Section 3.2) and accident site conditions (Section 3.3).

2.10 ASSESSING RESOURCES

The on-scene coordinator should identify the resources needed on-site to control the accident. This inventory should include such factors as personnel, equipment, materials and responders and also includes a comparison of available resources in the area (from the contingency plan). Based on the assessment of the hazards associated with the accident, made by responders and technical experts, the OSC may determine the accident resource requirements. Other factors useful for determining the resources required to mitigate the hazards include on-site observation of personnel combating the hazards and personal experience of the OSC.

Once the required resources have been identified, the on-scene coordinator would initiate action to acquire/deploy them.

2.11 DECISION-MAKING

The OSC needs to make decisions concerning deploying personnel and resources to the scene, initiating rescue, controlling access, evacuation, moving the command post and requesting additional assistance and resources. At the scene of a hazardous materials transportation emergency timely decisions must be made by the on-scene coordinator for these factors. A general discussion of training which on-scene decision makers should have is given in Section 1.1.

Basic to any transportation accident is the deployment of personnel and resources to the scene. When hazardous materials are involved, the interactions of responding personnel becomes much more complex. This is due to the fact that these materials are hazardous, therefore, a large number of specialist groups are involved and the situation continually changes, sometimes drastically, so the OSC must be very judicious, yet act promptly in assigning personnel, equipment and other resources.

During performance of USAF contract F04611-80-C-0046 an accident management strategy for decision-makers was developed. This strategy involved the development of logic needed for the assessment of and recovery from catastrophic spills of either aerozine-50 or nitrogen tetroxide during off-complex highway transportation emergencies. The accident management technique developed for these two commodities could be applied to any hazardous material. To further illustrate this methodology as it is applied to accident management for a hypothetical accident of aerozine-50, refer to Appendix K.

Upon receiving initial notification of an accident, the emergency service's (i.e., police, fire, medical) dispatcher deploys "first response" teams to the scene. This includes an officer who serves as the on-scene coordinator. If the accident situation worsens and onsite "first response" teams are not capable of handling the situation, additional personnel, equipment and materials need to be brought on-scene or a decision needs to be made to evacuate existing on-scene personnel. The decision to evacuate existing on-scene personnel should be made by the on-scene coordinator. If additional personnel, equipment or materials are needed onscene this request should be made by the OSC through the CCC to the appropriate organizations. It should then be the particular service's dispatcher or specialist group's representative who should locate and deploy the required resources on-scene. Mutual aid agreements should be made between communities and with county and state organizations to assure the availability of personnel, equipment and materials, when an emergency occurs. Many such agreements exist, but other jurisdictions need to develop programs.

Another source of specialized personnel, equipment and materials is a local DOD facility. Agreements should also be made between nearby DOD installations and local communities with the former being invited to participate in the development of contingency plans. Often local communities cannot afford the specialized training for personnel or the equipment and materials needed to handle hazardous materials transportation accidents. However, DOD facilities of any reasonable size usually have access to specialized personnel, equipment and materials capable of assessing and mitigating certain HM hazards.

When local fire, police or emergency medical service personnel arrive on-scene and it is determined that the area is safe to work, rescue of injured and exposed persons and removal of fatalities should be initiated. Local hospitals should be notified immediately by the service dispatcher, through the CCC, of an accident resulting in injuries, exposures, fatalities, and what HM is involved, so the hospital may ready itself for the arrival of these individuals. The communications link is usually through the hospital's emergency unit. It is recommended that hospitals which do not have emergency operation plans develop such a program. Also, this program, once developed, should be tested by hospital personnel and local emergency medical personnel at a mock-up accident.

During the removal of injuries and exposures from the scene, continuous monitoring for toxic vapors should be conducted. If proper breathing equipment and protective clothing are not available for use by emergency personnel and toxic vapors exceed the TLV, rescue should not be attempted. All emergency services should have such breathing apparatus and protective clothing and gear. In all cases, removal of fatalities should not be conducted when the concentration is above the TLV. A discussion of methods for assessing the on-site vapor concentrations is given in Section 3.4.1.

At all accidents, access to the scene should be controlled so unauthorized individuals do not enter the area. Only personnel such as emergency response, product transfer, cleanup/disposal, wreckage removal contractors, etc. should be permitted within the accident perimeter and then only those involved in on-going operations. If questions arise about the authorization of individuals on-scene, these inquiries should be directed to the on-scene coordinator. The enforcement of restricted access to an area should be performed by law enforcement personnel.

When the on-scene or downwind vapor concentration exceeds the TLV, evacuation of response personnel and members of the civilian population should be considered. Emergency response personnel, wearing proper protective clothing and breathing apparatus, may remain if engaged in essential operations and continuously monitored. Others should be withdrawn to a safe distance upwind. If the public is exposed or expected to be exposed to a dangerous concentration, instructions for self-protection and evacuation should be given.

Evacuation should be conducted in an orderly manner, in accordance with the contingency plan. Reasonable safeguards for evacuated citizens' property (e.g., by patrolling the evacuated area) need to be provided. Evacuation should be conducted by law enforcement personnel in conjunction with members of the civil defense organization. Communities and state agencies should establish a cooperative assistance plan in the event of such an emergency.

The area to be evacuated will be a function of the HM vapor dispersion pattern. A discussion of vapor dispersion in relation to estimating evacuation radii is given in Section 3.4.1.

The command post should be kept upwind from the spill site at all times. Basic to keeping upwind from the spill site is knowing the prevailing and actual wind direction.

In some instances, on-site personnel, equipment and materials may not be adequate to control the hazards of the accident. When this is the case, the on-scene coordinator can request additional assistance and resources. All requests for additional assistance and resources should be made to the on-scene coordinator or through the CCC.

2.12 WORKING WITH THE NEWS MEDIA

The news media can be a valuable resource or another complicating factor in handling a hazardous materials emergency. Obviously, the former is necessary. The news media deals in information and has direct contact with the public via TV and radio. Thus the news media can provide warnings and instructions when there is a danger, a potential danger or even if an evacuation is necessary.

The public and the news media are entitled to know what has happened, what's going on and what to expect. It is important for the OSC to hold periodic press conferences to provide factual information. Individual responders and experts can expect to be pursued by the news media. However, the overall operation can best be served, if there is a clear understanding and agreement among such individuals and the OSC that all the interviews will be held at press conferences. By using this approach, all concerned hear the same story. All those who wish to speak or are requested by the media to do so may be heard. The OSC should serve as the moderator. It would be wise for the group of speakers to meet together before the press conference, if possible, to make certain they are on the "same wavelength", so to speak, and to try to have the facts put together and answers to anticipated questions prepared, so that the press conference will proceed smoothly, satisfy the public and news media needs, and not detract from the emergency response efforts.

The OSC or the OSC's designated representative should keep in contact with the news media and determine what questions they have and what information they desire. This contact also facilitates requests to the media to make announcements promptly.

The news media should not be located with the OSC. However, appropriate accommodations should be made available nearby, as is done for the numerous other groups represented, so that there is no actual or implied discrimination against the media.

The OSC should arrange for the news media to be informed of the dangers that exist, personnel precautions that must be taken, why certain actions are taken and special instructions. Above all, the media members must understand that restrictions placed upon them are for their own safety and to prevent interference with operations, not to hide the facts.

The news media is in a unique position to allay public fears and prevent panic. News media officals should avoid the temptation to make technical assessments at the scene and should make certain that only factual information is reported. The best method for this is to work through the OSC or other officially designated spokesperson. Rumors may be easily confirmed or proven wrong by these persons. Even though the temptation for sensationalism may be very strong the media should exercise restraint, so as not to unduly alarm the public or to further complicate the serious problems with which the emergency responders are already faced.

A detailed discussion of the news media interface with on-scene responders is given in Section 2.2 (Initiating the Response Communications Network).

2.13 STATUS REPORTING FOR CONTINUAL ASSESSMENT

For the duration of the accident, frequent periodic status reporting should be made from each on-scene specialist and group to the on-scene coordinator, or his designated spokesperson, via the CCC. Status reporting serves as an excellent mechanism for facilitating information flow between organizations for changing accident conditions, success and problems encountered as well as for obtaining minute-to-minute information on accident site conditions. A discussion of status reporting in terms of news media interface is given in Section 2.2 (Initiating the Response Communications Network).

The CCC location depends upon the particular community and its contingency plan. It should be located far enough away from the accident scene so that its function is never endangered. Depending upon the circumstances, the on-scene coordinator, media interfacing representative and other technical experts may or may not be located at this facility. All communications should flow through the CCC, to and from the scene. Technical decisions should be made by the OSC based on continuous status reporting from the scene via the CCC. Once an appropriate technical decision has been made by the OSC, the duty should be given to the on-scene service chief whose personnel are performing the actual response activities. It cannot be overemphasized how critical it is for community contingency plans to pre-establish specific responsibilities for organizations responding on-scene and providing support.

2.14 HAZARDOUS CHEMICAL DATA

This section identifies the kinds of physical and chemical properties presented in this document for the 28 chemicals and propellants. The following information is given in Appendix A:

- Flash point;

- Vapor density (relative to normal air);

- Critical temperature;

- Critical pressure;

- Lower and upper flammability limits in air;

- Specific gravity;

- Color of material;

- Threshold Limit Value (TLV);

- **Short-term inhalation limits**; and

- **Odor threshold.**

3. HAZARD ASSESSMENT GUIDELINES

The first step in mitigating the effects of a hazardous materials transportation emergency is to view the accident site in its entirety; determine the materials involved; identify synergistic/antagonistic effects; determine which mitigation and cleanup/disposal options are available, applicable and viable; and then choose among the options those best suited to handle the situation. The accident site with all its specific meteorological, environmental, topographic, hydrogeologic and demographic considerations must be detailed before a course of response and mitigation actions can even be contemplated. Such things as material release, fire and fire impingement, amount and nature of container damage, meteorological conditions, terrain, population and property proximity and resource availability are all necessary inputs to the various on-scene decision-makers handling the accident.

The imperatives associated with response and mitigation, however, must have human safety as the first priority, followed by protection to the environment and surrounding property. Transportation industries (rail and highway) involved in accidents are confronted with additional operating and cost problems in re-establishing order and resumption of business after an incident. Furthermore, members of the local sociopolitical structure may place restrictions on response and mitigation activities for various reasons, all of which make the total assessment of an accident extremely complicated.

This document will attempt to delineate the necessary steps in assessing the technical and physical hazards associated with a transportation emergency. The sociopolitical and economic business aspects which are also relevent will not be discussed. However, every emergency responder and on-scene decision-maker ought to be aware that these issues can also be extremely important at an accident and may even dictate hazards mitigation activities.

3.1 ASSESSING THE ACCIDENT SCENE

Initially, the hazardous materials involved must be identified along with their physical, chemical and thermal properties; assessments of toxic, flammable and explosive vapor hazards associated with the particular hazardous material involved in the accident must be performed; and accident site conditions must be detailed.

In determining the accident site conditions, guidelines must be established to handle such situations as: hazardous materials on fire resulting in toxic or corrosive material hazards; massive liquid pool or small continuous leak as a result of loose, damaged or unseated fittings or valves; and situations where no release occurs but there is fire impingement on intact tanks containing hazardous materials.

Given both the hazardous materials involved and other accident conditions such as release, fire involvement, location and weather; hazards mitigation options may then be identified. In deciding which hazards mitigation options to use, personnel must be aware of the available alternatives, personnel and equipment requirements and appropriate specific applications for each method. Procedures need to identify available options to on-scene decision-makers so that the optimum solution considering both safety and cost-effectiveness is reached. The options also should be developed in an integrated form so that the total scene will be considered at every step in the wreck-handling process. (See Appendix K).

3.2 DETERMINING HAZARDOUS MATERIALS INVOLVEMENT AND IDENTIFICATION

The initial confusion and misleading reports following a transportation emergency are a natural result of the chaos and fear at an accident site. However, for a responder to be able to take adequate mitigating actions and alleviate the safety problems, fast, accurate accounting of the materials involved is essential. The first step is to determine whether or not hazardous materials are present in the train consist or on the truck. The waybill, train consist or bill of lading which accompany shipments by rail and highway are the appropriate indicators of container contents. In the highway mode, the bill of lading is carried in the driver's cab. For rail shipments, the train consist and waybill information is kept by the conductor in the caboose. These documents identify contents of a highway tank truck or rail tank car and provide the quantity and weight of the commodity, the DOT placards required, the DOT description and hazard classification of the material and the National Motor Freight Classification Number (highway) or the Uniform Classification Number (rail) for the specific commodities being transported.

If these documents are not available, a phone call to the transportation company's dispatcher can provide the required information.

Once the presence or absence of hazardous materials has been ascertained and their location identified, the level of involvement in the wreck itself must be determined. This involvement may be simply a derailed, undamaged/damaged loaded tank car, a leaking tank car, a leaking tank car with burning contents, a damaged/undamaged loaded tank car with fire impingement, etc. Under such conditions the involvement, location and identification of hazardous materials can be critical.

The identity of materials involved in an accident can be determined using any one or combination of the following methods:

● Visual methods such as documentation, placards, markings or container shapes/designs;

● External communications data systems such as CHEMTREC, USCG/NRC, OHMTADS, etc.; and

● Sensing methods using equipment specifically designed to identify commodities.

3.2.1 Visual Methods

Several visual methods for on-scene identification of hazardous materials contained in transport trailers, railcars or other shipping containers exist. These include:

● Waybill, consist or bill of lading documentation;

● DOT placarding system separately or in conjunction with the United Nations (UN) or Standard Transportation Commodity Code (STCC) identification numbers; and

● Observation of markings, specific coloration, size, shape and appurtenances on containers.

Optimally, these methods can be used in conjunction with other available methods to identify a material involved in an accident. Positive identification is necessary for response personnel to properly mitigate hazards associated with a specific accident.

Waybill, Consist or Bill of Lading Documentation

Waybill, consist or bill of lading documentation is an important tool for identifying the contents of a tank truck, tank car or other container involved in a transportation accident. In the highway mode, the bill of lading is carried in the driver's cab. For rail shipments, the train consist and waybill information is usually held by the conductor. These documents identify contents of a rail tank car or highway tank truck as well as providing the quantity and weight of the commodity, the DOT placards required, the DOT description and hazard classification of the material, the National Motor Freight Classification Number (highway) or the Uniform Classification Number (rail) for the specific commodities being transported and sometimes general emergency response information. An example of a sample waybill is given in Figure 2-2. Waybills, bill of lading or some exempted documentation are required under the Hazardous Materials Transportation Act to accompany a shipment of hazardous materials. In reality this does not always happen and then additional information must be sought to identify materials. Following an accident, rail or highway personnel should seek out representatives of the emergency response community and supply any documentation or assistance they can to help identify the materials involved. Further, the rail crew should also identify not only involved cars that contain hazardous materials but also their position in the train for possible interaction with other HM which could increase hazards and risks to arriving emergency responders. Many railroads and shippers currently provide printed emergency response procedures with the documentation for each commodity being transported.

DOT Placarding System

The DOT placards are indicators of the primary hazard associated with specific classes of hazardous materials. They indicate explosives, compressed gases (non-flammable and flammable), flammable liquids and solids, oxidizing materials, poisonous materials, irritating materials, corrosive materials and radioactive materials, etc.

According to the DOT the colors used for hazardous materials placards and labels are designed to readily identify the primary hazards of a cargo or material to emergency response personnel. Because of the various dangers, six distinctive colors are used to assist in identification of the most significant hazard involved. These six colors are important for emergency response personnel to remember when looking at vehicle placards or package labels, and are as follows:

1. Orange identifies explosives and blasting agents.

2. Red identifies flammable and combustible materials (liquids, solids or gaseous).

3. White identifies items such as poison, corrosive materials, poison gas, chlorine and any other material which may present a severe health hazard.

4. Blue designates materials which will react violently, when in contact with water, usually producing a flammability hazard or generating extremely high temperatures.

5. Yellow designates substances which will react violently upon contact with other chemicals, such products may produce toxic or flammable gases through spontaneous combustion or they may detonate if subjected to severe shock.

6. Green identifies materials which are highly pressurized. Such materials may explode without warning if exposed to intense heat.

Certain hazardous commodities, with multiple hazards, are identified by a multi-colored placard.

7. Yellow and White indicate Radioactive materials.

8. Red and White stripes indicate Flammable solid.

9. Red and White stripes with Blue top containing a slashed W indicate a flammable solid which is water-reactive. The slashed W indicates water is not to be used on the commodity.

Material Identification Numbering Systems

All DOT-regulated hazardous commodities shipped by highway or rail have been assigned a United Nations (UN) number by DOT. The railroads also utilize a Standard Transportation Commodity Code (STCC) number. If either or these numbers is known, but the commodity name is not known, existing response procedures may be identified by referencing the UN number in the DOT "1980 Hazardous Materials Emergency Response Guidebook[6]" or the STCC number in the AAR guide, "Emergency Handling of Hazardous Materials in Surface Transportation[8]". Each of these manuals has been designed for a particular purpose; consequently, they differ in details. Appropriate response procedures need to be available in a single source document for all hazardous materials emergencies. A problem associated with the UN classification system is that the responses are for generic hazard groupings (although primary, secondary and tertiary hazards have been considered), rather than being commodity specific.

Table 3-1 shows the hazard class, placards required, packaging exceptions and specific requirements for transport of the 28 chemicals/propellants addressed by this manual. Table 3-2 gives the DOT/UN and STCC number for each of the chemicals and propellants.

Specific Service Stenciling

Certain commodities in transportation require that the name be stenciled on the tank car or container. For example, tank cars of anhydrous ammonia, propane, chlorine and butadiene service are stenciled. This stenciling can be a useful identification tool as an indicator of tank contents. Also, to insure reliability, a check should be made prior to loading or unloading the container so that the lading conforms with the tank stencil. Operational procedures are needed to ensure this check prior to loading and unloading operations.

3.2.2 External Communications Methods

Telephonic assistance networks such as the USCG National Response Center and CHEMTREC can assist a caller in identifying a material given some on-scene information such as markings, placards, color, odor, dispersion pattern, behavior (e.g., reactivity), etc. If the information is adequate, these groups may be able to provide preliminary handling and firefighting procedures until expert assistance arrives. Computerized systems can further augment data transmission to an accident scene. These systems need to be accessible to personnel in remote areas; use real-time data; have quick turn around time, which will improve on-scene identification methods; and have 24-hour accessibility by personnel to the system. The personnel using these systems need to have knowledge of input parameters used to execute the models and have proper training to interpret the results. A detailed discussion of these systems, methods of operation and access information is given in Section 1.5.

3.2.3 Sensing Methods

The state-of-the-art of practical hazardous materials sensing technology is relatively unsophisticated and not

TABLE 3-1.   REGULATIONS APPLICABLE TO CONTAINER REQUIREMENTS*
(Code of Federal Regulations Title 49)

Hazardous Materials Descriptions and Proper Shipping Names	Hazard Class	Label(s) Required (if not excepted)	Packaging	
			Exceptions	Specific Requirements
1. Acetone	Flammable Liquid	Flammable Liquid	173.118	173.119
2. Acetone Cyanohydrin	Poison B	Poison	None	173.346
3. Acrylonitrile	Flammable Liquid	Flammable Liquid and Poison	None	173.119
4. Aerozine-50	Flammable Liquid	Flammable Liquid and Poison	173.118	173.119
5. Ammonia, Anhydrous	Nonflammable Gas	Nonflammable Gas	173.306	173.304 173.314 173.315
6. Butadiene, Inhibited	Flammable Gas	Flammable Gas	173.306	173.304 173.314 173.315
7. Chlorine	Nonflammable Gas	Nonflammable Gas and Poison	None	173.304 173.314 173.315
8. Ethyl Acrylate, Inhibited	Flammable Liquid	Flammable Liquid	173.118	173.119
9. Ethylene Oxide	Flammable Liquid	Flammable Liquid	None	173.124
10. Hydrazine, Anhydrous	Flammable Liquid	Flammable Liquid and Poison	None	173.276
11. Hydrocyanic Acid	Poison A	Flammable Gas and Poison Gas	None	173.332
12. Hydrogen, Liquefied	Flammable Gas'	Flammable Gas	None	173.316
13. Isobutane (LPG)	Flammable Gas	Flammable Gas	173.306	173.304 173.314 173.315
14. Methyl Alcohol	Flammable Liquid	Flammable Liquid	173.118	173.119
15. Methyl Bromide	Poison B	Poison	None	173.353
16. Methylhydrazine	Flammable Liquid	Flammable Liquid and Poison	None	173.145
17. Monomethylamine Nitrate	None	None	None	None
18. Nitrogen Tetroxide, Liquid	Poison A	Oxidizer and Poisonous Gas	None	173.336
19. Oxygen, Pressurized Liquid	Nonflammable Gas	Oxidizer	None	173.304
20. Propane (LPG)	Flammable Gas	Flammable Gas	173.306	173.304 173.314 173.315

* Source: Title 49 CFR, Section 172.101.

TABLE 3-1 (cont'd)

Hazardous Materials Descriptions and Proper Shipping Names	Hazard Class	Label(s) Required (if not excepted)	Packaging	
			Exceptions[1]	Specific Requirements
21. Propylene (LPG)	Flammable Gas	Flammable Gas	173.306	173.304 173.314 173.315
22. Sodium Hydro-sulfide Solution	Corrosive Material	Corrosive	173.244	173.245
23. Sodium Hydroxide Solution	Corrosive Material	Corrosive	173.244	173.249
24. Styrene Monomer, Inhibited	Flammable Liquid	Flammable Liquid	173.118	173.119
25. Toluene	Flammable Liquid	Flammable Liquid	173.118	173.119
26. Dimethylhydra-zine, Unsym-metrical	Flammable Liquid	Flammable Liquid and Poison	None	173.145
27. Vinyl Acetate	Flammable Liquid	Flammable Liquid	173.306 173.314 173.315	173.304
28. Vinyl Chloride	Flammable Gas	Flammable Gas	173.306	173.304 173.314 173.315

TABLE 3-2. DOT/UN AND STCC NUMBERS FOR SELECTED COMMODITIES*

	Commodity	DOT/UN Number	STCC Number
1.	Acetone	1090	4908105
2.	Acetone Cyanohydrin	1541	4921401
3.	Acrylonitrile	1093	4906420
4.	Aerozine-50	N/A[1]	N/A
5.	Anhydrous Ammonia	1005	4904210
6.	Butadiene, Inhibited	1010	4905704
7.	Chlorine	1017	4904120
8.	Ethyl Acrylate, Inhibited	1917	4907215
9.	Ethylene Oxide	1040	4906610
10.	Hydrazine, Anhydrous	2029	4906225
11.	Hydrocyanic Acid	1951	4920125
12.	Hydrogen, Liquefied	1049	4905746
13.	Isobutane (LPG)	1075	4905747
14.	Methyl Alcohol	1230	4909230
15.	Methyl Bromide	1062	4921440
16.	Methylhydrazine	1244	4906230
17.	Monomethylamine Nitrate	N/A	N/A
18.	Nitrogen Tetroxide, Liquid	1067	4920360
19.	Oxygen, Pressurized Liquid	1073	4904360
20.	Propane (LPG)	1075	4905781
21.	Propylene (LPG)	1075	4905782
22.	Sodium Hydrosulfide Solution	2922	4935268
23.	Sodium Hydroxide Solution	1824	4935240
24.	Styrene Monomer, Inhibited	2055	4907265
25.	Toluene	1294	4909305
26.	Dimethylhydrazine, Unsymmetrical	1163	4906210
27.	Vinyl Acetate	1310	4907270
28.	Vinyl Chloride	1086	4905792

* Source: 1982 AAR Emergency Handling of Hazardous Materials in Surface Transportation.

1. May be shipped as hydrazine.

adequate. Areas such as remote versus non-remote sensing and multiple (functional) versus single materials identification need to be developed and assessed in terms of safety, cost, availability and accessibility trade-offs. The most sophisticated technical equipment is not useful if it can not be used where needed by the personnel available.

Technology has perhaps outstripped the emergency response community's resources both to train and equip its personnel. Thus, an effort to identify those methods most immediately applicable and effective is necessary.

To date there are no operational or available instruments capable of remote specific hazardous materials identification. Several systems have been applied to atmospheric observations to measure the low-level concentrations of known species. However, these data are useful and have led to the development of many components which may be used for remote sensing of hazardous materials.

The U.S. Army is experimenting with an instrument which may prove promising in the future, but it is in preliminary developmental stages. The prototype, the XM21, is a passive long-path infrared instrument being developed for field detection of chemical warfare agents (nerve gas). This system is promising because it is being designed for use by an operator with limited training, is portable and rugged. Since the system is designed specifically for nerve gases, analysis and development of a microcomputer-based discrimination subsystem must be conducted to adapt this hardware for identification of many hazardous materials.

Recently, the Computer Genetics Corporation of Wakefield, Massachusetts has developed a mobile LIDAR (light detection and ranging) system using Raman techniques, Rayleigh and Mie scattering, fluorescence and differential absorption for making measurements. This system operates much like radar with 5 to 10 nanosecond (10^{-9} second) pulses of selected wavelengths of light penetrating a column of air or water. The back scattered light is detected as a function of distance by its time delay and computer processing of the spectra yields concentration profiles of the material. The data are rapidly obtained, with high resolution and are three dimensional.

However, the Computer Genetics system has not yet been adapted or used specifically for identifying unknown hazardous materials. This approach also shows considerable promise for future development as a portable field system. Using a single frequency laser, a Raman system has the potential to detect many materials; however, the large power requirements have meant bulky mobile systems to date.

These two areas are the most promising for progress in remote sensing of hazardous materials following transportation emergencies.

The non-remote sensing field has more currently available techniques with several commercial instruments using radiation absorption techniques; (IR, UV, visible) mass spectrometry; gas chromatography; gas chromatography/mass spectrometry (GC/MS); and specific material chemical reactions and parameter measurement techniques (pH, conductivity, colorimetric indicators, gas and vapor detectors).

The GC/MS and dispersive IR analyzer show promise for near-term development. However, the methods for specific materials presently appear the most practical and broadly applicable for accident site use. These methods include specific colorimetric detector tubes, water analysis kits, gas and vapor detectors and dosimeters. The following sections will describe these methods and their specific application to the 28 specified chemicals and propellants.

A. Colorimetric Indicators

Detector tubes are a type of visual colorimetric indicator comprised of a sealed glass cylinder with chemically-treated packings designed to react with a specific gas or vapor. Typically, a calibrated pump is used to draw a vapor sample through the tube and the length of stain or degree of color change determined from calibration charts. This method can be applied to the following:

1. Acetone
3. Acrylonitrile
5. Anhydrous Ammonia
6. Butadiene
7. Chlorine
9. Ethylene Oxide
10. Hydrazine, Anhydrous
11. Hydrocyanic Acid
12. Hydrogen, Liquefied
14. Methyl Alcohol
18. Nitrogen Oxides
19. Oxygen, Pressurized Liquid
20. Propane (LPG)
21. Propylene (LPG)
24. Styrene Monomer, Inhibited
25. Toluene
26. Dimethylhydrazine, Unsymmetrical

27. Vinyl Acetate
28. Vinyl Chloride

These indicators are manufactured by Mine Safety Appliances Company (MSA), National Draeger, Inc., Bendix/Gastee (National Environmental Instruments, Inc.) and Matheson Gas Products (Division of Hill Ross, Inc.), and possibly other firms.

One of the major shortcomings in the application of colorimetric detectors to hazardous materials emergencies is that they are generally material-specific and of very limited use for identification of unknowns or mixtures, which is the usual case in accidents. However, where the presence of a material is suspected, these indicators might add to the evidence toward verification.

B. Water Analysis Kits

Several kits have been developed for analysis of hazardous materials in water. The two major types differ basically in the nature of the tests involved. One uses non-specific, chemical-class tests for detection of pollutant presence, the other keys tests for specific contaminant identification. The first type kit is commercially available from HAC Chemical Co., while the second is still under evaluation by the EPA. The problem with both types of analysis kit is that training is required both to perform and interpret results.

C. Gas and Vapor Detectors

There are many different vapor detectors available for many different applications and varying levels of sensitivity. There are instruments which measure concentrations in percent by volume or percent lower explosive limit (LEL); instruments for specific ranges of explosives or flammable vapors (alkane hydrocarbons); instruments for broad ranges of combustibles; and instruments which do not depend on combustion for their operation.

The basic detection method for the first group of instruments is to burn or combust the gases and to use the combustion products or heat of combustion as an indicator of concentration. Flame ionization and catalytic combustion are the two specific applications. The instruments for detection of other gases or vapors utilize such systems as UV absorption, photoionization and colorimetric techniques. These instruments can provide selected vapor-specific detection. For example, CEA Instruments, Inc. sells a portable continuous colorimetric analyzer capable of detecting ammonia, chlorine, hydrazine, methylhydrazine and oxides of nitrogen.

The combustion-type devices are currently widely used by emergency response groups for monitoring flammable or explosive atmospheres associated with an accident site. They are portable, lightweight, relatively inexpensive and require little technical training to use. Several models are available including the MSA Explosimeter, the Grace Industrial Electronic Nose, the Bacharach TLV Sniffer, Infrared Industries Portable Hydrocarbon Analyzer and the Scott/Davis Portable Flame Ionization Meter.

D. Dosimeters, Personal Monitors, Alarms

These are also instruments which in some manner indicate danger levels of exposure for individuals in the vicinity of hazardous materials releases. These may be portable alarms designed to respond to a specific material such as the U.S. Army M43 alarm which responds to nerve agents and monitors used in mines and tunnels, or personal monitors like the Dupont Pro-Tek badges for toxic gases which could actually be worn by responders. MDA Scientific, Inc. produces personnel pocket-sized monitor/alarm units which can monitor for ammonia, chlorine, hydrazines and nitrogen dioxide. However, these units are specific for given materials and would not be applicable to a broad or unknown range of hazardous atmospheres.

The need for fast, accurate in-field sensing methods for detection and identification of hazardous materials involved in a transportation emergency is urgent. These methods are needed not only to facilitate mitigation and clean-up but also to monitor the environment during these post-accident efforts. Present methods utilizing visual (shipping documents, placards, markings) and external communications systems (CHEMTREC) are simply not adequate.

Currently no remote sensing instrumentation exists which is portable and field-ready for detection and identification of hazardous materials. The Army XM21, remote IR system and the Computer Genetics remote single frequency laser Raman system offer the greatest promise for future development of remote field monitoring systems.

There is a large number of non-remote instruments commercially available for specific applications during hazardous materials emergencies, but there is no instrument capable of identifying an unknown material. Detector tubes, water analysis kits, portable "sniffers" for flammable and explosive vapor levels and specific vapors are all available and can assist in verification of materials on-scene. Also, a dispersive IR instrument and portable gas chromatograph/mass spectrometer (GC/MS) systems are being developed for field use in hazardous materials identification.

However, the single instrument to use at hazardous materials transportation emergencies has yet to become a reality, especially in the area of remote sensing capabilities.

Based upon this review of hazardous materials identification methods Table 3-3 has been prepared to summarize appropriate HM identification methods to be used in on-site analysis.

3.3 DETERMINING THE MAGNITUDE OF THE ACCIDENT

Several factors contribute to the magnitude and severity of a hazardous materials transportation accident. These include the materials involved, accident site location and proximity to population centers, meteorological conditions, site topography and hydrogeology, soil characteristics, presence of fire and firefighting resources available, accident debris, public/observers and the duration of on-scene response activities. Many of these factors are discussed in a book by Al Smith, Jr.[2], Region IV EPA OSC, entitled, _Managing Hazardous Substances Accidents_. The following sections discuss these factors and the significance of their impact on post-accident procedures.

3.3.1 Materials Involved

The hazardous materials involved in a transportation accident dictate what containment measures, firefighting techniques and extinguishing media, hazard mitigation, and cleanup/disposal procedures are effective and available to response personnel. Therefore, the identity, amount, condition and hazardous properties of involved materials must be quickly determined.

3.3.2 Accident Site Location

The proximity of an accident to large cities, property or vital energy and communications systems and/or private property can adversely affect the extent of damages and personal injuries. Densely populated areas may require evacuation, relocation and for boarding during an emergency. Evacuation is a two-edged sword. On the one hand an adequate evacuation radius is essential to provide protection to the public in the event of a toxic vapor cloud. On the other hand, the risks associated with evacuation of the elderly or sick can bring punishing liability after the fact. Of additional concern is damage to private property and businesses as well as energy, communications and other community systems.

3.3.3 Meteorological Conditions

Weather is a critical factor in the response phases of a spill. Reliable information of precipitation forecasts, local temperatures and surface-wind and high-altitude-wind data can be continually available on-scene by the National Oceanographic and Atmospheric Administration (NOAA) (301) 655-4000 or local weather service. Where available, mobile meteorological monitoring equipment could be used at the site for more accurate assessment of evacuation priorities. Data should be obtained continuously, if possible, during critical operations such as plugging leaks, uprighting cars or transferring loads.

Wind speed and direction are critical when gases or extremely volatile liquids are released. Wind shift could mean that work would have to be stopped and the area evacuated. In the case of such a release, steady winds may help disperse toxic or flammable vapors or a fire column may help carry them away. Of course, this impacts communities downwind and evacuation may be a direct result.

Rain conditions can both help and hamper activities at an accident site and provisions for controlling contaminated runoff, preventing leaching of contaminants through soils into ground water and working under generally more dangerous conditions must be anticipated and dealt with.

The ambient temperature may also be an important safety factor, especially where toxic or flammable materials or fire situations are involved. High temperatures can further cause safety risks such as fatigue and stress for on-scene personnel and perhaps cause judgmental errors.

3.3.4 Site Topography and Hydrogeology

All areas, unless they are swamps or lakes, will eventually drain to some water body. Thus, essentially every transportation related hazardous materials accident can be considered a potential spill reaching water. If the material is not directly released into a body of water, it can be introduced as a

TABLE 3-3. SUMMARY OF APPROPRIATE HM
IDENTIFICATION METHODS FOR THE CHEMICALS AND PROPELLANTS*

Material	Service Stenciling	Colorimetric Indicator	Dosimeters, Personal Monitors, Alarms	Gas Detector
1. Acetone		*		*
2. Acetone Cyanohydrin				
3. Acrylonitrile		*		*
4. Aerozine-50				
5. Anhydrous Ammonia	*	*	*	*
6. Butadiene, Inhibited	*	*		*
7. Chlorine	*	*	*	*
8. Ethyl Acrylate, Inhibited				
9. Ethylene Oxide		*		*
10. Hydrazine, Anhydrous		*	*	*
11. Hydrocyanic Acid		*		*
12. Hydrogen, Liquefied		*		
13. Isobutane (LPG)				*
14. Methyl Alcohol		*		*
15. Methyl Bromide		*		*
16. Methylhydrazine		*	*	
17. Monomethylamine Nitrate				
18. Nitrogen Tetroxide, Liquid		*	*	*
19. Oxygen, Pressurized Liquid		*		
20. Propane (LPG)	*	*		*
21. Propylene (LPG)		*		*
22. Sodium Hydrosulfide Solution				
23. Sodium Hydroxide Solution				
24. Styrene Monomer, Inhibited		*		*
25. Toluene		*		*
26. Dimethylhydrazine Unsymmetrical		*	*	
27. Vinyl Acetate		*		
28. Vinyl Chloride		*		*

* Source: Manufacturer's literature. Refer to SRI Dictionary of Chemical Producers
for listing of chemical manufacturers in your area.

contaminant by rain or fire control runoff. Steep cliffs or banks at the site can make wreckage handling and cleanup/disposal very difficult and terrain effects can also alter vapor dispersion patterns impacting evacuation considerations and even on-scene approaches.

Soil characteristics at the site also play an important role in on-scene activities. The need to contain liquid releases and prevent them from entering the soil system and eventually reaching subsurface water is largely dependent on the soil porosity, permeability, sorption characteristics and degree of attenuation. For example, sandy or loamy soils or dry very plastic friable clays allow the rapid penetration and transport of liquids, while dense wet clays, peat moss or humus soils will attenuate and immobilize various contaminants and even buffer certain chemicals. Also certain soil microbia can act to biodegrade some materials once they have been attenuated in the soil system.

3.3.5 Fire and Firefighting Resources

Conventional fire training is not always adequate in chemical situations. Water may indeed worsen a fire involving chemicals and extreme caution must be exercised in using appropriate extinguishing materials. Water should not be used as an extinguishing agent for fires involving acrylonitrile, methyl alcohol, propane, styrene, toluene or vinyl acetate. Fire impingement on loaded containers is extremely dangerous and if sufficient water is available and applied early enough, containers may be cooled. In many cases, fire conditions may provide the best or possibly the only, method for a particular hazardous material. Acrylonitrile, butadiene, ethyl acrylate, styrene, vinyl acetate and vinyl chloride can both undergo polymerization when exposed to intense heating and are safer to let burn. In other instances, it may not be practical to extinguish a fire because there is the grave risk of flash back, reignition and possible explosion. In all cases involving fires, an adequately trained, equipped and coordinated firefighting unit is a necessity.

3.3.6 Accident Debris

Serious accidents always involve twisted, flattened, punctured pieces of metal, wood, plastics and other debris. This material must at some point be moved and properly disposed of which imposes safety and regulatory requirements. Wreckage removal is an integral step in handling a transportation accident and the presence of hazardous materials may complicate these efforts. The accident site must be stabilized from toxic or flammable vapor levels and care must be taken to monitor the area when moving disoriented or damaged cars. See Sections 5.1 and 5.2 on the precautions for cargo transfer and wreckage removal operations.

3.3.7 Public/Onlookers

Onlookers must not be permitted near the scene of a hazardous materials accident. An adequate "public safety perimeter" must be established in the interest of public safety for the safety and efficiency of on-scene personnel. The news media can do much to solve this problem.

3.3.8 Duration of Response Activities

The time and effort spent in the initial phases of accident response can do much to alleviate the needs for extensive subsequent cleanup and disposal. The more rapidly the situation is stabilized for safety, the less damage to property and the environment will be done. Also the steps taken early to mitigate hazards will indicate what actions are required in the later stages of wreckage removal, and cleanup/disposal.

3.3.9 Assessment of Injuries, Exposures and Fatalities

In Section 2, initiating guidelines for rescue and removal of injuries, exposures, and fatalities from the scene of a hazardous materials emergency are discussed. It needs to be emphasized that, even though the primary on-scene responsibility of emergency medical personnel is to provide medical assistance to those who require it, they should not enter a contaminated area when the concentration exceeds the TLV, unless completely protected and fully qualified in self protection, and never when the minimum vapor concentration mixture exceeds the LEL.

Information is needed on the injuries and exposures to the crew or driver in the immediate vicinity of the accident. The crew or driver should be accounted for and rescued if necessary and possible without jeopardizing the safety of the would-be rescuer. It is of prime importance that rescue personnel be adequately clothed and equipped to perform search and rescue operations, or further injuries/fatalities will occur.

The major hazards associated with the 28 chemicals and propellants, upon release in a transportation accident, are the toxic, flammable or explosive vapor levels attendant. Thus, data on hazardous atmosphere, vapor clouds and meteorological conditions are vital to rescue personnel.

3.3.10 Determining Who and What Are at Risk

When a hazardous materials transportation accident occurs, the on-scene coordinator must determine who and what are at risk. Under these conditions, risk may include such factors as personal exposures or injuries, pollution threat or property damage. Once the accident risk is determined, it should be the on-scene coordinator's responsibility to take remedial actions to mitigate these and any further risks.

The risk associated with personal exposures and injuries should be determined for on-scene response personnel as well as members of the local community.

Risk to on-scene response personnel may be assessed by continuously monitoring the accident site for toxic, flammable and explosive vapors, the weather, the integrity of the containers and personnel behavior. When the TLV or LEL threshold exceed the minimum safe concentrations on-site, the on-scene coordinator must immediately evacuate personnel from the scene, until the vapor concentrations are below the TLV or LEL or other precautions are taken. The exception being those personnel especially protected, qualified and who of necessity must work in the toxic atmosphere (not flammable).

Assessing the risk to members of the local community should be performed by applying an appropriate vapor dispersion model (see Section 3.4.1). By inputting basic accident information such as source strength, meteorological and topographic conditions into one of the vapor dispersion models, the on-scene coordinator can estimate the downwind vapor concentrations for a specified time. This tool will enable the on-scene coordinator to establish evacuation radii based on the specific material released, and to determine the exclusion area in any case.

The pollution threat (i.e., water and air) associated with an accident will be a function of the accident site, hydrogeology, topography, meteorological, chemical/physical properties and quantities of the materials released. For a detailed discussion of the behavior of dense gases under various topographic conditions, see Section 3.4.1.

The threat of property damage is based upon the location of an accident with respect to populated/industrialized areas. In populated areas, residents are in potential danger as well as their homes, valuables, pets and any utility systems. Industrial areas may be even more threatened, when public systems such as utilities (power, water supplies), communications (telephone, TV, radio, special satellite), and services (hospitals, schools, retirement homes) are endangered. Decisions need to be made as to whether sufficient resources are available for handling these eventualities, and if not, what alternative actions can be taken to minimize the danger.

In all these cases a local/community emergency action plan to address hazardous materials transportation emergencies that has been developed, implemented and tested is the best mitigation option available.

3.4 ESTIMATING DANGER AREAS

3.4.1 Downwind Vapor Cloud Dispersion

Several vapor dispersion models have been examined including the USCG HACS, Shell R&D SPILLS, DDESB Downwind Chemical Hazard Slide Rule, AFCRL Ocean Breeze/Dry Gulch and prototype dense gas vapor dispersion models.

U.S. Coast Guard Hazard Assessment Computer System (HACS)[7]

HACS is built on the mathematical models that were created for the CHRIS Hazard Assessment Handbook, Volume 3, together with several specialized models developed specifically for computer application. Subroutines for modeling phenomena such as liquid spread and fire, dispersion of vapor, radiation from fires, and dissolution and dispersion in water for some 900 commonly shipped chemicals are included.

The major subroutines are:

(A) Venting Rate Model. This computes the rates and time of release, and total quantities released for gases and liquids which are discharging from a punctured tank or container;

(B) Vapor Flame Size and Thermal Radiation Model. This is used for estimating venting of a flammable gas under pressure from a hole in a tank and is comprised of three segments for computing length and distance of the flame jet (B1);

safe separation distances from the flame and whether or not an intact tank containing compressed gas will rupture if exposed to the flame (B2); and how long to tank rupture given fire exposure (B3);

(C) Vapor Dispersion Model. This computes the dispersion of neutrally buoyant gases in air for either instantaneous or continuous releases of gases or vapors evolving from holes in tanks, evaporating pools of spilled liquid or both;

(D) Spreading Rate and Movement Model. This is used for spills of liquids less dense than water which are insoluble or slightly soluble in water and have a boiling point less than ambient temperature;

(E) Liquefied Flame Size and Thermal Radiation Model. This is used for potential or actual ignition of a pool of spilled flammable liquid;

(I) Boiling Rate Model. This is used to compute time for all discharged liquid to vaporize and is used for liquids more dense than water, insoluble or slightly soluble, with boiling points less than ambient temperature;

(P) Mixing and Dilution Model. This computes the concentration of a water-miscible liquid or solid at a specified point and time resulting from a discharge in a lake, river or tidal estuary;

(R) Boiling Rate Model. This is utilized for volatile liquids soluble in water and having boiling points greater than ambient temperature but less than $100^{\circ}C$;

(T) Spreading Rate and Movement Model. This is applicable to the continuous or instantaneous release of chemicals which are soluble or slightly soluble in water, less dense than water and having boiling points greater than ambient temperature;

(V) Boiling Rate Model. This computes pool size and area, volume of chemical remaining, temperature of the chemical, and evaporation rate for volatile chemicals which are insoluble in water, less dense than water and having boiling points greater than ambient temperature but less than $100^{\circ}C$; and

(X) Movement in Water Model. This is used for chemicals insoluble or slightly soluble in water, more dense than water and having boiling points greater than ambient temperature.

Basic Assumptions of HACS Vapor Dispersion Model (C)

The model is based on the Gaussian diffusion model and the experimentally determined Pasquill variances of the Gaussian concentration profile. This model is comprised of two submodels or segments to compute (C1) the downward distance over which a flammable or toxic cloud or plume is hazardous and (C2) the time of arrival, duration and width of the cloud or plume for given concentration at a specified downwind location and time. The wind direction and velocity are assumed to be constant (invariant with height and distance of travel of the cloud or plume). The model also assumes a flat terrain in the direction of travel. The output from these dispersion submodels is based on values of lower flammable and lower toxic limit concentrations for the spilled chemical.

Interface Capabilities of HACS Vapor Dispersion Model (C)

The basic dispersion model (C) was developed to describe dispersion of gases or vapors released directly from a tank. Vapor dispersion models for releases under other conditions were developed as separate modules interfacing with the basic model. These are:

- Vapor dispersion from insoluble or slightly soluble liquids less dense than water with boiling points lower than the ambient temperature (G). Options are provided to model the vapor release as either instantaneous or continuous.

- Instantaneous or continuous vapor release from insoluble or slightly soluble liquids more dense than water and having boiling points less than ambient temperature (J).

- Vapor dispersion hazards associated with spills of soluble chemicals with boiling points less than ambient temperature (N). This model assumes all vapor is evolved instantaneously and uses estimates of the size and shape of the vapor source.

- Dispersion of vapor from spills of volatile liquids which are soluble in water and have boiling points greater than ambient temperature but less than $100^{\circ}C$. (This chemical type has a considerable vapor pressure at ambient temperature and is miscible in water) (S). The model assumes all of the vapor liberated is generated at the spill origin.

● Dispersion of vapors from spills of volatile insoluble chemicals having a boiling point greater than ambient temperature and which are less dense than water (W). Either instantaneous or continuous vapor release is modeled.

It should be noted that these models do not take into account the disturbances caused by obstructions, wind direction change or wind velocity nor do they include the effects of the vapor being heated by the ground or air and the consequent rise of the plume. Therefore, it is important that the output values be properly interpreted by trained persons as guides for assessing and evaluating hazards and not taken as absolute concentration values.

Accessibility to HACS System

HACS is primarily accessible through the National Response Center under the aegis of the OSC. In addition, there is a mechanism for helping communities with pre-emergency contingency planning, again through the appropriate OSC in each region.

Shell, R&D SPILLS Vapor Dispersion Model[10]

The Shell model can be used to analyze the evaporation and atmospheric dispersion of a chemical spill on land. The unsteady state model estimates vapor concentration as a function of time and distance downwind of the spill.

The model incorporates three options depending on the nature of the spill:

(1) Instantaneously formed pools of liquids or liquefied gases;

(2) Continuous spills, such as leaks from tank cars, tanks or pipelines; and

(3) Stacks, where the emission rate is assumed to be known.

For options (1) and (2), the thermophysical properties of the 36 chemicals in the system are used to calculate the evaporation rate which then becomes the emission rate for the atmospheric dispersion calculations. The mathematical model for calculating evaporation rate is based on heat and mass transfer mechanisms. The air dispersion model is based on the Gaussian puff model which uses the same approach and assumptions as the Gaussian plume equation. This three-dimensional Gaussian puff model is used to generate the following three different outputs: maximum concentrations and their downward positions at given elevations and elapsed times since the spill; concentrations at given times and positions in space; and constant concentration contour plots (isopleths) for given elevations and elapsed times.

The thermophysical properties necessary for the calculation of evaporation rates are vapor pressures, heats of vaporization, saturated liquid enthalpies and binary diffusivities in air. The properties of air required are thermal conductivity, kinematic viscosity and thermal diffusivity in the temperature range of 0-100°C. The necessary soil properties are thermal conductivity, density and specific heat for dry, unfrozen and frozen soil.

Accessibility to SPILLS Vapor Dispersion Model

The computer program is very user oriented, written in a conversational mode using Fortran V, and designed to run on an IBM 370 computer. In addition, it can be easily accessed on a portable terminal at the time of an accident to assist in mitigation efforts. For example, the input parameters to the model can be varied to predict minimum and maximum isopleths upon which estimates of evacuation zones can be based.

DDESB, Downwind Chemical Hazard Slide Rule[11]

The chemical hazard slide rule was developed to provide simple solutions to the complicated problems of making atmospheric dispersion predictions in the field. This system does not solve mathematical relations, it replots computer generated solutions to such simulations using recognized procedures. Graphical slide rules are different from conventional logarithmic instruments in two basic ways:

1) Sets of data are acted upon by constants to arrive at new sets of answers, and

2) Data and constants may be treated as parameters and not values.

The information required to use the Chemical Hazard Slide Rule for determining downwind hazard predictions are:

1) Agent;

2) Source strength;

3) Local meteorological data needed to identify the applicable Pasquill category including wind speed and direction, cloud cover and solar radiation level;

4) Determination of the source as instantaneous or continuous;

5) For a continuous source, length of time of release; and

6) Level of human activity downwind, which influences breathing rate and therefore, population exposure.

The slide rule uses positive film type acetate overlays to reproduce many graphs. Some parts are fixed over a set of locators and other parts slide to make estimates from many combinations of contributing factors. This assembly may be used to estimate downwind dosages from the accidental atmospheric releases of toxic chemicals near ground level. Two sets of components may be required:

1) A set of components to estimate dosages as a function of downwind distances. Slide overlays are provided for both instantaneous and continuous sources.

2) The second set of components is used in the estimation of evaporation rate for accidental spills. The evaporation rate and the total quantity spilled are used to estimate the time required for complete evaporation.

General Operating Principles

Precalculated solutions are plotted graphically on a transparent slide so when proper alignment is made with a base graph, the coordinate axes reflect a valid data set by the intersections of coordinate points on the plotted curves.

A new set of solutions is generated by moving the curve to a new position. Scales are plotted, generally on the slide, to aid in the relocation of the slide at a new position and thus reproduce the precalculated solution for a specific change in a parameter. When more than one parameter is plotted, a cursor is needed to locate the slide properly as two or more parameters are varied.

The functional graphs of this slide rule are plotted on a full logarithmic scale.

The user needs to be trained in the use of the system and requires background information on the several input parameters needed. This system was developed for military agents and explosives, and does not have the data necessary to address release of any of the 28 chemicals and propellants in this study. The Chemical Hazard Slide Rule is relatively easy to use and can be applied for field use; however, further development of slides for other hazardous chemicals must be undertaken before the system can be used for across-the-board hazardous materials emergency transportation response activities.

The AFCRL Statistical Vapor Dispersion Model[1,2]

The AFCRL model is a steady state model representing a ground level release of vapors from a spill of UDMH-hydrazine fuel or nitrogen tetroxide oxidizer. It was developed to determine the dispersion and toxic vapor levels of these propellants at Titan II installations. Experiments have shown that low level atmospheric diffusion depends on the following parameters: (1) wind direction fluctuation as an indication of the horizontal rate of mixing or diffusion; (2) vertical temperature gradient as an indicator of the vertical rate of diffusion; (3) mean wind speed as an indicator of the dilution rate of the contaminant as it is emitted at the source; and (4) source strength, the amount of material introduced into the atmosphere per unit time.

The AFCRL dispersion model assumes that: (1) only vertical and lateral mixing occurs; (2) steady state conditions are present; and (3) there are homogeneous horizontal atmospheric conditions. The model was empirically/statistically developed based on the following tracer experiments simulating ground level continuous point source releases: (1) Prairie Grass at O'Neill, Nebraska in 1956; (2) Ocean Breeze at Cape Kennedy, Florida in 1963; and (3) Dry Gulch at Vandenberg AFB, California in 1963.

The equation developed using these data is as follows:

$$\frac{C_p}{Q} = .000175 \; x^{-1.95} \; (\Delta T + 10)^{4.92},$$

where C_p is the peak concentration in gms/cubic meter at a height of approximately 5 feet above the ground at a given downwind travel distance, X (in meters)

Q is the source strength in gms/second

ΔT is the difference, in ^{o}F, between the temperature at

54 feet and 6 feet above the ground.

ΔT is defined by $(T_{54}-T_6)$ so that a negative ΔT means a decrease of temperature with height, and a positive ΔT, an increase of temperature with height. The quantity 10 is added to ΔT to avoid raising a negative number to a power. The constants are parameters of fit determined by least squares regression techniques. The model can be applied only to releases of short duration, 3 minutes or less, and up to a maximum downwind direction of six miles. This model can not be applied to releases that are instantaneous or have elevated sources.

Based on the results of these tests, nomographs and tables have been developed which predict the normalized peak concentration of contaminants as a function of distance downwind and extent of hazard area as defined by a given concentration and source strength. If an accident was to occur, data necessary to execute this model could be obtained at the meteorological equipment stations at the missile site.

Overview of Dense Gas Dispersion Models

The HACS, SPILLS, DDESB Slide Rule and AFCRL vapor dispersion models are not designed to predict the concentration levels and atmospheric dispersion of negatively buoyant or dense gases. Other groups of models are being developed with this purpose in mind but have not been validated by field testing. Dense gases fall into four categories based on either their chemical composition or specialized shipping requirements. These categories are: (1) high molecular weight gases (e.g. Cl_2); (2) pressurized liquefied gases at ambient temperature and elevated pressures (e.g. LPG); (3) refrigerated liquefied gases (e.g. LNG); or (4) refrigerated pressurized liquefied gases.

For predicting the atmospheric dispersion of high molecular weight gases it should be noted that they experience gravity spreading with entrainment and turbulent mixing in the atmosphere. Pressurized liquefied gases stored at ambient temperatures and elevated pressures experience gas releases from two effects: (1) flash evaporation due to reduction of vapor pressure and temperature to reach equilibrium with the atmosphere; and (2) slow pool evaporation resulting from heat transfer to the cold liquid pool. Gravity spreading and dispersion of the cold gas are influenced by surface heating of the cloud, since vapors are emitted at the boiling point of the gas; thus, cloud mixing is enhanced with heating along the cloud path. Refrigerated liquefied gases emanate from pool evaporation after a spill. The resultant vapor is denser than air and disperses with a gravity spread component until mixing and cloud heating cause the gas to become neutrally or positively buoyant. Atmospheric diffusion of refrigerated pressurized liquefied gases would result from the combination of flash and pool evaporation and cloud heating.

Atmospheric dispersion models for dense gases are typically multicomponent mathematical descriptions of the three phases of gas release. These models can best be defined as a:

● Source model which describes gas emission to the atmosphere;

● Gravity spread model which simulates spreading and dilution of the cloud under the influence of gravity and edge mixing or entrainment; and

● Neutral tracer dispersion model which accounts for final transport and dispersion of the gas from the time the cloud becomes neutrally buoyant with respect to air until it no longer presents hazards.

Two distinct features of source/gas generation models are that pressurized liquefied gas is subject to two components of vaporization upon release as follows: (1) a flash as the liquid vapor pressure goes from pressure vessel environment to ambient air pressure and cools the liquid to its boiling point; and (2) heat transfer to the liquid pool from the substrate (land or water).

Gravity spreading models are based on the understanding that gravity acting on the density difference between the cloud and air results in an outward motion. The outward motion continues until the density difference is eliminated. It should be noted that confined land spill models do not normally include gravity spread submodels. Various gravity spread models consider cloud-air entrainment, convective heating and wind speed.

Dispersion models are of two types as follows: (1) numerical models (based on LNG simulations) developed primarily for Lawrence Livermore Laboratory and; (2) analytical models. In the numerical models, gravity spreading after vaporization and dispersion are coupled in numerical solutions to equations for mass, heat and momentum conservation. Analytical models, however, are empirical solutions to a diffusion equation for neutrally buoyant gases whose fundamental concepts are equated to Gaussian puff (instantaneous) and (continuous) plume solutions derived by Pasquill.

The dispersion parameters used in dense gas models are somewhat controversial because of their temporal and spatial variability. Presently dispersion parameters are empirical relations based on limited measurements over short distances on flat terrain for neutrally buoyant gases which may not be representative particularly over water or varying terrain.

While a comprehensive but usable dense gas model does not presently exist, field experiments are planned to further develop applicable models. Once a comprehensive vapor dispersion model with capabilities of existing models for spills on land and water is combined with dense gas and terrain effects, the emergency response community will have a tool broadly applicable to the wide range of vapor hazards presented at hazardous materials transportation emergencies.

3.4.2 Blast Overpressure, Fireball and Fragment Dispersal Areas

There are three different phenomena which may occur alone or in combination and because they are closely associated, they are being treated together. A fuel-air vapor-phase explosion (deflagration/detonation) is possible with those chemicals and propellants which form flammable mixtures with air. The magnitude and severity of the reaction depends upon such things as: how well the chemical or propellant mixes with air before ignition occurs; the fuel-to-air ratio; the quantity of chemical or propellant mixed; thermochemical properties of the chemicals and propellants; and the meterological conditions. Explosions create blast waves which are expressed as overpressures in pounds per square inch gauge or bars gauge and a time duration (e.g., milliseconds). The military has done a considerable amount of research on fuel-air explosives. However, most of the reports have been classified, so the information is not available for use in this publication. Suffice it to say that unclassified portions of reports indicate that it is possible to produce explosive reactions with vapors, so the potential for such reactions must be recognized when these chemicals and propellants are spilled, and appropriate countermeasures taken.

Liquefied Hydrogen. ORI, Inc. reports[21] that the theoretical explosive energy of hydrogen in confinement (e.g., pipe) is approximately equivalent to 24 grams of TNT per gram of hydrogen and that only about 10% of this explosive yield can be expected in open air. However, it should be kept in mind, that in confinement, hydrogen-air mixtures react more violently than in the open and there are many ways to confine the mixture. The quantity-distance relationships for the protection of personnel near liquid hydrogen storage and experimental areas (unbarricaded) are shown in Figure 3-1.[21] These data were obtained from National Bureau of Standards Technical Note 690. The figure contains curves for fireball radius, a range of overpressures and shrapnel. Assuming 32,000 gallons of liquid hydrogen in a tank car and a liquid density of .0708 gm/cm, this works out to 8,575 kilograms. From the chart (Figure 3-1) the fireball radius for this quantity of hydrogen is about 239 feet. However, dangerous radiant heat extends beyond this distance. The chart does not distinguish safe personal distance for the individual phenomenon but indicates one distance for all three. Overpressure distances range between 787 and 1542 ft. and the fragment distance is 3,346 ft. Fatality and injury ranges downwind for liquid hydrogen pool fires appear in Figure 3-2.[21] Figure 3-2 also indicates the estimated safe distances for given spill quantities involved in the pool fire.

Although not specifically designed for liquid hydrogen, Baker's workbook[22] should be of value for determining at least a rough prediction of blast pressure and fragment effects for hydrogen and other chemical and propellant spills and container ruptures. It is cautioned that these distances are approximations and do not ensure absolute safety because of the wide variation in conditions that occur at different accident scenes as well as at different times at a particular site.

A tank car tends to rupture such that the ends, if thrown, will travel in a direction roughly along the logitudinal centerline of the tank. Therefore, nothing and no one should be located or positioned in those two directions. Other fragments or debris may be hurled in any direction so precautions must be taken to deal with this potential danger.

Vinyl Chloride. Hokason and Wenzel[23] studied the explosive and flammability characteristics of vinyl chloride monomer (VCM). They reaffirmed that the flammability limits in air were 2.5% to 30% and that VCM should be treated as a

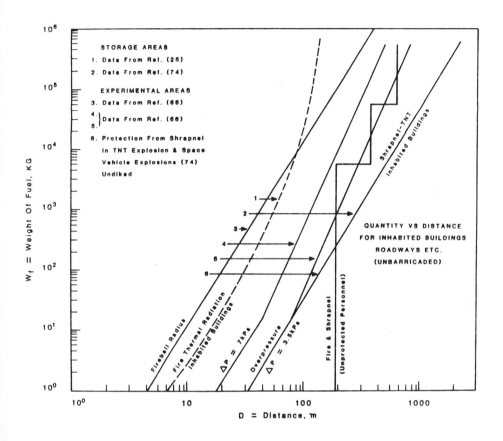

SOURCE: NBS TN 690

FIGURE 3-1.   QUANTITY DISTANCE RELATIONSHIPS FOR THE PROTECTION OF PERSONNEL NEAR
LIQUID HYDROGEN STORAGE AND EXPERIMENTAL AREAS (UNBARRICADED)

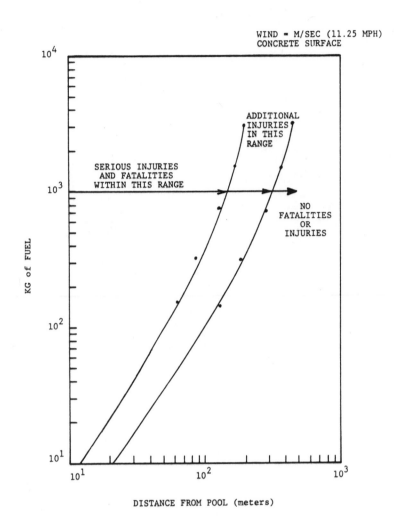

FIGURE 3-2. FATALITY & INJURY RANGES (DOWNWIND) FOR LH$_2$ POOL FIRES

flammable gas even in the presence of water vapor. Although no detonations were observed in the experiments, the authors cautioned that these tests did not involve ignition from electrostatic discharges. They further cautioned that they had difficulties measuring propagation velocities.

Propane. Jones[24], et al, shows maximum theoretical fireball diameter versus volume of liquid propane released. The possible fire damage radius due to 32,000 gallons (a full tank car) of burning propane is given as 640 feet and the radius of possible projectable damage from a ruptured propane tank car is 2500 feet.

Ethylene Oxide. Bowen[25] briefly discusses some tests on an ethylene oxide-filled bomb. It does not provide any blast overpressure data. It does say that ethylene oxide (EO) can not be detonated in the liquid state but the vapor-in-air detonation limits are 6% to 24% by volume. Inasmuch as EO is completely miscible in water, the vapors can be scrubbed out of the air or the liquid EO may be diluted by water. The flammability range for ethylene oxide vapors is 3% to 100% in air.

Ethylene oxide may violently decompose or polymerize in the presence of such catalysts as metallic chlorides and oxides, alkali metals and hydroxides, acids and organic bases.

3.5 CONTAINER INTEGRITY ASSESSMENT

For many years, wreck clearing operations have been hampered by the risk of tank cars damaged by collision or derailment. A number of serious incidents have occurred in recent years because apparently stable tank cars have exploded without warning, causing extensive property damage and, in some cases, loss of life. The potential dangers of such explosions have increased in recent years because of the increasing sizes of tank cars and the necessity of transporting more volatile and dangerous materials. In order to provide some means of ascertaining the structural integrity of damaged tank cars, guidelines based on direct visual inspection of the damaged tank cars have been developed. The principal purpose of these guidelines is to recommend courses of action that will minimize the risks associated with the wreck clearing operations.

The emphasis is placed on actions directly associated with the tank car and not with other aspects of the wreck clearing operations. For example, the problems associated with atmospheric dispersion and cleanup of hazardous materials are not addressed in this section. Within this context, the subject guidelines are comprehensive because they address all of the major items which should be included. They include information pertaining to the initial inspection, assessment of different types of damage and mechanisms of failure.

One of the major difficulties with these guidelines is that they offer no means of anticipating an impending explosion of the tank car. They do provide for different degrees of caution, depending on the extent of damage, but they offer no suggestions as to when the condition of the tank car becomes so dangerous that the area should be evacuated. The difficulty in providing such guidelines with a reasonable degree of confidence is recognized and this situation is discussed in greater detail in this section.

The purpose of this effort is to provide an assessment of the existing guidelines, emphasizing both their strengths and weaknesses so that the risks associated with wreck clearing operations can be minimized. Emphasis is placed on those portions of the guidelines assessing the structural integrity of damaged rail cars.

3.5.1 Inspection

It is apparent that the initial inspection of the damaged tank car represents the most critical step in the assessment process, because the immediate risks and the consequences of an error are greatest at this point. Because of the unknown possibility of explosion, the inspection should be as thorough and accurate as possible, while at the same time minimizing the exposure of personnel to danger. This represents a major shortcoming associated with visual methods, because a careful inspection for cracks can involve a considerable expenditure of time in situations where the inspectors' life is at risk. The risks associated with an incorrect assessment can be even greater because more personnel would be normally in the immediate vicinity of the tank car after it was declared safe. Several violent explosions of tank cars, which were thought to be in a stable condition, have occurred in recent years resulting in considerable damage and loss of life.

A major difficulty with the inspection process, in addition to the time and risk factors, is that the bottom portion of the car is normally unavailable for inspection. In many cases where the car is partially embedded in the ground or otherwise unexposed, one-half or more of the car cannot be inspected. Because the lower portions of the car are most likely to have received the worst damage, the inspection process may be misleading, even when performed in the best possible fashion.

Another significant problem with the inspection process is the difficulty associated with the inspection of insulated tank cars. The damage observed on the jacket is immaterial to the car's structural integrity, so it is necessary to ascertain the extent of damage to the tank itself. Assessment of tank damage may be difficult or impossible without extensive preparation to expose the tank surface. Such efforts naturally increase the inspection times and uncertainties associated with the evaluation process.

Aerial surveillance could assist at least in preliminary inspection and assessment. Use of a high resolution video camera in an aircraft (e.g., helicopter) could permit zooming in from a safe distance on areas of the wreckage that are not visible from the ground. This could provide some of the information required for such things as dent analysis, hot spot locations, twisting and bulging, as well as the conditions of external valves, piping and appurtenances which are not buried. This technique is practical because exposure of inspection personnel is eliminated.

3.5.2 Damage Assessment

Damage assessment includes consideration of most types of damage that would be expected to occur to tank cars during collision or derailment. Rail burns are not explicitly discussed, although the nature of the damage is similar to wheel burns and may be combined with the latter for discussion purposes. Rail burns have been shown to be the critical mechanism leading to explosions in tank cars, for example, the tank car failure in Cuming, Iowa in 1969. Punctures and other types of damage causing rupture and leakage are not considered here because they preclude pressure build-up and subsequent explosive fractures.

3.5.3 Cracks

The current treatment of cracks is qualitative in that the existence of cracks of any size is considered adequate justification for unloading the tank car as soon as possible if it is safe to do so. In addition, cracks in

conjunction with a dent, score or gouge warrant unloading without moving the car, if possible. One exception to these rules is that cracks in fillet welds of attachment brackets or reinforcement plates are not considered critical unless they extend into the base metal of the container.

It is well known from fracture mechanics that the deleterious effects of cracks are strongly influenced by their size and shape. For example, the maximum value of the stress intensity factor for a semi-elliptical surface flaw is given by:

$$K_I = \frac{1.1 \ M \ \sigma_k \sqrt{\pi} a}{E \ (a/b)} \tag{1}$$

where K_I = stress intensity factor,

a = crack depth,

b = crack length,

$E(a/b)$ = elliptical integral of the second kind,

M_k = back-face correction factor, and

σ_k = nominal applied stress.

For a crack oriented along the length of the tank car the nominal tangential stress (hoop stress) is:

$$\sigma = \frac{pD}{2t} \tag{2}$$

where p, D and t represent the internal pressure, the diameter and the shell thickness, respectively, of the tank. If the crack were oriented perpendicular to the length of the tank, the stress would be exactly one-half of the value given by equation (2).

At the point when the internal pressure is just large enough to initiate unstable fracture, equation (1) can be written:

$$K_{Ic} = \frac{1.1 \ M_k \ \sigma_c \sqrt{\pi} a}{E \ (a/b)} \tag{3}$$

where σ_c is the critical value of the applied normal stress and K_{Ic} is the critical stress intensity factor or the fracture toughness. The fracture toughness is considered to be a material property, independent of the structure or flaw geometry.

Application of the fracture mechanics to the interior is not a simple matter because it is necessary to establish reasonable values for the length and depth of the crack, the pressure, and the fracture toughness. In addition, values must be obtained for E (a/b) and M_k, which are available in tabular form, if a, b and the thickness are known. The difficulties associated with obtaining the necessary input data suggest that the use of a fracture mechanics failure criterion may be too sophisticated for application at a wreck-clearing site. Fracture mechanics methods are, however, quite valuable for and are often employed in determining the influence of cracks on unstable fractures, after they occur (post failure analysis). No other quantitative treatments of cracks are available for assessment of tank car structural integrity, so the qualitative approach currently used is probably the most appropriate under existing circumstances.

3.5.4 Dents

Dents are quantitatively defined in the subject guidelines as having the critical radii less than certain specified values. These minimum values are $R_{min} = 4.0$ inches for tank cars built before 1966 and $R_{min} = 2.0$ inches for those built in 1966 or later. The rationale for these requirements is based on the maximum normal strain (at the surface) caused by bending. Correlations between the minimum bend radius and fracture may be obtained experimentally by the cold bend test or by consideration of the maximum normal strain criterion.

The correlation between the minimum bend radius and the maximum normal strain criterion for fracture is indicated by the following analysis. From the theory of bending, relationships have been established between the minimum bend radius, R_{min}, the thickness, h, and the reduction of area, q, obtained from a tensile test. For values of q less than 0.2 the relationship has the form:

$$\frac{R_{min}}{h} = \frac{1}{2q} - 1 \qquad (4)$$

or

$$q = \frac{h}{2 \, (R_{min} + h)} \qquad (5)$$

The analysis of the parameters in a tensile test has also resulted in the following relationship between q and the normal strain, ε_f, as

$$q = 1 - \exp{(-\varepsilon)_f} \qquad (6)$$

Equation (6) can be solved for ε_f to yield

$$\varepsilon_f = \ln{(\frac{1}{1-q})} \qquad (7)$$

Then from equations (5) and (7), the critical normal strain can be written in terms of R_{min} and h as:

$$\varepsilon_f = \ln{\frac{2(R_{min} + h)}{2R_{min} + h}} \qquad (8)$$

The relative influence of R_{min} and h on ε_f is indicated in Table 3-4. Table 3-4 shows that both R_{min} and h exert strong influence on ε_f so that the analysis is somewhat incomplete if R_{min} is used only as input data.

The maximum normal strain criterion for fracture states that a structure or component will fail when the maximum normal strain attains the value determined from a tensile test on the same material. A steel commonly used for the fabrication of tank cars prior to 1966 was an ASTM A-212 Grade B steel, which had a required minimum ε_f of 21 percent. Comparison of this value of ε_f with Table 3-4 shows that the critical strain permitted by the guidelines is approximately one-third of the minimum value for that material. This represents a reasonable safety factor considering that the actual tank car will have fabrication welds, various amounts of damage (cold work) and will be subjected to various environmental conditions not experienced by the test specimens.

For more information on the specifications and design requirements for tank cars, refer to Title 49 CFR Part 179, Specifications for Tank Cars. This provides information on required plate thickness, bursting pressure, materials, insulation, safety relief valves design and setting, etc. Of course under accident conditions, it is best to consult someone with experience in assessing tank car structural damage such as the shipper, the car manufacturer or the AAR.

3.5.5 Additional Failure Criteria

Another failure condition, which conceptually is the same as the maximum normal strain criterion and perhaps more widely used, is the maximum normal stress failure criterion. However, the maximum normal strain criterion is more

TABLE 3-4.   INFLUENCE OF THICKNESS AND MINIMUM BEND
RADIUS ON THE CRITICAL NORMAL STRAIN

Minimum Bend Radius (in)	Thickness (in)	Critical Normal Strain ($)
4.0	0.6	6.7
4.0	0.7	7.7
4.0	0.8	8.7
2.0	0.6	12.3
2.0	0.7	13.9
2.0	0.8	15.4

useful when the material is somewhat ductile, as indicated by the requirements that ε_f is greater than or equal to 0.21 for the A-212 Grade B steel.

Several other failure criteria are widely used under various conditions and should be mentioned for comparison purposes. The maximum shear stress or strain criteria states that a structure or component will fail when the maximum shear stress or strain attains a value equal to the maximum values obtained from a tensile test on the material. Thus failure will occur when:

$$\tau_{max} \quad \frac{\sigma 1 - \sigma 2}{2} = \frac{\sigma 1}{2}$$

or   (9)

$$\gamma_{max} \quad \frac{\varepsilon 1 - \varepsilon 2}{2} = \frac{\varepsilon 1}{2}$$

where σ_1 and ε_1 are the principal values of the stress and strain obtained from the tensile test ($\sigma_2 = \varepsilon_2 = 0$). Then, values of ($\sigma_1 - \sigma_2$)/2 or ($\varepsilon_1 - \varepsilon_2$)/2 are obtained for the structure to be examined and are compared with τ_{max} or γ_{max} obtained from the tensile test.

Another widely used failure condition is the distortion energy or Von Mises failure criterion. This criterion states that the structure or component will fail when the distortion energy given by:

$$\sigma_o = \frac{1}{\sqrt{2}} \ (\sigma_1 - \sigma_2)^2 + (\sigma_3 - \sigma_1)^2 +$$

$$(\sigma_2 - \sigma_3)^2 \ ^{1/2}$$

or

$$\varepsilon_o = \frac{1}{\sqrt{2}} \ (\varepsilon_1 - \varepsilon_2)^2 + (\varepsilon_3 - \varepsilon_1)^2 +$$

$$(\varepsilon_2 - \varepsilon_3)^2 \ ^{1/2} \qquad (10)$$

becomes equal to their values calculated at fracture during a uniaxial tensile test. In equations 10, σ_1, σ_2, and σ_3 are the principal (maximum) stresses and ε_1, ε_2, and ε_3 are the principal (maximum) strains.

Many other failure conditions have been developed but the ones cited in the previous paragraphs are the most widely used. As a general rule, the maximum normal stress or strain failure criteria are used when the material response is

brittle, whereas the maximum shear stress or strain or the distortion energy criteria are most effective for ductile materials. Also, increasingly, biaxial or triaxial states of stress or strain (in which σ_2 and σ_3 or ε_2 and ε_3 cannot be neglected in relation to σ_1 or ε_1) provide better agreement with the maximum shear stress or strain and distortion energy criteria. Considering all of the uncertainties associated with the damage evaluation process, the maximum normal strain failure criterion is probably as effective as the others and is easier to apply to the evaluation of dents.

One major limitation for this assessment of the minimum bend radii of dents is that it includes no guidelines identifying sufficiently great damage as to warrant precautionary evacuation of the area around a tank car. These guidelines mainly suggest different procedures for handling the tank cars when different magnitudes of damage have been observed. Development of the ability to predict accurately the point of unstable fracture is a very difficult matter and will probably require a completely different approach from the one presented in the subject guidelines. One approach which appears to have considerable promise for providing such data is the acoustic emission (AE) method. This method is based on the ability to identify when the acoustic signals emitted by a structure represent the onset of unstable fracture. This method is currently subject to much development and may be quite applicable to tank assessment.

3.5.6 Scores and Gouges

The guidelines for the assessment of scores and gouges is partially quantitative and partially qualitative. Scores are generally considered to be noncritical unless they cross a weld seam and then are considered potentially critical only if they remove more weld material than the amount extending above the base metal. The depth of the scoring is treated quantitatively by reducing the allowable internal pressure in proportion to increasing depth of scoring or gouging. The relation between allowable internal pressure and depth of scoring included in the guidelines has been plotted in Figure 3-3 for 340W and 400W tank cars (340 psi and 400 psi proof tests). The relationships between these two variables appears to be essentially linear and suggests that the allowable pressure is primarily dependent on the thickness of the remaining material. Inasmuch as the thickness of the tank is not required to apply these guidelines, they appear to

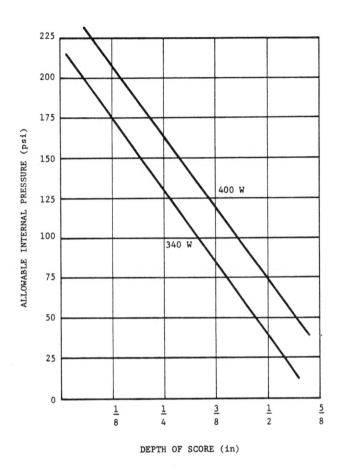

FIGURE 3-3.   RELATIONSHIP BETWEEN ALLOWABLE INTERNAL
             PRESSURE AND DEPTH OF SCORING

be based on an average value of thickness in the range 5/8 to 3/4 inch. It is also noted that a fixed stress concentration factor of 2.0, rather than a variable factor, was used because the permitted pressures were not a function of either the thickness of the tank or the score or gouge radius. To a lesser degree than the fracture mechanics analysis, more accurate treatments require additional information (the tank thickness and the gouge radius) which may be difficult to obtain reliably and quickly. The scoring also introduces cold work at the outer surface which tends to alter the material properties, making them less ductile and more subject to brittle fracture.

This suggested approach for determining the internal pressure of the gas-vapor mixture is valuable and should be considered whenever the temperature can be determined with a reasonable degree of accuracy. In recent years, remote infrared thermometers have been developed. These appear to be potentially useful for making rapid temperature scans of the entire tank car and from that obtaining improved estimates of the pressure in the tank. Possibly the guidelines should be modified to suggest use of these devices because they should permit considerable improvements in temperature measurements.

The guidelines suggest that scoring in a dent is more serious than either type of damage by itself. This is certainly true and additional caution in quite properly directed toward such situations.

3.5.7 Wheel and Rail Burns

The damage caused by wheel or rail burns can be treated similarly to scoring and gouging. The depth of the burn is used to recommend immediate unloading (minimum depth greater than 1/8 inch). These recommendations appear to be based on prior field experience rather than on technical grounds. Again, it is noted that currently there is no specific level of damage that is cited or known to be serious enough to warrant evacuation of personnel from the vicinity of the tank car, although such criteria are badly needed.

3.5.8 Unloading Methods

Guidelines for off-loading or transfer techniques may be found in Section 5.3.

3.5.9 Moving of Tanks

The moving, lifting and uprighting of invalued or damaged tank cars is one reason for an accurate damage and structural integrity assessment following a derailment or vehicle overturn. For specific guidelines on lifting provisions, rigging and other wreckage removal considerations see Section 5.2.

3.5.10 Mechanism of Failure

The impact strength of the differing grades of steel give different strengths to each different steel tank cars. However, in any case, the transition temperature at which the properties of steel go from brittle to ductile increases due to cold work. Cold work occurs when steel is deformed at atmospheric temperatures or is permanently distorted by an impact.

Failure of a tank can occur in the following way: First, the tank shell is struck, causing an inward dent; this dent develops high tensile stress on the inside surface and small cracks form; the projectile which caused the dent deforms and cold works the outside surface; stress concentration occurs at the root of micro cracks, particularly in the cold work outside surface. Thus critical stress is developed and only a slight crack growth or increase in stress could cause a catastrophic failure. The general relationship between crack length and stress illustrating crack growth and propagation can be seen in Figure 3-4.

At present there is no technique to detect a crack which has become critical and which could propagate and cause a leak or violent rupture. However, acoustic emmission technology shows promise in detecting and monitoring flaws or cracks in accident situations.

Aerial surveillance could assist at least in preliminary container integrity assessment. Use of a high resolution video camera could permit zooming in from a safe distance on areas of the wreckage which are not visible from the ground. This could provide some of the information required for much things as dent analysis, hot spot locations, twisting and bulging, as well as the conditions of external valves, piping and appurtenances.

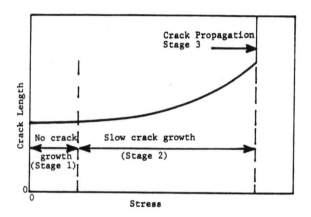

FIGURE 3-4.   CRACK GROWTH AND PROPAGATION

4. HAZARD MITIGATION GUIDELINES

4.1 CONTAINMENT

Containment methods for spilled hazardous materials will vary based upon the specific nature of the chemical and the physical location of the spill. The EPA[5] has identified guidelines for the containment of spilled hazardous materials on land or water, in water or air, or underwater. The appropriate containment guidelines for each of the chemicals and propellants addressed by this manual are given in Table 5-5.

4.2 VAPOR SUPPRESSION

Volatile liquids as well as compressed gases pose toxic and flammable vapor hazards. Vapor control has been attempted using water curtains, fog and spray but for mitigating the vapor hazard from spilled hazardous chemicals, foam systems appear to be the most efficient and effective.

Foam blankets act to isolate spill surfaces from ignition sources and radiant energy. This slows the vaporization rate but vapor release is reduced primarily by the limited permeability of the foam, its capacity to absorb the chemical, or by dilution of the surface layer. Foam can also be of use for strongly water reactive materials by allowing careful application of water to the surface to effect dilution or conversion to less hazardous forms without violent reaction. Guidelines for selection of an acceptable foam system depend on the compatibility between the foam and the spilled chemical. Not all foams are applicable to a volatile material. Polar materials for example, require special foam systems. On the basis of some EPA sponsored work[17] on foams done by MSA, the matrix presented in Table 4-1 has been developed.

The specific nature of the spill, on-scene accident conditions and resources available will in large part determine which, if any, foam system is appropriate or applicable. Low expansion foams are less influenced by atmospheric effects of wind, rain or high temperature and so will provide the longest safe period before break through of vapor occurs. However, they require larger volumes of water than do high expansion foams so the spill may be spread further or the containing dike, dam etc. may overflow.

Specific work on foam systems applicable to the chemicals and propellants in this study has been done for ammonia, chlorine, hydrazine, nitrogen tetroxide, propane and butadiene. In a paper entitled "The Use of Foams to Control the Vapor Hazard from Liquefied Gas Spills"[20] by R. H. Hiltz and S. S. Gross of MSA, the results of efforts on chlorine and ammonia were discussed. The investigations[16,17] of the effect of foam on chlorine have given mixed results. It is certain that for the current grades of commercially available foam systems, foam application to liquid chlorine results in rapid destruction of the foam and a gross exaggeration of the boil off rate. Depending on the foam type, the expansion, and the rate of application this effect may persist through several successive applications.

The interaction between the chlorine and the collapsing foam produces a layer of ice and chlorine hydrate which tends to float on the chlorine surface. With continued application of foam the layer eventually becomes sufficiently continuous that a foam blanket can be built on top of it. When this occurs, the rate of vapor release of the chlorine is slowed and a net positive effect is achieved in the downwind area.

There is not yet sufficient data to determine what foam or expansion is best nor what application rate or duration is necessary per square foot of spill surface to achieve coverage. It does appear best to work with medium expansion foams (300 to 350:1) but low expansion foams exclusive of AFFF can also provide benefit. At the present time only generalizations can be made. If the spill conditions are such that a short term exaggeration of the chlorine cloud can be tolerated in return for long term reduction of the hazard, foam should be considered.

The data for ammonia[17,18] are more definitive. As with chlorine, the initial foam application may be destroyed, but even this may be advantageous. One approach to an ammonia spill is dilution with water. Due to the large heat of solution the direct application of water to anhydrous ammonia results in a violent reaction. Foam offers a means of applying water at a slow rate, providing dilution with a minimum of reaction.

With low expansion foams such dilution will probably be the major benefit. With medium to high expansion foam a blanket can be developed with a subsequent reduction in the downwind gas concentration. Figure 4-1 shows a comparision of gas concentration at 4 feet and 15 feet downwind from the spill edge for application of low and high expansion foams.

63

TABLE 4-1. MATRIX FOR SELECTING FOAMS* FOR USE IN
MITIGATING VAPOR HAZARD FROM SPILLED VOLATILE CHEMICALS**

| | Low Expansion | | | | High Expansion | | |
	Protein	Fluoro-protein	Alcohol	Surfactant	Acrylic	AFFF	Surfactant
Esters	E	E	A	E		E	E
Alcohols	E	E	A	E		E	E
Ethers	E	E	A	E		E	E
Aldehydes	E	E	A	E		E	E
Ketones	E	E	A	E		E	E
Phenols	E	E	A	E		E	E
Halogenated Compounds	A	A	C	A		C	A
Alkanes	A	A	C	A		C	A
Alkenes	A	A	C	A		C	A
Alkynes	A	A	C	A		C	A
Dienes	A	A	C	A		C	A
Cycloaliphatic	A	A	C	A		C	A
Aromatic	A	A	C	A		C	A
Nitrogen Tetroxide					A		
Hydrazine Fuels					A		

A - Recommended

C - Satisfactory

E - Not recommended

* Foam designations are for commercially available materials in common usage.

** Source: EPA 68-03-2478, Evaluation/Development of Foams for Mitigating Air Pollution from Hazardous Spills, 1976.

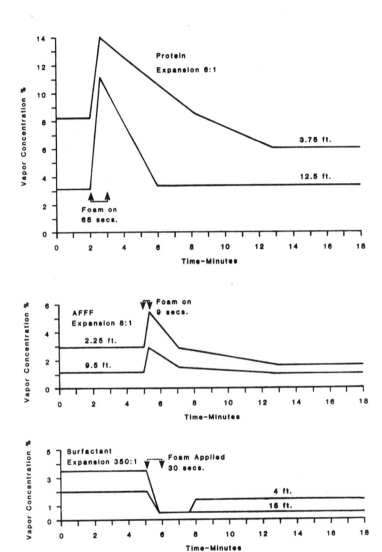

FIGURE 4-1.   EFFECT ON DOWNWIND VAPOR CONCENTRATIONS OF
FOAM ADDITIONS TO ANHYDROUS AMMONIA SPILLS

The benefit from the high expansion foam is due to a combination of effects. The high expansion foam causes a smaller increase in boil off than does the low expansion foam. The ability to develop a persistent blanket results in some vapor scrubbing as the gas rises through the foam. Most importantly, however, is the warming of the vapor both by normal heat transfer and also from the heat of solution of ammonia in water. This is believed to be the explanation for the greater reduction at 15 feet downwind than at 4 feet; the warm vapor being buoyant tends to disperse upward.

The importance of imparting buoyance to ammonia vapor clouds has been shown by recent tests and spill analyses in England.[19] This work provides an explanation of the long downwind, extensive crosswind and upwind movement of ammonia vapor clouds. It predicates such movement on the collapse of the initial vapor column, the entrainment of significant quantities of air, the concurrent cooling of the entrained air and the difficulty of raising the temperature of such a mixture simply from the surrounding atmosphere.

4.2.1   Recent Laboratory Efforts

The use of foam to induce gas warming and buoyance would minimize those events and aid in cloud dissipation as well as restrict downwind travel. It has been proposed that similar events occur with other liquefied gases but there is no supporting data.

MSA has performed laboratory studies and field tests for EPA to determine and evaluate the best procedures to treat spills of hydrazine and nitrogen tetroxide. The evaluations included testing of foam acrylic plus surfactant and mineral oil as suppressants. The foam by itself was only partially successful in reapplication with fresh foam and did not produce an effective cover. The test with mineral oil showed that the oil was permeated by hydrazine.

In the tests on nitrogen tetroxide, the ability of mineral oil to suppress vapors is temperature dependent. At temperatures less than $60°F$, the oil provided an effective barrier to N_2O_4 vapor (NO_2); however foam control appeared effective only for a short time. During the first application the foam was more effective than oil. After about 15 minutes breakthrough occurred and vapor control was lost and cannot be reestablished.

In a more recent study, initiated in September 19, 1981 and currently still in progress, improved foam systems for hypergol propellant spills were developed. After laboratory experimentations, two systems judged to exhibit superior vapor suppressant properties were further evaluated in larger scale field tests simulating spill scenarios expected in space program operations. These scenarios include spills at launch site storage areas, transportation spills (highway), etc. Foam, prepared from Rohm Haas ASE 95 (polyacrylic)/MSA surfacant solution with an expansion ratio of approximately 8:1, persisted for over two hours when placed on top of a contained monomethylhydrazine pool; and a second foam, prepared from Rohm Haas ASE60 (polyacrylic)/MSA surfaciant plus a pectin additive (expansion ratio, approximately 150:1), maintained a cover over N_2O_4 pool for approximately 15 minutes. In both cases the cover could be maintained indefinitely by reapplication of fresh foam. In the oxidizer case, even after the total breakdown of the foam, the amount of rocket propellant vaporization was considerably reduced by the surface film formed by the collapsed foam. The capability of the foam in extinguishing a fuel (hydrazine) fire was also demonstrated. Based on the successful results obtained in this study, the U.S. Air Force is currently fabricating a portable foam generating system, equipped with a spill collection system. The unit is completely self contained with its own power generator for operation in a remote location.

Work done on extinguishment and control of LPG (propane) fires by Applied Technology Corp. under contract to DOE showed that:

- LPG fires can be controlled but not extinguished by high expansion foam.

- Dry chemical agents like potassium bicarbonate and urea potassium bicarbonate are effective extinguishants when applied with properly designed systems.

Further testing done by Energy Analysts, Inc., on fighting liquefied gas fires showed that use of low expansion protein and fluoroprotein foams did not extinguish a butadiene fire because they floated on the surface and did not form a complete seal. The most effective foam is high expansion fluroprotein for extinguishing butadiene fires. However, the butadiene vapors eventually permeate the foam and this presents grave problems of vapor travel, ignition and flashback. Thus, in this case as with other heavier than air hydro· rbon liquefied gases, control of burning may be preferable to extinguishment.

4.3 HANDLING LEAKS

One can approach the problem of leaks or product releases from containers punctured or otherwise damaged in transportation accidents from three options:

1. Stopping the leak;

2. Leaving the leak "as is;" or

3. Further opening up the car or tank (venting) and disposing of the lading (burning).

Depending on the size, shape, and orientation of a hole in a container, a leak may be patched or plugged. If the leak is from damaged or loosened car fittings (gauging devices, valves, safety vents, thermometer well cap, etc.), they may be tightened or repaired. Often, leakage from fittings can be stopped by tightening mounting nuts and closure plugs. However, if the mounting gaskets or valves have deteriorated, tightening nuts will not stop the leak. Replacement may be possible by specially trained personnel with special equipment.

Leaks can occur in fittings that have not been broken off. When the tank is upright, vapor will be released if the following fittings are loose or defective:

a. The gasketed joint between the manway cover plate and the manway nozzle.

b. The gasketed joint between the base of the vapor valve and the manway cover plate.

c. The gasketed joint between the base of the safety valve and the manway cover plate.

d. The gasketed joint between the base of gauging device and the manway cover plate.

e. The closure plugs of the vapor valve.

f. The thermometer well closure cap.

g. The packing gland of the gauging device.

Liquid will be released if the following fittings are loose or defective:

a. The gasketed joints between the liquid valves and the manway cover plate.

b. The sampling valve.

c. The gauging device at the valve handle.

d. The closure plugs of the liquid valves sampling line and gauging device.

All openings in a tank car containing flammable compressed gas except the safety valve are equipped with gravity-activated excess flow check valves which are designed to close automatically when their external closure is fully open or broken off. Because of these devices, contents of the tank can only be transferred with the tank in an upright position. A device known as an excess flow check valve float lifter, developed in Canada, can be applied to a closure valve that will permit unloading regardless of the position of the fitting. Unfortunately, there are not very many of these devices available nor do they fit all closure valves being used today.

The following items must be strictly adhered to in attempting to approach a leaking container:

1. A leaking container is approached only after monitoring for and assuring safe toxic or flammable vapor levels;

2. Some efforts have been made to assess the overall structural integrity of the container;

3. Response personnel use appropriate protective gear and equipment when approaching a leaking container;

4. All sources of ignition such as mechanical refrigeration units, lamps, stoves, markers, etc. must be extinguished;

5. Only "non-sparking" tools must be used when making emergency repairs;

6. Patching or plugging materials must be compatible with the hazardous material;

7. Trains are not permitted to pass on adjacent tracks or motor vehicles on the highway or street;

8. Moving of leaking tank cars or cargo tanks is not attempted; and

9. If the container has a fire at the safety relief valve or from a tank

puncture, no attempt be made to extinguish the fire unless the leak can be secured because of the problem of vapor travel, reignition and flashback.

When a tank car or tank truck containing compressed flammable gases such as butadiene, isobutane, liquefied hydrogen, propane, propylene and vinyl chloride is involved in a transportation accident, leakage is likely to develop, especially if structural damage has occurred. These gases are heavier than air and can travel and accumulate in low-lying areas, posing fire, explosion and flashback hazards. If a leaking tank car is on fire it can be benign or pose BLEVE potential. A more severe BLEVE situation, however, is fire impingement on an adjacent car which is not on fire.

In cases where a container is inaccessible, or the damage too severe, or where fire impingement has reached dangerous proportions, or the container is punctured and its contents burning; trying to stop a leak may not be feasible or desirable. There may, in fact, be times when a tank car or other container needs to be emptied of its contents because of potential critical damage precluding moving, rerailing or even off-loading. In the past few years there have been a few successful attempts (i.e., Claxton, Kentucky; Molino, Florida) at "venting" tank cars and "burning" contents using explosives. These procedures are still at very preliminary stages and thus must be used with extreme caution and only when conditions indicate no other solutions. The following issues must be addressed in developing this technology:

1. Assessment of critical shell damage to container precluding moving or an in-field transfer;

2. The decision to utilize explosives for "vent" and "burn" must be one mutually arrived at and agreed upon by the experts who have critically assessed the situation;

3. The area must be sufficiently remote to reduce exposure of public and property;

4. Experts must be located to perform the operation;

5. Explosive materials such as shaped charges, thermite grenades, etc. must be available;

6. The accident scene must be sufficiently stabilized to permit access

to place charges and other equipment as required;

7. There must be adequate prior assessment of impact and expected results;

8. The public and all non-essential response personnel must be removed to a safety perimeter beyond the site;

9. If any liquid release is expected, dikes, dams or containment pits must be constructed; and

10. After fire has subsided the container be checked for presence of flammable or other vapors and be flushed clear, if any remains, in order to allow safe resumption of wreck clearing operations.

In terms of handling leaks involving the chemicals and propellants addressed by this manual metals should not be used for acrylonitrile (i.e., copper, copper alloys, aluminum), anhydrous ammonia (i.e., copper and galvanized surfaces), chlorine (i.e., most metals, especially copper), hydrazine (i.e., most metals), nitrogen tetroxide (i.e., most metals), sodium hydrosulfide solution (i.e, most metals) and sodium hydroxide (i.e., aluminum, tin, lead, zinc).

4.4 FIREFIGHTING

The NFPA and other professional firefighting organizations, nationwide, provide excellent training courses and manuals on firefighting techniques. Thus, this manual will not presume or attempt to add anything to those efforts. However, it would be prudent to point out in this section some of the special problems and considerations facing firefighters confronted with transportation accidents involving hazardous materials as well as some of the options available for vapor suppression and extinguishants.

Fires involving hazardous materials present not only the expected thermal hazards but can also involve toxic or corrosive combustion products and present large scale explosive hazards. If a container itself is not mechanically damaged or structurally weakened in a fire, the combination of fire impingement causing increase in internal pressure and the resultant lessened integrity of the container could cause a rupture.

Structural failure of the container may cause a massive explosion with an accompanying fireball and tank fragments propelled at high velocities in every direction. In such cases the principal firefighting tactic is to cool the tank shell by localizing streams of water at the following main vulnerable points: the vapor-phase area of the tank and the point of flame contact. According to the NFPA, the application of 500 gal/min is considered minimal if cooling of the structure is to have any effect. This technique is extremely risky and the use of unmanned monitors to apply water is recommended providing they may be safely set up. Water has been synonymous with fire extinguishment for many years and, when applied as a stream or a fog or in several intermediate forms, sees greater use than any other single material. It extinguishes basically by cooling the burning surface to temperatures below those necessary to sustain combustion. The steam generated by its absorption of heat acts to dilute the oxygen concentration and, when used as a fog or curtain, blocks radiant energy release.

Water is most useful against fires involving solid fuels like wood, paper, other cellulosic materials and some liquid fuel fires. However it is not effective for hydrocarbon liquids because it is more dense than these fluids and sinks giving little fire reduction. In fact, application of water can worsen a situation by causing overflow of contained liquids or frothing, boiling and spattering of pooled liquids. Water is ineffective against gases and cryogenic liquids and cannot be used for fires involving energized electrical equipment because of hazards to personnel and damage to electrical circuitry.

Water can be more efficient as an extinguishant by adding surface active agents (surfactants) or sealing it into the structure of a gel or foam. A surfactant reduces the surface tension of the water and thus imparts better wetting of organic surfaces, better penetration into material surfaces and openings. To expand the types of fires where water could be applied, the water-surfactant combination was further developed by mechanically inducing dispersion of air in water to form a continuum of bubbles known as foam. Foam offers several advantages, such as the following, for a range of fire scenarios:

- Can be floated on the surface of liquids;

- Mechanism to deliver water slowly but continuously;

- Cuts down smoke, fumes;

- Easier conversion of water to steam;

- Method to build a 3-dimensional water barrier; and

- Provides a lessened shock hazard or damage potential to electrical circuitry.

The main disadvantage of foam is the possibility of saturation by the burning liquid, usually a result of improper application of the foam blanket. Foam is divided initially into high expansion (a volume expansion to foam greater than 100 to 1) and low expansion (a volume expansion less than 20 to 1).

There are six major types of foam agents in use: protein, synthetic, AFFF fluoroprotein, alcohol and polar solvents foams.

Protein foam agents are materials derived from animal matter which provide good cooling and burn back resistance. Its fire knock down capability is acceptable but not as good as AFFF. It is limited to low expansion application.

AFFF is a descriptive term for a fluorocarbon based surfactant which has excellent fire knock-down capabilities but is poor for cooling a structure and maintaining a blanket. Its principal action is the formation of a special oriented floating monomolecular film which is effective as long as it is continuous. AFFF is normally used in the low expansion mode.

Synthetic or detergent foams are long-chain organic hydrocarbon compounds with capabilities parallel to AFFF. They are primarily restricted to high expansion use but a few agents can be used for low expansion also.

Fluoroprotein is a blend of protein and fluorocarbon materials to provide lower surface tensions and greater fluidity than are possible with protein, while maintaining the persistence absent in AFFF materials. However, the result is a compromise rather than an optimization of characteristics of each. Fluoroprotein is restricted to low expansion use.

The last two are specialty low expansion foams for polar solvents and some low molecular weight chlorinated hydrocarbons which degrade normal foams: alcohol foams and polar solvent foams. These foams either precipitate or gel into an insoluble layer on the chemical surface to block foam degradation and provide a base for foam build-up. There are protein, surfactant and AFFF forms of alcohol foams and all are restricted to low expansion use.

Low expansion foams in addition to fire control can provide vapor suppression from spilled chemicals and smoke and fumes from deep seated fires. High expansion foams complement the low expansion type and are utilized in enclosed areas. High expansion foam provides the fastest extinguishment of contained pool fires.

Carbon dioxide also functions as an extinguishant by blanketing the fire and is available in liquid form in extinguishers or in mechanical foams.

Several halogenated hydrocarbons or halons are extremely stable to heat and are useful as fire extinguishants for such applications as electronic equipment, computer circuits, aircraft interiors, museums, vaults, hospitals, etc., where only minor residue resulting from use is desirable. However, the decomposition of these agents under fire temperatures creates toxic gases or vapors; therefore these agents would probably be of only limited for transportation emergencies.

Several dry chemical extinguishers are also available and potentially applicable. Sodium chloride, sodium bicarbonate and/or potassium bicarbonate can be used to reduce the intensity of fires. Graphite, which is the major component of several other dry extinguishants, is effective on fires of certain metals like magnesium and sodium which are water or CO_2 reactive.

The following sections present brief paragraphs for each chemical and propellant involved in fire. Details of cautionary emergency response guidelines for each HM ound in the DOT, AAR, EPA and USCG Response Guidebooks are given in Appendices G through J, respectively.

4.4.1 Acetone

Acetone is a colorless flammable liquid which has flammable limits in air of 2.6 - 12.8%. Use of water as a fire fighting agent in a straight hose stream will scatter and spread the fire, so it should not be used. Acetone fires may flashback along vapor trail; containers should be cooled with unmanned hoses and water nozzles; and fires should be extinguished with dry chemical, alcohol foam or carbon dioxide.

4.4.2 Acetone Cyanohydrin

Acetone cyanohydrin is a poisonous material which supports combustion when its vapor concentration is between 2.2 - 12% in air. Appropriate fire fighting agents include water spray, dry chemical, alcohol foam or carbon dioxide.

When the material is on fire, toxic hydrogen cyanide is generated. Wear chemical protective suit and self-contained breathing apparatus. Containers should be cooled with water from a safe and protected location. Firefighting runoff will be harmful to aquatic life in very low concentrations, so proper methods of containment must be used.

4.4.3 Acrylonitrile

Acrylonitrile is a flammable gas when the vapor concentration in air is between 3.05 - 17%. Fires of acrylonitrile should be extinguished with only dry chemical, alcohol foam or carbon dioxide. Use of water or foam as a firefighting agent may cause frothing. When heated or burned, acrylonitrile may evolve toxic hydrogen cyanide gas and nitrogen oxides. Flashback along vapor trail may occur. Combat fire from a safe distance or protected area. Water may be ineffective on fire. Cool exposed containers with water. Firefighters should wear goggles, self-contained breathing apparatus and rubber overclothing. Spills may be harmful to aquatic life in very low concentration.

4.4.4 Aerozine-50

Aerozine-50 is flammable in both liquid and vapor states. Since the vapor over the fuel blend at 75°F is predominantly UDMH, the flammability hazards of the mixture are the same as for UDMH. The fuel blend vapors are flammable in air in concentrations from 2.3 - 100%. Large quantities of water should be used to extinguish Aerozine-50 fires. Aerozine-50 fires behave essentially as UDMH fires and may be extinguished by water sprays, alcohol foam, and dry chemical powders containing primarily sodium bicarbonate. Acrylic foam may also prove beneficial. Neither Freon 13B1 (bromotrifluoromethane) nor carbon dioxide are effective. The TLV is 0.1 ppm and ER personnel should be equipped with appropriate breathing apparatus. If a fishy odor is detected the TLV has been exceeded, evacuate the area and seek proper medical assistance (see Section 4.2.1).

4.4.5 Ammonia, Anhydrous

Anhydrous ammonia is a non-flammable, toxic compressed gas but it will support combustion within certain vapor concentration limits (15.5-27.0%). It can increase fire hazards when oil or other combustible materials are also involved. Ammonia has no chemical incompatibilities with any fire extinguishing agent and the appropriate agent for the surrounding fire conditions should be used. Firefighting runoff water will be mildly corrosive and extremely toxic to aquatic life, so care must be exercised to contain and prevent it from reaching water sources.

4.4.6 Butadiene, Inhibited

Butadiene is a flammable, compressed gas with vapors heavier than air. Under fire conditions, the vapors may travel to an ignition source and then flashback. Containers may explode in a fire due to polymerization of contents. Butadiene has no restrictions on fire extinguishants. Flooding quantities of water are generally effective. However, it is important to stop and secure any leak sources, if attempts are made to extinguish a fire involving butadiene because of flashback problems.

4.4.7 Chlorine

Chlorine is a non-flammable, toxic compressed gas which may cause fire on contact with combustibles. Chlorine does react with many metals vigorously at high temperatures. There are no special restrictions on fire extinguishing agents and any agent suitable for the fire is appropriate. A fire of combustibles in chlorine atmospheres can produce toxic and corrosive combustion products. Chlorine reacts vigorously with water and forms a corrosive solution; therefore, any firefighting runoff water should be contained because it can pose a threat to aquatic life.

4.4.8 Ethyl Acrylate

Ethyl acrylate is a flammable liquid having flammable limits in air of 1.8 - 9.5%. When ethyl acrylate is heated by fire toxic and irritating vapors are generated. Containers may explode in fires causing flashback along its vapor trail. In cases where the material is released goggles, self-contained breathing apparatus and rubber overclothing must be worn. Fires should be extinguished with dry chemicals, foam, or carbon dioxide. Vapors of ethyl acrylate are heavier than air and may travel a considerable distance to a source of ignition and flashback. May polymerize and cause container to explode.

4.4.9 Ethylene Oxide

Ethylene oxide is a flammable liquid whose flammable limits in air range from 3-100%. These air-ethylene oxide mixtures of 6%-24% can detonate. The vapors are heavier than air and may travel some distance to an ignition source and flashback. The container may explode when heated. Ethylene oxide may also polymerize violently, if contaminated with alkaline or acidic materials, metal oxides or chlorides. In a fire involving this material, the first step is to secure the release or leak if possible before attempting to put out the fire because of flashback potentials. One method of combating an ethylene oxide fire is to flood it with water. According to the NFPA, however, this method is sometimes ineffective. Another recommended method is to use alcohol foam. Because alcohol foam is not always available, there will be occasion when there is no alternative but to use water. Ethylene oxide must be diluted with water 22 to 1 before it will no longer burn. Small pool fires are most effectively extinguished using fluidized (bicarbonate base) commercial dry powder extinguishers.

Standard foam must not be used, because it may assist the burning rather than retard it. Ethylene oxide vapors may detonate, if some initiating heat source is present. Ethylene oxide vapors, in a tank exposed to a fire, may be rapidly heated to their ignition temperature unless the tank is cooled with water spray.

4.4.10 Hydrazine and Monomethylhydrazine (MMH)

Hydrazine and MMH are flammable, poisonous liquids with flammable limits of 4.7 - 100% and 2.5 - 98%, respectively. In both cases, flashback along a vapor trail may occur and the vapors may detonate if ignited in a confined or enclosed area. Water, which acts by cooling and diluting, is the most effective agent for completely extinguishing air-supported hydrazine and MMH fires. The most efficient means of applying water is in a coarse spray. Water fog and bicarbonate-base (powder) extinguishing agents may be used for combating spill-type fires. In large fires, there is a danger of flashback with these agents, because hydrazine and MMH accelerate the disintegration of foam. Effective use of water minimizes the re-ignition and flashback hazard in hydrazine and MMH fires. Halogenated firefighting agents are generally ineffective on this type of fire. For oxidizer-supported fires (flare burning), water fog or spray is the most effective extinguishing agent if it is acceptable for use on the specific oxidizer feeding the fire. Also, acrylic foam has been demonstrated to show flame extinguishant capabilties (see Section 4.2.1).

4.4.11 Hydrocyanic Acid

Hydrocyanic acid is flammable in 5.6 - 40% concentrations in air as a liquid or gas. When a fire occurs an attempt should be made to stop the flow of the gas. Fires should be allowed to burn; however, exposed containers should be cooled with water. Extremely toxic vapors are generated even at ordinary temperatures. In case of fire emergency response personnel should wear a chemical protective suit with self-contained breathing apparatus.

4.4.12 Isobutane

Isobutane is a liquefied compressed gas having flammable limits in air of 1.8 - 8.4%. Isobutane floats and boils on water. Water should be used to cool exposed containers and men effecting shut off (stop discharge if possible). Stay upwind and use water spray to "knock down" vapor.

4.4.13 Liquefied Hydrogen

Liquefied hydrogen is a flammable, compressed gas with flammable limits in air ranging from 4 - 75%. The most effective control of hydrogen fires is by securing the leak or release of hydrogen. Fires from hydrogen gas can also be controlled effectively with very high concentrations of the common extinguishing agents, such as water, CO_2, and steam. Equipment should be designed for effective control and isolation in case of failure. It should be noted that, if hydrogen flames resulting from leaks are extinguished, hydrogen will continue to leak and form a cloud of combustible gas that may explode if ignited. It is also important to note that the outer limits of hydrogen flame or fire cannot generally be seen. Where possible, use large quantities of water, preferably in the form of spray, to cool adjacent exposures.

4.4.14 Liquefied Oxygen

Liquefied oxygen is a liquefied gas that is not flammable but will support combustion. The presence of liquid oxygen will intensify a fire and when mixed with a fuel, organic or combustible material can form a detonable mixture. Procedures for controlling fires involving liquid oxygen vary with the type and circumstances of the fire. Some general guideline recommendations follow. When the fire results from a leak or flow of liquid oxygen onto wood, paper, waste, or other similar material, first stop the flow if possible. If the leak or flow can be stopped, use water to put the fire out quickly. When the fire involves liquid oxygen and liquid fuels, control it as follows:

a. If a fire is supported by liquid oxygen flowing into large quantities of fuel, secure the release of oxygen, and put the fire out with firefighting agents appropriate to the fuel.

b. If fuel and liquid oxygen are mixed, but not burning, isolate the area from sources of ignition, quickly evacuate personnel, and allow the oxygen to evaporate.

c. If large pools of oxygen and water-soluble fuel are burning, use water to dilute the fuel and reduce the intensity of the fire. This method cannot be used with fuels which do not mix with water. Appropriate extinguishing agents may be used to put out fuel fires after the oxygen has evaporated.

4.4.15 Methyl Alcohol

Methyl alcohol is a flammable liquid having flammable concentrations in air of 6 - 36.5%. In the case of fire flashback along vapor trail may occur; extinguish with dry chemical; do not use water because it is ineffective as a firefighting agent; and cool exposed containers with water. When containers holding methyl alcohol are subject to fire they may explode.

4.4.16 Methyl Bromide

Methyl bromide is a compressed liquefied gas having flammable limits in air of 10 - 15%. When exposed to fire or heat toxic and irritating gases are generated. Exposed containers should be cooled with water. In the case of fire poisonous and irritating gases are produced. Emergency response personnel should be equipped with self-contained breathing apparatus, goggles and protective impervious overclothing. Fires should be extinguished by water, foam or carbon dioxide.

4.4.17 Nitrogen Tetroxide

Nitrogen tetroxide is a compressed, toxic gas which is also a strong oxidizer. It is not flammable, but supports combustion of combustible materials and can cause fire or explosion upon contact with these materials. Nitrogen tetroxide dissolves in water to form a corrosive solution of nitric acid, thus any firefighting runoff poses a threat to aquatic life and should be contained. It should also be noted that poisonous nitrogen oxide fumes are produced in a fire involving nitrogen tetroxide. In case of fire, an attempt should be made to secure the leak of N_2O_4. The continued application of large quantities of water will eventually flush away the oxidizer so that combustion is no longer supported. Any remaining air-supported fuel fire may be extinguished by using techniques applicable to the fuel involved (see Section 4.2.1). In addition, all ER personnel should be equipped with impervious clothing.

4.4.18 Propane

Propane is a flammable, compressed hydrocarbon gas with flammable limits in air ranging from 2.1 - 9.5%. Propane vapors are heavier than air, may travel some distance to an ignition source and flashback, or can detonate if ignited in an enclosed area. Containers may explode in a fire and the fragments rocket in every direction causing additional hazards. In a situation where a bulk propane shipment is leaking and on fire, no attempt should be made to fight the fire unless the leak source can be secured and there has been no fire impingement on any container vapor space. In such cases, allowing the fire to burn and even further opening (venting) the container for more rapid burning of contents may be warranted and has been used in the past. For small propane fires, dry chemicals may be used.

4.4.19 Propylene

Propylene is a liquefied compressed gas having flammable limits in air of 2 - 11%. When fire occurs container may explode; flashback along vapor trail may occur; flow of gas should be stopped if possible; fires should be allowed to burn; and cool exposed containers and protect men effecting shut off with water. Vapors of propylene are heavier than air and may travel considerable distance to a source of ignition and flashback.

4.4.20 Sodium Hydrosulfide

Sodium hydrosulfide is a non-flammable gas. In cases where sodium hydrosulfide is released an attempt should be made to stop discharge, keep people away, and isolate and remove discharged material. Sodium hydrosulfide reacts corrosively with most metals, but the reaction is not hazardous.

4.4.21 Sodium Hydroxide

Sodium hydroxide is a non-flammable solid, however, may cause fire in contact with combustibles. May also form a flammable hydrogen gas when in contact with metals such as aluminum, tin, lead and zinc. Exposed containers should be cooled with water. Emergency response personnel should be equipped with rubber overclothing. NaOH dissolves with the liberation of heat in water and may steam and splatter.

4.4.22 Styrene

Styrene is a flammable liquid having flammable limits in air of 1.1 - 6.1%. Styrene vapor is heavier than air and may travel considerable distance to a source of ignition and flashback. At elevated temperatures such as in fire conditions, polymerization may take place which may lead to container explosion. Water may be ineffective as a firefighting agent. Appropriate firefighting agents include water fog, foam, carbon dioxide or dry chemical. Emergency response personnel should wear chemical protective suits with self-contained breathing apparatus. Exposed containers should be cooled with water. Combat fires from safe distance or protected location.

4.4.23 Toluene

Toluene is a flammable liquid having flammable limits in air of 1.27 - 7%. Toluene vapors are heavier than air and may travel a considerable distance to a source of ignition and flashback. Firefighting precautions include wearing goggles and self-contained breathing apparatus; extinguish with dry chemical, foam or carbon dioxide because water is an ineffective firefighting agent; and cool exposed containers with water.

4.4.24 Unsymmetrical Dimethylhydrazine (UDMH)

UDMH is a poisonous, flammable liquid with flammable limits in air ranging from 2 - 95%. UDMH fires supported by air may best be extinguished by the application of water in relatively large amounts in proportion to the fuel. When this fuel has been diluted with water (one to three times the original fuel volume), the resulting solution is non-flammable. The amount of water required to render the solution non-flammable is dependent on the temperature of the mixture. The most efficient method of applying water is in a coarse spray. Water fog, carbon dioxide, and bicarbonate-based fire extinguishing agents are not recommended for extensive fires, since with these agents there is danger of flashbacks and explosive re-ignitions. In any case, these agents should not be used for extinguishing this type of fire.

4.4.25 Vinyl Acetate

Vinyl acetate is a flammable liquid having a vapor concentration in air of 2.6 - 13.4%. Vinyl acetate vapors are heavier than air and may travel considerable distance to a source of ignition and flashback. Polymerization can occur when in contact with peroxides and strong acids, but only under extreme conditions. Appropriate firefighting agents for vinyl acetate fires should be used including carbon dioxide or dry chemical for small fires and ordinary foam for large fires. In case of fire emergency response personnel should wear goggles and self-contained breathing apparatus; combat fires from safe distance or protected location; extinguish with dry chemical, foam or carbon dioxide; and cool exposed containers with water.

4.4.26 Vinyl Chloride

Vinyl chloride is a flammable, compressed gas with flammable limits in air ranging from 4 - 26%. Vinyl chloride vapors are heavier than air, may travel a distance to an ignition source and flashback, and may detonate if ignited in an enclosed area. Vinyl chloride polymerizes in air, sunlight or when heated unless inhibited by phenol stabilizer. Under fire conditions the container may explode. Further hazards include the formation of toxic and corrosive combustion products such as hydrogen chloride, phosgene and carbon monoxide.

For small fires, dry chemicals or carbon dioxide may be used. To address large fires, the leak source must be secured and adjacent exposed surfaces cooled. However, in this case, as with propane, it may be in the interests of safety to allow the fire to burn.

4.5 EVACUATION

When the on-scene or downwind vapor concentration exceeds the TLV or the atmosphere has reached the LEL, the on-scene coordinator must make a decision whether or not to evacuate on-scene emergency response personnel and civilian members of the surrounding community.

It is not as important to evacuate emergency response personnel from the scene if they have proper protective clothing and breathing apparatus, as it is if they have limited or no resources available. Members of the local community are not generally equipped, could be unaware that an accident has occurred or they may simply not know what self-protective steps to take.

Evacuation of a 1- to 2-mile radius around the accident site can be a good effective tool for safeguarding the general public. However, evacuation is an option which must be weighed carefully for it can be a two-edged sword. On the one hand, the public must be protected from exposures threatening their health and general safety. On the other hand, there must not be needless over evacuation because of the social disruption, fear, cost, and potential danger to the sick and elderly who must be moved. There is the potential to cause more chaos, confusion and problems with an over zealous, uncoordinated and unanticipated evacuation. The Department of Transportation has identified isolation and evacuation distances for specific hazardous materials. Table 4-2 has been prepared to show initial isolation and initial evacuation distances from a spill of DOT recognized HM addressed by this manual. Isolation and evacuation distances are given for acrylonitrile, anhydrous ammonia, chlorine, ethylene oxide, hydrocyanic acid, methyl bromide and nitrogen tetroxide.

Evacuation should be conducted by law enforcement personnel in conjunction with members of the state's civil defense/emergency preparedness organization. Communities and state agencies should establish a cooperative assistance plan in the event of such an emergency.

The area to be evacuated will be a function of the material released and local meteorological, topographic, hydrogeologic and demographic conditions. A discussion of vapor dispersion for estimating evacuation radii is given in Section 3.4.1. The initial evacuation must be continually reevaluated during the mitigation, cleanup and disposal and wreckage removal phases following a transportation emergency for modification, extending or collapsing the hazard perimeter based on prevailing meteorologic conditions, the material released and other accident conditions.

An excellent walk through on evacuation excerpted from Smith[2] is presented below.

"Within minutes of the accident, the first officials arrive on or near the scene. The first order of business is to get the immediate area evacuated. The people involved here require little urging, but simply a direction in which to go. If fire is a big problem, perimeter cooling can begin simultaneously with initial

TABLE 4-2. ISOLATION AND EVACUATION
DISTANCES OF SELECTED HAZARDOUS MATERIALS

NAME OF MATERIAL SPILLING OR LEAKING	INITIAL ISOLATION SPILL or LEAK FROM (drum, smaller container or small leak from tank) ISOLATE in all Directions feet	INITIAL EVACUATION LARGE SPILL FROM A TANK (or from many containers, drums, etc.) FIRST ISOLATE in all Directions feet	THEN EVACUATE IN A DOWNWIND DIRECTION Width miles	Length miles
Acrylonitrile	30	60	0.1	0.2
Anhydrous Ammonia	100	200	0.4	0.7
Chlorine	250	520	1.3	2.0
Ethylene Oxide	40	70	0.2	0.2
Hydrocyanic Acid	90	190	0.5	0.7
Methyl Bromide	50	90	0.2	0.3
Nitrogen Tetroxide	110	220	0.5	0.8

evacuation. There is little you can save on-scene with water; the best you can hope for is explosion control. Initial fire-control efforts should always be defensive. Be ready to retreat, and have your equipment arranged in withdrawal positions. Get EMT units into the area as quickly as possible. Civil defense workers, sheriff, local police, and spillor officials are to begin the next stage of evacuation immediately. Use bullhorns or whatever is available, and set up teams moving in concentric circles. Have one team move clockwise, the next counterclockwise. The theory is that the overlapping amplified warning may prewarn those in the next block before the team arrives. Finally, have follow-up teams moving in the same pattern, closing and locking doors, checking ovens, windows, lights, etc. If the situation is too volatile, move back. You can continue later when you have received proper equipment and additional help. Don't forget to tell everyone where to go. Pick out a well-known spot (not too far away, since some may be walking), and make sure every announcement relays this location to the evacuees. Immediately send one of your staff members to receive them, and get ready for the Red Cross and Salvation Army to begin sheltering them.

"When the area is evacuated and secure, roving patrols (with adequate breathing equipment) should continually move throughout the area, keeping a sharp eye for curiosity seekers, looters, and people going back for something they forgot.

Reoccupation is a happy time, but it must be done with some formality. Prior to leaving the shelters, everyone should be briefed as to what happened and where and when to file claims they may have for any and all damages. The spillor should be involved in this meeting. Last of all, everyone should be warned that cleanup is continuing on-scene and that they must stay out the cleanup area. Individuals who have suffered specific damage such as contamination of water wells, gardens, etc., must be instructed individually as to what they can or cannot do."

5. CARGO TRANSFER, WRECKAGE REMOVAL AND CLEANUP/DISPOSAL GUIDELINES

5.1 CARGO TRANSFER GUIDELINES

5.1.1 Cargo Transfer Team

When the tank cars containing the hazardous materials must be transferred at the scene the carrier has the authority to select the group to perform any cargo transfer operations. Because of the value of the cargo, the shipper's knowledge of the cargo's characteristics and expertise in handling the particular hazardous material and the fact that the carrier is performing a service for the shipper, the carrier should, and usually does, seek the advice and assistance of the shipper for cargo transfer. Some shippers have qualified in-house experts available to perform actual transfer and provide on-scene advice to others. In any event, no cargo transfer should be attempted without supervision by fully-qualified experts and the prior approval of the carrier and shipper, both of whom should fully coordinate the plans and actions with the OSC. The shipper must decide what personnel and equipment are needed to accomplish the job and determine what resources (equipment, materials, etc.) must be acquired outside the company and arrange for them to be delivered to the site if necessary. In some cases, the shipper may elect to hire a contractor to perform the transfer. In the best interests for everyone concerned the shipper and carrier should be knowledgeable about the capabilities and qualifications of a potential cargo transfer contractor.

Qualification and Training

Individuals who perform cargo transfer and cleanup/disposal activities at the scene of a hazardous materials transportation accident should have training in material properties including thermophysical/chemical and material compatibility; use of personal protective clothing; vapor monitoring; Federal waste disposal regulations (see Section 5.3); and transfer operations and options.

Transfer Team Preparations

Before any decision or attempt is made to transfer cargo, the transfer team must know what hazardous materials are present; quantities involved; container structural integrity, structural designs (detailed drawings are useful) and orientation. Depending upon the situation, empty specification tank trucks/rail tank cars or other containers have to be obtained. Appropriate hazardous materials monitoring instruments and personal protective clothing, breathing equipment and other gear must be obtained and checked out. After careful study of the container designs a sketch should be made of the proposed transfer scheme. A list of all necessary pipes, fittings, adapters, valves, gauges, pumps, containers and other items required to construct the transfer should be made. An important reason for having detailed container design drawings is the need to be certain that all connections from the transfer system to the tank will be properly sized and threaded; a misfit could create a very serious accident. Then, an overall plan should be written (if not already available) for every aspect of constructing the transfer system and its operation. The SOP should include an appropriate checkoff list to assure all steps are followed, leaving nothing to chance.

Upon arriving at the scene, the transfer team should make personal contact with the OSC and appropriate other officials, e.g., railroad, shipper (if the team is not from the shipper's organization), environmental monitoring groups and any other necessary support groups such as earth movers or wreckage handlers to discuss the transfer plan; make necessary modifications if the situation has changed; arrange for any needed support; and establish the communication linkage.

5.1.2 Container Status

Presently, there is no accurate way to assess container structural integrity at the accident scene. The technology has yet to be developed and applied to the assessment of a hazardous materials tank car or cargo tank. The propane tank car explosion at Waverly, Tennessee, is clear evidence of this deficiency; nevertheless, certain observations can be made to give some indication. First look for visible leaks and use detectors for hidden/gaseous leaks. Insulation on tank cars or motor vehicle cargo tanks adds to the difficulty in locating leaks. If torching of the ullage space (vapor space) has been observed or there is evidence to that effect on the tank, it should be assumed that the metal has been weakened. Discolorations, scrapes, scouring marks and indentations are indications that the container may have been weakened. Bulging indicates internal overpressuring has occurred. Dynamic stresses and strains also can occur to the tanks without any visible signs. If part of the tank is buried, the condition of the hidden part can not be determined without removing the dirt from around it and this is not recommended.

In addition to the aforementioned physical markings, one should look for damaged or missing external valves, fittings, piping or other appurtenances as well as damage at those points where the tank has been mounted to the rail car or truck chassis. Some external fixtures are designed to shear off, if impacted, and are backed up by internal valving to prevent product release. The appearance around such damaged areas needs to be carefully examined for indications of damage to the container itself. Significant external damage and signs of dynamic stress/strain also indicate the possibility that internal piping may have been broken or weakened; all these considerations must be taken into account when producing the transfer system scheme.

The utilization of an AE device attached to the inner cargo tank is one area of technology which needs exploration as a possible means to provide warning that the container may be weakening towards possible rupture. Remote sensing and remote monitoring of internal tank pressure and temperature are other examples of technology needing development which could lead to improved assessment of container integrity. Currently, a great deal of evaluation is left to intuition or experienced judgment for assessing the container's integrity. This is not a comforting situation from a safety standpoint.

Even if there is no apparent damage to the tank car or larger tank of a tank motor vehicle, it should be assumed that there has been damage and all actions should be conducted with this in mind.

In addition to determining the container's integrity, it is very important to shore up, anchor with cables and secure the container by other means before attempting any transfer activity.

5.1.3 Container Accessibility

It is necessary to examine the detailed design drawings for the particular tank car or cargo tank involved to determine internal piping arrangements, valving and other access points, and their position relative to the orientation of the container the quantity of hazardous materials and liquid level. The Car and Locomotive Cyclopedia[13] contains diagrams of a number of rail tank cars. The railroad or company official may know something of the container design. It may be necessary to get the drawings from the tank car or cargo tank owner, trade associations (e.g., the Chlorine Institute and CHLOREP Teams may have this information) or from the manufacturer. It is critical that the design be known with certainty. Knowing this permits a decision as to how a connection can be made to the transfer system and whether or not the access point can be opened. Also it reveals how much the container needs to be reorientated to provide a suitable access point; or if the container would have to be breached to insert an adapter, and if so, where the best location to breach the container would be. It should be kept in mind that liquid is what needs to be transferred. Gaseous transfer is completely impractical.

The Chlorine Institute has developed sophisticated "Go Teams," experts knowing container designs, and equipment to seal leaks and repair certain items like valves and seals on chlorine containers. Other associations are attempting to develop comparable equipment and programs for other specialized hazardous materials.

The ideal situation is to have the normal unloading valves and piping intact and in a usable position. Often this does not happen, so it is necessary to utilize other means to reach the remaining cargo.

In the event there is no access to the inside of the container and it is necessary to establish one tapping is a possible technique. This requires special tools and equipment especially designed for the particular commodity and container. Much technology remains to be developed in this area. Obviously, the greater the internal pressure, the more difficult, risky or impossible this technique becomes. Unless expertise with appropriate tools and equipment are available to perform the operation, it should not be attempted. Consideration needs to be given to container design, so that, regardless of orientation, both the liquid and ullage areas would be accessible (permit installation of a valved adapter and still be capable of being opened with the adapter in place). Such a design would do away with the need for the tapping procedure. It may prove worthwhile to develop improved tapping techniques.

In any event, continuous monitoring of the containers, meteorological conditions and personnel is necessary. Only persons essential for the performance of product transfer operations should be allowed in the area when this operation is being conducted.

5.1.4 Connecting Up

When the product transfer team finds that the on-site conditions are safe to transfer the hazardous material, careful consideration must be given to the reactivity of the material with metals, stability of the material (see Section 4.3) and availability of authorized transfer tanks. Attention must be paid to the container specifications for transport of each material given in 49 CFR.

5.1.5 Reaching the Liquid Product

Bulk containers are designed for top/bottom unloading depending upon the particular hazardous material being transported in them. As mentioned earlier, liquid transfer is a practical approach. When in the normal position, this is not a problem. However, the usual accident scene finds the containers in anything but normal orientation. The wheels or undercarriage may be sheared off and the container could be resting on, or partially buried in, the ground. Obviously this makes transfer from the bottom impractical unless it is possible to dig an access through the ground to a fitting underneath. If an access is partially below the liquid level, it may be possible to remove some of the liquid. However, a point is going to be reached when it will be necessary to insert some kind of dip tube or snorkel to reach the bottom of the liquid in order to remove it. Technology should examine the feasibility for developing a snorkel-type device during container construction which would provide reliable access to the liquid, even when pressurized, regardless of the tanks orientation in an accident.

Special expertise and equipment are required to insert some type of tube into the liquid level; this should be performed only when no pressure exists in the container. The outlet to any such device must be closed off before insertion into the liquid, so that when the system is sealed no product will inadvertently run out. In fact that piece of equipment, as well as the entire transfer system and receiving container should be flushed free of air and be blanketed with an inert gas.

5.1.6 Minimizing Internal Pressure

The chances of increased leakage or rupture of the container can be reduced if the excess internal container pressure can be safely reduced prior to commencing transfer operations. If the container is equipped with an adjustable safety relief device which is free and located in the ullage space it may be possible to utilize this method. This may not be possible or it might still be unadvisable even if it can be adjusted. If the vapors are flammable or toxic the release must be done in such a manner that released vapors do not create either a flammable or toxic hazard. If venting is to the atmosphere, the release rate and meteorological conditions must assure atmospheric concentrations will be below the dangerous level to those working at the scene and the community at large. Any person engaged in a venting operation must have full protective (fire and toxicity) clothing and gear. Unless it is mandatory to do otherwise, the venting system should be rigged so that it can be controlled remotely to provide adequate safety to the persons involved.

It may be advisable to flare venting vapors. If this is the case, a line must be run a sufficient distance away from the wreckage to pose no fire danger. The line must be located such that the combustion products (they might be toxic) do not endanger the on-scene workers or the public. Flaring may speed up the pressure released but the rate of release must be controlled so that the concentration of combustion products released is not hazardous.

Depending upon the particular hazardous material; it may be possible to reduce the tank pressure by water-cooling the container (not to be done with cryogens or refrigerated products). With certain chemicals and propellants it might not be possible to reduce significantly the internal pressure unless essentially all the product is released. Water-cooling the container might have to be done if conditions indicate that transfer can not be accomplished or moving the loaded container risky.

As a last resort when cargo transfer is considered dangerous, it may be necessary to release the pressure by rupturing the container. This requires the services of qualified explosives experts working in coordination with persons knowledgeable in the construction of the particular container and the characteristics of the hazardous materials in an explosive environment. All effects (fire, toxicity, fragments and blast overpressure) must be carefully estimated and the necessary prior evacuation and other precautions taken beforehand. Provisions must be made to assure immediate ignition of the vapors to reduce vapor-phase explosion intensity.

All pressure-reducing venting/flaring systems must be equipped with flow control valves, check valves, flame arrestors and other necessary safety features to prevent air/flashback into the container.

5.1.7 Transfer System Design/Layout Components

Because of the differing hazards associated with hazardous materials and their incompatabilty with other materials, threading and other aspects of valves, connectors, etc. are deliberately designed to prevent interchange. For that reason, and to make certain no leak occurs, it is critical that fittings and connectors are matched between the tank and the transfer system. Certainly, the precaution must be observed throughout the transfer system.

Materials of Construction Compatibility

The 28 chemicals and propellants under consideration possess widely diverse physical and chemical properties (see Appendix A). Liquefied oxygen and hydrogen are cryogens and they require very specialized materials for storage facilities and handling tanks. Oxygen systems require special cleaning to ensure that no organic matter is present which could result in shock-sensitive materials. Nitrogen tetroxide systems must be cleaned and passivated because, in the presence of moisture, it is very strongly acidic, thus corrosive, and also is capable of spontaneously igniting fuels (inorganic and organic). The hydrazines, particularly hydrazine, itself, are hydroscopic and form corrosive alkaline solutions. Ammonia behaves likewise. These materials are given as examples to show that each of the 28 chemicals and propellants has peculiar properties which must be fully understood when the transfer system components are selected (e.g., seals, fittings, pipes, valves, gauges, pumps, etc). If any of these fail during the transfer operation, new problems are created.

The chemical manufacturers can provide information about the materials of construction and equipment suitable for handling their respective commodities and should be consulted when designing a particular transfer system. Equipment manufacturers (e.g., for pumps) should be able to recommend equipment suitable for service with particular hazardous materials. In most instances the manufacturer or shipper will be represented at the scene and can provide technical expertise to transfer operations of their HM.

Capacity and Specifications

All hazardous materials which are transferred will also be transported. Unless the hazardous materials are to be delivered, recovered or disposed in the local jurisdiction where the accident occurred, its transport will be subject to state and Federal regulations. More and more states are adopting the Federal Hazardous Materials Transportation Regulations (49 CFR). Therefore, it is strongly recommended that receiving containers for the particular hazardous material involved meet the 49 CFR specifications. In addition to avoiding penalities for violating the regulations, their use avoids unnecessary second transfers to specification containers and the hazards, risk and expenses that an operation entails.

Regardless of what receiving containers are used, it is absolutely critical that they have been thoroughly cleaned, so that there is nothing present that could react with the HM to be placed in them. Furthermore, their integrity needs to be verified so they will not leak.

In order that transfer operations proceed without unintended interruption, the receiving containers must be positioned so they will be stable when loaded and be able to be moved out without any problem. Also, the capacity of the receiving container must be adequate to accept all the product to be transferred.

Grounding

Several of the HM addressed by this manual are flammable (See Table 3-1). Sound safety procedures dictate that all sources of ignition be removed from any place where flammables are present. Static or electrical sparks can easily ignite flammable vapors so it is important that the entire transfer system, including the original HM container and receiver, be properly grounded, so that the possibility of sparking and igniting any inadvertent vapor release is minimized. Fluid flow is a notorious generator of static electricity. Pumps are also.

In the event it is necessary to reorient the container prior to conducting transfer operations, heavy equipment is usually involved. Such equipment is capable of developing high static charges. Grounding of such equipment in consonance with the container is absolutely essential.

5.1.8 Transfer Operations

Adequate continuous monitoring of all aspects of the scene, operations and personnel is necessary so that corrective actions if needed may be taken immediately. Accident case histories reveal serious neglect in this area.

Leaking vapors could be flammable or toxic. People working in close proximity are particularly susceptible to such hazards and must be alerted immediately. Weather radar is a valuable tool for tracking a hazardous materials vapor cloud. Weather predictions and meteorological data are needed on a continuing basis for downwind vapor dispersion calculations. The calculations are used for the deployment of personnel and management of operations.

Changes in tank pressure or temperature may be indicative of a potential problem within the container and are particularly significant if the container has sustained damage. Initial determination of a container's structural integrity is an area where technology is deficient at hazardous materials transportation accidents. Even if the utilization of AE or other warning techniques proves technically feasible, such device must be placed on the container at the scene. However, there is some unknown inherent risk to the person who approaches the tank car or cargo tank. A much greater AE technological breakthrough would be required to make the installation of a device on every bulk container practically and economically feasible.

Nevertheless, hazardous materials containers involved in an incident, need to be continually observed for any abnormal indications, particularly damaged or scraped areas. Dampening may be the first indication of a leak. Hissing (e.g., escaping gas) or creaking are audible danger signals. Flexing or bulging would indicate a strong structural deformation was taking place. Preferably, these observations would be done through high-powered optics at a safe distance. However, if the decision has been made to permit transfer operations to proceed regardless of the unknown risk involved, a qualified expert investigator should personally examine each car, making actual field measurements of distortions and noting all abnormalities.

Obviously, the structural integrity is most critical for containers whose contents are under significant pressure due to the possibility of violent rupture. Loaded cargo tanks if already weakened could experience additional stress and cause severe rupture during reorientation or movement; this type of handling even strains normal tank cars or cargo tanks. This reason indicates why cargo transfer before container movement is generally advisable.

Wind behavior must be known so operations can be performed upwind from hazardous materials containers. Transfer operations should generally not be performed in severe weather if possible; meteorological information is necessary to manage the operations properly. Likewise meteorological data is necessary to make decisions about possible evacuations when transfer operations are to be performed and while underway.

Persons working on the accident scene are under stress and usually are breathing heavily due to the physical nature of the work. If a person is exposed to a toxic vapor, the amount entering the lungs would increase. Personnel must wear full protective clothing and equipment for such operations. There is a finite time limit for a person to perform so personnel need to be observed for any unusual behavior.

5.1.9 Controlling Transfer

Transfer operations should be completed as quickly as is practical and safe. Most hazardous materials are moved as a liquid because with the quantities involved; an extremely long time would be required to transfer the hazardous material as a gas or vapor form. Three basic options that can be used for moving the liquid are gas/vapor pressure, gravity flow or pumps. If the conditions are such that the top of the receiving container is lower than the bottom of the tank car or cargo tank, gravity flow can be used. This would be considerably slower than the other two methods but is the safest because it does not involve the addition of a pressurizing gas or mechanical equipment. Depending upon the orientation and design of the container and the condition of internal piping, gravity flow might involve direct flow from the lower portion of the container. Siphoning may be required and extra precautions and special techniques (e.g., applying some inert gas pressurized or some equipment) may be required to establish the liquid siphon head.

With those hazardous materials which are already under pressure, the liquid driving force is already present and can be utilized to accomplish transfer. Unless there is no access to the liquid this method is faster than liquid this method is faster than gravity flow and does not require any auxiliary help.

There is a good likelihood that pumping may be necessary, particularly if those HM are flammable liquids. Because there is a risk that introduction of a pressurizing gas could stress the container, pumps offer a viable alternative. It is important to remember that the pumps must be compatible to operate in the presence of the vapors of the particular hazardous material involved and that it be compatible with the hazardous material itself.

Regardless of the method employed, the transfer flow rate needs to be controlled so that the ability of the grounding system to prevent any static charge buildups is not exceeded, nor is a negative pressure created in the tank car or cargo tank. Mention is made that a closed transfer system is to be used. An important reason for this is to maintain an open line between the vapor (ullage) spaces of the container being emptied and the receiver, so that the pressure in the two will be at equilibrium. This is necessary to prevent a negative pressure from developing in the tank car or cargo tank due to rapid drawing which could collapse the container and cause a rupture or leak. Flow rate must be controlled so the ability of the connecting line between the two vapor spaces to maintain an equilibrium pressure is not exceeded.

There may be tremendous pressure brought to bear to get everything cleaned up so rail service may be resumed or the roadway opened. Safety must be paramount to expediency, so transfer must be done efficiently but not hurriedly.

5.1.10 Communications

The product transfer team, upon being contacted by whatever source, needs to obtain as much information as possible about the accident - what HM are involved, quantities, conditions, what resources and special equipment are available at the scene or nearby, the name and phone number of the OSC and of the shipper's and carrier's representatives, etc. The name and phone number of the transfer team leader and a list of information that will be needed by the team in order to implement the transfer scheme should be provided the OSC.

If the transfer team is not a part of the shipper's organization, the team needs to maintain close contact with the shipper, obtain any necessary information about the hazardous materials and to be certain how the shipper wants the product handled for transport from the scene. The shipper may also be able to provide design and construction details for the tank car or cargo tank involved. The transfer team certainly needs to contact the carrier promptly to seek the latter information because these details are essential for designing the transfer scheme and preparing the transfer operations. These communications links must be maintained so that additional information may be obtained if needed.

Before commencing transfer operations, the transfer team should brief the OSC and other appropriate officials, particularly those who will be providing a support or backup role. This plan should include continuous two-way communications between the OSC and the team so that the OSC can coordinate support activities and be kept advised of progress, problems, and requests for assistance.

5.2 WRECKAGE REMOVAL GUIDELINES

5.2.1 Initial Precautions

Before wreck clearing is initiated, the accident scene must be stabilized. This includes:

● Reduction of hazards from toxic, explosive, and flammable vapors;

● Hazardous materials transfer where advisable; and

● Assessment of the structural integrity of derailed or overturned tank cars containing hazardous materials.

Guidelines to be followed to carry out these precautions are discussed in other sections of this report. In the case of a freight train derailment, it is also advisable to pull to safety those cars that are still intact on the track at the front and/or rear of the train. The derailment will have ruptured the air lines in the train brake system causing automatic application of emergency brakes to the cars still on the track. Therefore, it will be necessary to close the angle cock on the intact car at the break in the train to permit the build up of pressure in the pneumatic brake system in order for the emergency brakes to release. Thereafter, the intact cars can be pulled to safety away from the accident scene.

5.2.2 Separating Derailed Rail Cars

The wreckage in a derailment is frequently in a jumbled, partially interlo 'ked condition. Some rail cars may still be coupled together with the couplers inoperative. Damaged trucks may be intertwined with other parts of the wreckage. Even after hazards from vapors have been minimized and hazardous materials transferred, removal of damaged rail cars should not be initiated until these cars have been detached or mechanically separated. Otherwise movement of the rail cars would be subjected to unexpected jolts and banging could breach the integrity of the car with possibly disastrous results.

If possible, mechanical separation of the rail cars should be accomplished by gentle moving and lifting of juxtaposed portions of the wreckage. If portions are inextricably tied together, as for example in coupled rail cars where the couplers are inoperative, then cutting torches may be required. Extreme caution must be used, particularly in the case of tank cars that contain flammable liquids or gas. Cutting torches must not be used on tank car tanks either empty or loaded. Some applicable guidelines from B.E. Pamphlet No. 1[8] are as follows:

"Wrecking operations or transfer of contents of tank cars of flammable gas should not be attempted until all vapors in that vicinity are dispersed. Cutting torches must not be used on tank car tanks, either empty or loaded.

Wrecking operations or transfer of contents of tank cars of flammable liquid should not be attempted until all vapors are dispersed. Cutting torches must not be used on tank car tanks either empty or loaded. Many liquids regarded as safe under ordinary conditions and transported as combustible or non-regulated materials should be treated as dangerous in handling a wreck. An empty or partially empty tank car, with or without placards, is very liable to contain a vapor-air mixture which may ignite. Fumes in any empty tank car should be considered as injurious to a person entering it. An empty tank should not be entered before it has been cleaned by steaming and checked for residual vapors. When using cutting torches, care must be exercised to avoid contact with leakage or ground saturated with even such materials as lubricating oils, asphalts, or other petroleum products, vegetable oils, and animal fats, for they can be ignited and will burn as do flammable liquids."

In the case of an inoperative coupler, it may not be necessary or desirable to use a cutting torch. Often, the knuckler can be disengaged by knocking out the knuckle pin with a driving pin and sledge hammer. This would then free the two coupled rail cars. When feasible, this procedure is preferred over the use of cutting torches to disengage an inoperative coupler.

5.2.3 Sequence of Wreckage Removal

After the accident scene has been stabilized, it is necessary to establish a sequence for wreckage removal that minimizes hazards to personnel. The wreckage may contain a mixture of hazardous and non-hazardous materials laden cars with various degrees of damage. It is not possible to state fixed rules for the sequence of wreckage removal because it depends on the particular accident configuration. In general, non-hazardous materials cars should be removed first, if they are readily accessible and their removal does not endanger the integrity of hazardous materials tank cars. (It is assumed that hazardous materials containers in box cars have been removed to a place of safety, and the contents of broken containers disposed of safely, after which these cars can be treated as non-hazardous).

Next comes the removal of hazardous materials tank cars. This must be done with extreme caution, avoiding sudden shocks or jars that might produce sparks or friction. If any leaks are likely during movement of these cars, their contents should be transferred first. Upright intact tank cars should probably be removed first in order to reduce the number of hazardous materials laden cars at the accident scene as quickly and safely as possible. Damaged and/or overturned tank cars containing hazardous materials are probably the last to be removed. Their structural integrity should be continually monitored, both before and during wreckage removal. After uprighting these cars, their contents would normally be transferred before proceeding in their removal.

In the last analysis, the decision on the safest sequence of wreckage removal, as well as on all other aspects of wreckage removal, must depend on the expertise of the wreck supervisor at the accident scene.

5.2.4 Transporting Derailed Rail Cars

If a derailed rail car has not suffered appreciable damage to its underframe, including the car body holster, then the car can be retrucked and transported by rail in the normal manner. Its own trucks can be used if these are available and in operable condition. Otherwise spare trucks should be brought in to the accident scene for this purpose. In the case of a derailed tank car carrying a hazardous material, it is also necessary to assess the structural integrity of the tank shell before retrucking and transport by rail. If a leak is considered likely during transport, the car's contents should be transferred.

If the derailed rail car cannot be safely retrucked, then transport on a flat car or gondola is usually the only alternative. The car body should be blocked and securely tied down in such transport to avoid further damage. The contents of a hazardous materials tank car should be transferred before the car is transported in this manner.

5.2.5 Rigging Equipment Used in Wreck Clearing

Wreck clearing requires the use of mobile cranes. Some types suitable for use in railroad wreck-clearing operations are the locomotive crane and the crawler crane, shown in Figures 5-1 and 5-2 respectively. Also used frequently in railroad wreck clearing is the side boom tractor, shown in Figure 5-3. Side boom tractors are commonly used in pairs, on opposite sides or opposite ends of a rail car, for lifting and moving the car. For highway wreck clearing, the automotive truck crane shown in Figure 5-4 is appropriate. Prior to their use at an accident site, these mobile cranes should be inspected to insure their safe operation. Standard inspection procedures include the following:

"To inspect these cranes, have the operator lower the boom nearly horizontally or until the load block rests upon the ground; then stop the engine. Examine the boom carefully, both from the ground and by walking out on it. Strike all rivet heads with a machinist's hammer to detect any loose ones. Note all bent structural members (legs, lattice members, gusset plates, etc.) and any parts worn by the cables. Check for excessive corrosion. Also inspect the structural members that form the anchorage for the boom hoist cable. Note any loose bolts.

Strike each sheave with the hammer to detect any cracks. Of course, check the cables, anchorages, etc. Inspect the crane engine and hoist mechanism, paying attention to loose or worn pins, keys, cotter pins, broken gear teeth, etc. Check the running gear, including wheels, crawler treads, axles, gears, sprockets, turntable, rollers, center pin, and other vital parts. Make sure that the rail clamps and/or out-riggers are in good condition.

Have the operator start up the engine and raise the boom to the normal operating position, then pick-up a fair-size load and test the brake and frictions. Check the latch (if provided) on the foot brakes to ensure positive holding."[14]

Vehicle mounted winches are also used in wreck clearing, both railroad and highway, for exerting large pulling forces. Of course, the vehicle must be sufficiently braced to remain stationary while the winch is exerting these forces on the wreckage; this is particularly true in railroad wreck clearing where the required pulling force may reach 100 kips or more. Dragging of a hazardous materials tank car, whether by winch or crane, should be attempted only as a last resort and then only after following all safety precautions. This includes laying down a bed of foam along the path to be traversed and keeping all personnel at a safe distance. If leaks are expected, the contents should be transferred first.

Trackmobiles (small tractors) are often used for pulling derailed, but upright, freight cars with intact trucks. Up to 50 kips of car weight can be transferred onto the trackmobile at the pulling face of the coupler (15 inches inside of striker). This provides sufficient traction to the trackmobile to enable it to pull derailed cars longitudinally.

Wire rope, or steel cable as it is frequently called, is used in all aspects of rigging including slings, hoisting cables, winch cables, and crane

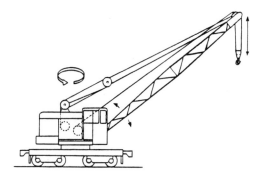

FIGURE 5-1.   LOCOMOTIVE CRANE

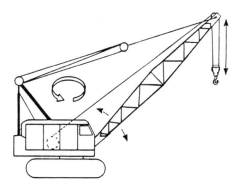

FIGURE 5-2.   CRAWLER CRANE

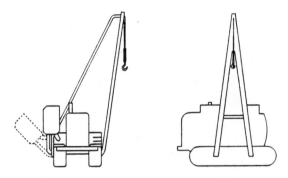

FIGURE 5-3. SIDE BOOM TRACTOR.

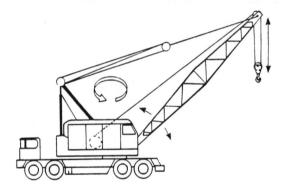

FIGURE 5-4.   AUTOMOTIVE TRUCK CRANE

cables. It is essential that all wire rope be inspected periodically for wear and broken wires to determine when a wire rope has reached the limit of its safe usage and must be discarded. It is dangerous, particularly in wreckage removal, to continue its use beyond a certain stage.

The safe working loads for various types of wire rope slings are shown in Table 5-1. The braided sling is made up of a number of smaller size wire ropes that form a continuous, uniform spiral throughout the entire length of the sling. The spiral braiding gives a much lower modulus of elasticity that a single cable of the same capacity. This greatly reduces the stress on the individual wires when a load is applied suddenly, permitting its safe use with a smaller factor of safety as indicated in Table 5-1. Braided slings are also constructed so as to be almost flat in the general cross-section; these being used particularly for basket-type hitches. These slings may have application in lifting railroad tank cars since their flat cross-section would minimize stress on the tank car body.

Another sling with a flat cross-section is the chain mesh sling, shown in Figure 5-5. This type of sling would also be effective in reducing the stress on tank cars during lifting. It could also be used to an advantage in minimizing the damage to the jacket of insulated tank cars.

is important. When a wire rope sling passes over sharp edges, lifting operations will often cause breaking of wire strands, with a resulting deterioration in the overall strength of the wire rope sling. A chain sling can resist this abrasion much better.

On the other hand, chains are not as resistant to sudden loads or shocks as wire rope. Moreover, chains can fail with little warning. Wire rope failure usually occurs over a period of time, with progressive breaking of wire strands, which allow detection during periodic inspection of the wire rope. Thus, chains require very careful inspection prior to their use in wreck clearing. Danger signs are elongated links (due to overloading), butt links, cracked links, and excessive wear the links bear on each other. The chain should be removed from service if any of these conditions are present.

Shackles, eyebolts, and turnbuckles used in rigging require the same careful periodic inspection as chains. These components can also fail with little warning, due to cracks, deformations, or excessive wear and corrosion.

The hook should be the weakest part of any rigging assembly, since it can provide visible evidence of overloading prior to failure. It seldom breaks, but may fail by straightening out and releasing the load. Hook distortion due to overloading is shown in Figure 5-6.

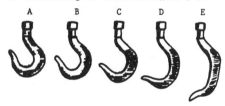

FIGURE 5-6. HOOK DISTORTION
DUE TO OVERLOADING

Reforging and/or assembling of spread hooks should not be permitted.

After long usage, all hooks should be carefully inspected for flaws and cracks.

FIGURE 5-5. CHAIN MESH SLING

Finally, wreck clearing involves the use of hoisting chains, hooks, shackles, etc. Although largely superseded by wire rope, chains are still used in many aspects of rigging, particularly where abrasion resistance

After many years of active service all loadhooks should be carefully inspected. Hooks of 2 tons capacity or less may be economically junked and replaced by new hooks. Those of 3 to about 40 tons capacity should be dipped in or coated with thin lubricating oil

TABLE 5-1.   SAFE WORK LOADS ON VARIOUS TYPES OF SLINGS

Type of sling	Nominal size, in.	Single sling, lb	Choker sling, lb	U sling, lb	Basket sling, lb	Total load on two-leg slings (For three-leg sling multiply by 1½. For four-leg sling multiply by 2)			Weight per ft (exclusive of hook, ring, thimble, or splice), lb
						60-deg bridle, lb	45-deg bridle, lb	30-deg bridle, lb	
0 x 19 improved plow steel rope (Federal spec. RR-R-571)	3/8	1,350	1,010	2,700	2,360	2,330	1,910	1,350	0.23
	7/16	1,840	1,380	3,680	3,220	3,180	2,600	1,840	0.31
	1/2	2,420	1,815	4,840	4,240	4,180	3,420	2,420	0.40
	9/16	2,900	2,175	5,800	5,080	5,000	4,110	2,900	0.51
Factor of safety = 8	5/8	3,800	2,850	7,600	6,650	6,570	5,400	3,800	0.63
	3/4	5,260	3,940	10,520	9,200	9,100	7,450	5,260	0.90
Splice efficiency = 80%	7/8	7,000	5,250	14,000	12,250	12,100	9,900	7,000	1.23
	1	9,000	6,750	18,000	15,750	15,550	12,750	9,000	1.60
Rope diameter	1 1/8	11,200	8,400	22,400	19,600	19,600	15,900	11,200	2.03
	1 1/4	13,800	10,350	27,600	24,200	23,900	19,550	13,800	2.50
8-part braided wire strand sling	1/8	1,540	1,150	3,080	2,700	2,670	1,630	1,540	0.18
	3/16	3,420	2,560	6,840	5,990	5,920	4,850	3,420	0.42
Factor of safety = 5	1/4	6,500	4,870	13,000	11,380	11,300	9,220	6,500	0.80
	5/16	10,800	8,100	21,600	18,850	18,700	15,300	10,800	1.28
	3/8	14,120	10,600	28,240	24,650	24,400	20,000	14,120	1.84
Splice efficiency = 100%	7/16	18,820	14,150	37,640	33,000	32,600	26,600	18,820	2.48
	1/2	24,200	18,150	48,400	42,300	41,900	34,300	24,200	3.20
Strand diameter	9/16	30,240	22,700	60,480	53,000	52,300	42,900	30,240	4.08
Use factor		1.000	0.750	2.000	1.750	1.732	1.414	1.000	

*Source: Handbook of Rigging (14)

and then wiped thoroughly dry. Then the hook should be painted with a coat of whitewash and allowed to dry. Flaws or cracks will be indicated by discoloration of the white-wash as the oil is leached out of the tiny surface defects. Hooks of 50 tons and larger should be scientifically inspected by using a commercial Magniflux method.[15]

5.2.6 Moving Derailed Rail Cars Without Lifting Provisions

Wreckage removal of a derailed rail car may involve uprighting and pulling of the car, in addition to lifting, depending on the condition, orientation and location of the derailed car. The aim is to move the derailed car alongside the track where it can be retrucked and retracked if feasible or else loaded onto a flatcar or gondola.

Uprighting and lifting operations require the use of one or two mobile cranes as well as appropriate sling configurations. Some typical sling configurations used in rigging, which may be applicable to moving derailed cars, are shown in Figure 5-7.

It is important to recognize that the forces exerted on slings may be much higher than the lifting force exerted by the crane, depending on the sling configuration and the sling angle. This is illustrated in Figure 5-8. As shown in this figure, an angle of 5^0 for the sling, would result in sling tensions over five times the lifting force involved. Very shallow sling angles are to be avoided in lifting operations in order to avoid overstressing of the sling cables.

Another reason for avoiding very shallow sling angles is illustrated in Figure 5-8. Even if the sling can withstand the large tensile forces, there is a real danger of one end of the sling slipping off the hook and dropping the load.

Basket slings, either single or double, are sometimes used for lifting one end or all of a derailed car. These types of slings can slip during lifting if the direction of force exerted by each sling deviates too much from vertical. The car can drop as a result, endangering personnel as well as causing further damage.

Another danger during lifting is the instability of some higher center of gravity cars such as tank cars. This type of car can roll during lifting and cause the crane to topple. Where there is a possibility of car rolling a

steadying line should be attached to the car during lifting.

The corners of freight cars are strongest in the vertical direction. Lifting forces at these locations should therefore, be in a vertical or near vertical direction. Appreciable lateral forces at these locations are to be avoided. Movement of an upright car laterally can be done by lifting and moving the entire car or else by lifting and moving one end of the car while the other end serves as a pivot. In the latter mode, care must be exercised to avoid additional stresses on an already damaged car, particularly in the case of hazardous materials tank cars. It may be useful to lay down a bed of foam under the pivot end prior to such movement.

Uprighting of a derailed freight car involves rigging procedures similar to turning a load over on its side. Some correct and incorrect hitches for accomplishing this are shown in Figure 5-9. The objective naturally is to upright the car without banging or jolting it, particularly when the car contains (or contained) hazardous materials.

A hitch used frequently for uprighting (rolling over) a tank car is the cross hitch illustrated in Figure 5-10. As a long tension is maintained on each leg of the hitch, the attachment hooks are not likely to slip.

Often times, it is unsafe or impractical to attach hooks or slings to the underframe of a derailed car because the car is buried in mud, water, or chemicals. A safer procedure may be to first drag the car longitudinally to a better location via hook and sling attached to the coupler, which can withstand large longitudinal forces. A hook adapter nicknamed the "ding-bat" can facilitate such pulling. It is substituted in place of the knuckler, which is removed by knocking out the knuckle pin with a drive pin and sledge hammer. In the case of hazardous materials cars, dragging should be done only on a bed of foam to minimize dangers from jolts and sparking.

In all movement and lifting of rail cars during wreck clearing, care must be exercised to avoid forces on structural members that are not designed to withstand it. Tearing away of the structural member can occur with potentially disastrous results even if the structural member holds, it can be badly damaged. Thus, the wreck-clearing supervisor must be familiar with car body construction, the relative

Bridle Sling

Four-leg sling with
hooks for use when
lifting holes or
eyebolts are provided

Double Basket Sling

Double choker sling with
hooks attached for more
readily attaching and
detaching

NOTE: In using the double
      basket sling, watch that
      one part does not tend to
      slip along the load and
      allow it to tilt and drop

FIGURE 5-7. TYPICAL SLING CONFIGURATIONS AND THEIR USES

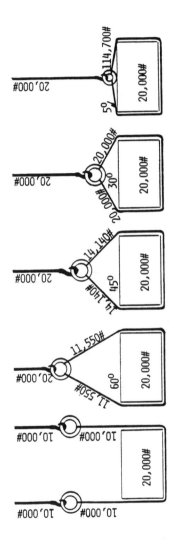

THE TENSION ON A SLING ROPE (OR CHAIN) DEPENDS UPON ITS ANGLE AS WELL AS THE LOAD TO BE LIFTED.

FIGURE 5-8.   VARIOUS ANGLES AND TENSIONS ON SLING ROPES

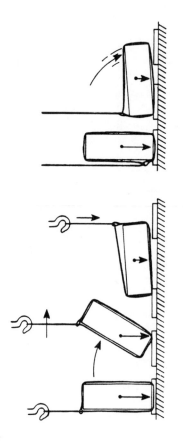

FIGURE 5-9. PROPER AND IMPROPER HITCHES

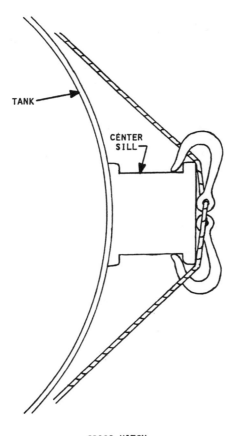

CROSS HITCH

FIGURE 5-10.   CROSS HITCH

strengths of various structural members, and the likely forces and directions of force that would be applied to these members during wreck clearing.

Another potential danger is slippage of the hooks during rigging operations. In order to prevent hook slippage, as well as tearing away or damage to the structural members, the use of hook attachment fixtures similar to that shown in Figure 5-11 is recommended. Such fixtures would be designed to clamp on to appropriate structural members and provide eyebolts for secure attachment of hooks. The fixture would distribute the stress on the structural member and thus minimize the risk of tearing away or damage to the structural member. Perhaps 3 or 4 fixture designs would be sufficient to accommodate key structural members on most freight cars. Each fixtures would be designed to be portable and readily attached to the appropriate structural member.

5.2.7 Moving Derailed Rail Cars with Lifting Provisions

AAR Standard S-234-78, shown in Figure 5-12, gives the specifications for the provision for lifting a freight car. Freight car manufacturers are now required to meet this standard in new car design and construction. Discussions with AAR reveal that a revision to Standard S-234-78 is in process. Instead of specifying the minimum dimensions of the required opening, the revised standard will require the opening to be compatible with two standard crane hooks that will be specified.

Although not mandatory, the preferred location of the lifting provision is in the car body bolster which is designed to withstand the lifting forces. This location is particularly desirable in the case of tank cars. Attachment of lifting provisions to the tank itself should be avoided, since damage to the lifting provisions could then affect the integrity of the tank. Tank car manufacturers are generally using the recommended location for lifting provisions in their car designs.

When lifting provisions are available on a derailed freight car, their use in lifting operations can reduce the hazards of wreck clearing. Some advantages of lifting provisions in wreck clearing are as follows:

- Lifting provisions attached to car body bolster can withstand lifting forces.

- Use of lifting provisions can reduce most hazards and equipment damage associated with conventional hook and sling attachments.

- Reduces exposure of wreck-clearing personnel in handling derailed car.

- Avoids danger of hook slipping or tearing of car body structural member not designed for lifting.

- Avoids damage produced by slings on jacket of insulated tank car.

- Avoids stress produced by slings on tank shell during lifting.

- AAR provision for lifting not restricted to car type, or hazardous versus non-hazardous service.

- Speeds up wreck clearing, return of track to normal and return of derailed cars for repair.

- Increases safety and reduces cost of wreck clearing.

AAR Standard S-234-78 requires that each lifting provision be capable of withstanding a force of 40% of the gross rail load applied within 15 degrees of the vertical axis of the car. This would restrict its use to a lifting force that is essentially vertical, since the allowable horizontal component would be only $0.4W \sin15^0 = 0.1W$, where W is the gross rail load. However, in the case of tank cars, the lifting provision must be tested with a force that has a larger horizontal component. This is required by AAR Standard 5.1.9 shown in Figure 5-13. This testing standard requires a force of 25% of the gross rail load applied at 45 degrees from the vertical in a vertical plane parallel to the longitudinal centerline of the car. This translates into a horizontal component, parallel to the car centerline, of $0.25 W \sin45^0 = 0.18W$.

Thus, in the case of tank cars, the lifting provision must be capable of withstanding a vertical force of 0.4W (to satisfy AAR Standard S-234-78) and a horizontal force parallel to the car centerline of 0.18W (to satisfy AAR Standard 5.1.9). Assuming that the lifting provision is in the tank car body bolster, which is the recommended location, the specified direction for the horizontal force component is a worst case. The reason for this is that a tank car body bolster is invariably weakest in a horizontal direction parallel to the car centerline and stronger in a horizontal direction perpendicular to the car centerline. Thus, the testing requirements of AAR

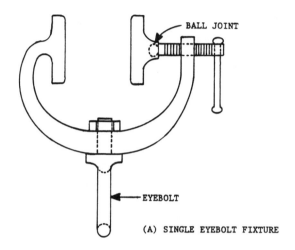

(A) SINGLE EYEBOLT FIXTURE

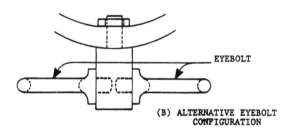

(B) ALTERNATIVE EYEBOLT CONFIGURATION

FIGURE 5-11. HOOK ATTACHMENT FIXTURES

Association of American Railroads

Mechanical Division

Manual of Standards and Recommended Practices

PROVISION FOR LIFTING FREIGHT CAR

Standard

S-234-78

Adopted 1977

Effective: Cars Ordered New After July 1, 1978

1. The purpose of this provision is to provide a means to vertically lift a loaded upright car. This provision is for new cars to facilitate rerailing operations and to improve the method of handling derailed cars.

2. The provision shall be made available at four places, preferably in or near the body bolster at the side sill.

3. The design force at each provision for the upright car must be 40% of the gross rail load applied within 15 degrees of the vertical axis of the upright car. Each connection zone must be designed to support the above load without exceeding the yield strength of the material except that local deformation is permitted to achieve hook bearing area.

4. The provision may be similar to that shown below and should have rounded ends and provide sufficient opening to accommodate lifting means.

Longitudinal Centerline of Car

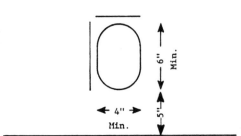

Outboard Vertical Surface of Side Sill

Typical Arrangement When Opening
is Utilized in Horizontal Structure

FIGURE 5-12. PROVISIONS FOR LIFTING FREIGHT CAR

THIS TEST REFERS TO THE LIFTING PROVISION REQUIREMENTS SHOWN IN STANDARD S-234 OF THE MANUAL OF STANDARDS AND RECOMMENDED PRACTICES. EACH DESIGN OF A TANK CAR LIFTING PROVISION IS SUBJECT TO A TEST BY LOADING AT LEAST ONE OF THE LIFTING PROVISIONS AS FOLLOWS:

- THE VERTICAL COMPONENT OF THE LOAD APPLIED TO EACH LIFTING PROVISION TESTED MUST BE A MINIMUM OF 25% OF THE GROSS WEIGHT ON RAIL.

- THE DIRECTION OF THE APPLIED LOAD MUST BE AT 45° FROM THE VERTICAL AND AS NEAR AS POSSIBLE TO A VERTICAL PLANE PARALLEL TO THE LONGITUDINAL CENTERLINE OF THE CAR AND EXTENDING THROUGH THE CENTER OF THE LIFTING PROVISION.

- AFTER APPLICATION AND RELEASE OF THE REQUIRED LOAD, VISUAL INSPECTION MUST REVEAL NO EVIDENCE OF PERMANENT DEFORMATION IN THE TANK CAR, BOLSTER OR LIFTING PROVISION EXCEPT THAT LOCAL DEFORMATION IS PERMITTED IN THE HOOK BEARING AREA.

FIGURE 5-13. LIFTING PROVISION TEST (AAR STANDARD 5.1.9)

Standard 5.1.9 imply that the lifting provision would withstand a horizontal force of 0.18W in any direction.

It should be noted that the terms "vertical" and "horizontal" in the preceding discussion refer to directions for an upright car. If the derailed car is not upright, the "vertical" and "horizontal" directions would be relative to the instantaneous position of the derailed car. Thus, if a derailed tank car were on its side, i.e., rotated 90 degrees from its upright position, the allowable "vertical" force of 0.4W would be applicable initially to the horizontal direction while the allowable "horizontal" force of 0.18W would be applicable initially to the vertical direction. Of course, these directions would change as the car orientation changes. It should also be noted that the limits of applied force, both "vertically" and "horizontally", apply to a structurally sound car. If the body bolster or its attachment to the car has been damaged in the accident, these limits would have to be reduced. The wreck supervisor would have to make this decision.

To summarize, the requirements of AAR Standards S-234-78 and 5.1.9 mean that each lifting provision on a derailed, but structurally sound freight car, can withstand the following forces:

- A "vertical" force of 0.4W.

- A "horizontal" force of 0.10W for any freight car.

- A "horizontal" force of 0.18W for a tank car in which the lifting provisions in incorporated in the body bolster.

The "vertical" and "horizontal" directions are relative to the instantaneous orientation of the derailed car.

In the case of a tank car, the relatively large allowable horizontal force (0.18W) can simplify uprighting operations. Instead of makeshift hook and sling attachments, hoods can be securely attached to the lifting provisions and the car uprighted in a controlled, safe manner, via standard rigging procedures, without exceeding the allowable force levels. This can be of particular value in the case of hazardous materials tank cars.

In the case of freight cars other than tank cars, the lifting provisions may still be usable for uprighting operations. If the freight car is only partially loaded, the car could be uprighted without exceeding the 0.

horizontal force limit. Even if fully loaded, the lifting provision design may be such as to be capable of withstanding a higher horizontal force limit. Lastly, uprighting operations of a fully loaded car may still be possible without exceeding the 0.1W horizontal force limit on a lifting provision, depending on the orientation and configuration of the derailed car and on the rigging procedures used. The wreck supervisor, who should be familiar with all of these factors, must make the final decision. If he deems it undesirable to use the lifting provisions for uprighting, then conventional hook and sling attachments could be used as discussed in Section 5.2.6. Hook attachment fixtures similar to that shown in Figure 5-11 would then be useful in reducing the hazards of uprighting operations.

Lifting provisions on a freight car are not suitable for car pulling operations where large longitudinal forces can be applied. The coupler, which can withstand these forces, should be used for pulling operations as discussed in Section 5.2.6.

5.2.8 Accident Prevention During Rigging Operations

In addition to the dangers of working around hazardous materials, wreck-clearing workers are subject to the considerable hazards associated with rigging operations in general. Recently, according to industry sources, a wreck-clearing worker was killed when a rail car collapsed on him after a rigging cable snapped. This accident was preventable by following a basic safety maxim in rigging, namely, no persons should be allowed below a suspended load. There have been other fatalities in wreck-clearing operations resulting from improper safety practices. In March, 1978 on the Union Pacific Railroad, an employee was killed between two couplers while the car was being pushed onto another car .[15] In May 1978, also on the Union Pacific, a cable hook slid along the side of the car with the result that the car fell down on and killed an employee[15]. In February, 1978 on Santa Fe, while a hopper car was being erected, the lifting hook was applied to the bolster cover plate which tore away and fell on a man killing him[15]. These last two fatalities are indicative of the hazards associated with the improper attachment of hooks and/or application of lifting forces.

The following are general safety guidelines for rigging operations in wreck clearing to minimize danger to personnel:

1. Prior to their use at an accident site, mobile cranes must be inspected using standard procedures to insure their safe operation.

2 All wire ropes must be inspected periodically for wear and broken wires to determine when a wire rope has reached the limit of its safe usage and must be discarded.

3. Hooks, chains, and eyebolts should be inspected periodically for cracks or other flaws and any faulty equipment removed from service. Hooks should be checked for signs of spreading (caused by overloading).

4. Boom cranes should not be slewed rapidly while carrying a load. During operation of these cranes, the chassis should be on an even keel and properly stabilized.

5. Avoid a very wide angle in a basket or bridle sling, even when strong enough to carry the load, since one sling may readily slip off the crane hook (See Figure 5-8).

6. All wreck-clearing personnel should wear safety shoes and hard fiber safety helmets and appropriate protective clothing.

7. No persons should be allowed below a suspended load.

8. No persons should be allowed between portions of wreckage that are being moved.

9. During car movement, no persons should be allowed between crane and point of attachment to car (to avoid injury in event of failure of cable, hook or car attachment point).

10. Extreme caution must be used during crane operations near overhead electric lines, to avoid contact between electric lines and any part of the crane or load (particularly applicable to wreck clearing on highways).

In addition, extreme caution should be exercised in the attachment of hooks to car body structural members, in order to avoid hook slippage or tearing away of the structural member with potentially disastrous results. Even when slippage or tearing away does not occur, considerable damage to the structural member can result. It is essential that the wreck-clearing supervisor be familiar with the car body construction, the relative strengths of various structural members, and the likely forces and directions of force that would be applied to these members during rigging operations. An area that may yield significant improvement in safety is the design of hook attachment fixtures, similar to the one described in Section 5.2.6, that could be readily fastened to appropriate structural members. The purpose of such fixtures would be to prevent hook slippage and to distribute the stress on structural members during rigging operations.

5.3 CLEANUP AND DISPOSAL GUIDELINES

5.3.1 Cleanup and Disposal Team

The cleanup and disposal team may or may not be the same one that handles product transfer. This primarily depends upon the particular hazardous material involved and the shipper's choice. It is conceivable that the cleanup crew might be different from the disposal crew. However, in recent years, a whole new specialized industry, cleanup and disposal contracting, has developed.

Certain companies alone, or as part of a trade association, have made available technical experts (specially trained and equipped teams) to assist with advice and handling of hazardous materials on-scene. The CHLOREP teams illustrate a cooperative industry effort to assist in handling chlorine incidents.

It is absolutely mandatory that the handling and cleanup/disposal of hazardous materials be done only by persons who have been specially trained and are fully qualified to deal with them. They must know such things as: the inherent hazards and physical/chemical characteristics of the materials to be handled; the reactions they undergo; the alternative safe neutralizing techniques; the neutralizing alternative which will result in the least disposal burden; whether or not recovery should be attempted; whether the hazardous materials should be disposed of on-site or at an EPA regulated waste disposal site; proper protective clothing and equipment; and applicable DOT and EPA regulations. Thus, the team must possess a broad spectrum of knowledge and capabilities. The team member must assure that the material to be disposed is packaged properly for shipment off-site.

5.3.2 Communications

As soon as the cleanup/disposal team is alerted that their services will be required, it is critical that communications be established with the OSC, the carrier and shipper's representative. The purpose is to obtain as many details about the accident scene and situation as possible, particularly for the teams involvement, quantities of HM involved, physical terrain, weather conditions, etc., so that preliminary operating plans can be drawn up and actions taken with regard to ordering, arranging and packaging. Communications should be two-way and provide for periodic updating of the on-scene situations to the team as well as the status of the team preparation to the OSC. The OSC should be made aware of the time when the team is expected to arrive.

The cleanup/disposal team can often provide the OSC with advice on handling or treating the spilled/leaking HM, managing effective control of them, while minimizing the quantitiy of HM that has to be cleaned up and disposed of. Good communications can assist in accomplishing these objectives.

On the scene, the cleanup/disposal team communicates primarily with the OSC. While working at the scene, the OSC and the team members should have continuous direct communication with each other and the team leader should have continuous, direct contact with the OSC. The OSC must know at all times what is happening and be able to respond to requests from the team.

By participating in periodic or special meetings called by the OSC to obtain the current assessment of the situation or to handle special problems, the cleanup/disposal team leader can communicate suggestions, concerns and requests.

Again, it needs to be pointed out that communications, equipment and procedures, used at the accident scene, must be safe to use in the vicinity of the HM involved. SOP's, as well as assigned frequencies, are necessary to assure that proper communications are maintained at all times.

All communications equipment should be checked immediately before use and be frequently checked between uses and malfunctioning items be promptly repaired or replaced.

5.3.3 Cleanup and Disposal Regulations

With the exception of bulk marine shipments, interstate shipment of hazardous materials is governed by Title 49 Code of Federal Regulations (49 CFR), Parts 100 to 199. Specifically, these derive from the Material Transportation Bureau, Research and Special Programs Administration, U.S. Department of Transportation. Most states utilize all

or parts of these DOT regulations for intrastate or interstate shipments. Therefore, if there is any hazardous materials or contaminated material which will have to be transported from the site, such chemicals or waste should be placed directly in DOT-approved shipping containers. This avoids the hazards of additional transfer handling operations. An early estimate of what containers will be needed and having them on hand before transfer and cleanup is initiated will do much to speed up these operations and disposal.

EPA requires certain types of information on a hazardous waste manifest which is different from information normally required by DOT on shipping papers. Efforts are in progress toward the development of a nationally agreed upon system (See Federal Register, Volume 45, No. 219, Monday, November 10, 1980, page 74642).

Docket No. HM-1450C Amdt. No. 172-66 (Federal Register, Volume 45, No. 53, Thursday, March 19, 1981, pages 17738-17750) contains the amendments to the DOT Hazardous Materials Transportation Regulations to conform to the Comprehensive Environmental Response Compensation and Liability Act of 1980 (CERCLA).

The EPA policy is to encourage and help states to establish effective environmental pollution control programs and then give the enforcement authority to the states. The following two documents furnish good insight into EPA's intent as well as guidance for the cleanup/disposal team:

1. SW-612, "State Decision-Makers Guide for Hazardous Waste Management", 1977, U.S. Environmental Protection Agency.

2. SW-635, "Model State Hazardous Waste Management Act (Annotated)", 1977, U.S. Environmental Protection Agency (Murray Newton).

It should be kept in mind that, although the HM addressed in this study are liquids and gases, ground which becomes contaminated as a result of their being spilled would be solid waste. Although EPA's intention is to have as much uniformity as possible, there may well be some specific variations from state-to-state, so one must be fully aware of the EPA requirements as well as those of the state where the spill occurs and where the hazardous waste is to be disposed of. It is extremely important that written disposal approval be obtained in advance of the time such materials will be ready for shipment. This means that the cleanup and disposal team, at or before the time shipping containers are being ordered, should undertake the actions to get disposal approval. The team has to perform some kind of preliminary analysis as to what hazardous materials and quantities will be involved.

Even if hazardous materials are proposed to be disposed of on-site, Federal, state and local environmental protection laws, regulations and ordinances must be obeyed. A full understanding of all applicable is necessary. The OSC should have this information or be of assistance in obtaining it. When the cleanup/disposal team make their initial contact with the OSC -- and this should be prior to reaching the scene -- the OSC should be reminded that the team will require this regulatory information, unless the team already has it. The Regional EPA office should also be contacted for a listing of approved disposal sites and persons to contact at these locations.

5.3.4 Monitoring

Cleanup and disposal operations normally begin after the situation has been stabilized. However, remaining materials (e.g., pools of the originally spilled hazardous materials or mixture with suppressants or the like; or hazardous materials in containers which have been patched or temporarily sealed) actually may be giving off flammable or toxic vapors or these could occur if container leaking reoccurred. Also if the materials are being deliberately burned or otherwise reacted, it is important to know what vapors are present and their concentrations where people are working within the exclusion areas and beyond the perimeter of the area. Persons engaged in cleanup/disposal work must be wearing full protective clothing, breathing apparatus and other gear suitable for the hazardous materials involved. Continuous monitoring of the site is necessary to assure that persons are not experiencing toxic concentrations or dosages beyond the capability of this protection. Continual observations of these persons (e.g., by closed circuit TV monitoring), for unusual behavior, augments vapor monitoring and also provides an alerting that the person might be getting exhausted simply from extended work under the confined, cumbersome conditions. Insufficient oxygen in the air is another aspect which monitoring must be able to spot immediately. Monitoring is also of paramount importance to provide warning that a flammable concentration is being approached or has been reached. Trapped

pockets of liquid or vapor can exist and be released as earth during cleanup. Monitoring is necessary to detect such occurrences. (See Section 3.2)

In the event damaged tank cars or tank cargo tanks still contains hazardous materials and it is necessary to perform any cleanup or disposal, it is vital that the integrity of these containers be continually monitored for structural integrity (See 3.5.). Cleanup/disposal operations should be confined to that which is absolutely necessary to prevent further problems. Examples might be to vent (might include flaring) vapor to reduce internal pressure or to divert a pool or stream of liquid into a catchment in order to provide working access to the container.

The basic technology exists from the aerospace, undersea, and nuclear programs to develop a remote-controlled robot for hazardous materials cleanup and disposal operations without the need to expose people. The same is true for product transfer operations and monitoring of container structural integrity and hazardous materials releases. Such a robot could be air-lifted and be designed to operate on any kind of terrain or in the water. Until such hardware is developed and made available, it is necessary to utilize the relatively unsophisticated techiques currently in use.

5.3.5 Personnel Protection

It is absolutely mandatory that all persons engaged in hazardous materials cleanup/disposal work be provided and required at all times to use protective clothing, gear and equipment (e.g., breathing apparatus) which are adequate for the particular hazardous material involved and the concentrations that could be encountered. Table 5-2 has been prepared to show the types of personal protective clothing which must be worn by emergency response personnel when handling the 28 specific chemicals and propellants. Only fully qualified people should be engaged in cleanup/disposal. Even though they are fully protected, such persons should avoid walking in, or other direct contact, with the hazardous materials. Working upwind of the spill is the recommended approach to avoid vapors.

It should be emphasized that cartridge/cannister-type breathing apparatuses, which filter outside air are extremely limited as to the concentration and exposure time they are good for. They can easily be overwhelmed. Self-contained air breathing equipment is the only kind recommended for

TABLE 5-2. TYPE OF PERSONNEL PROTECTIVE CLOTHING REQUIRED*,**

Hazardous Material	1	2	3	4	5	6	7	8	9	10	11	12	13
1. Acetone	*	*	*	*	*								
2. Acetone Cyanohydrin		*	*	*	*	*	*	*		*			
3. Acrylonitrile		*	*	*	*	*	*	*		*			
4. Aerozine-50	*	*	*		*		*				*		
5. Anhydrous Ammonia			*	*			*				*		
6. Butadiene, Inhibited			*	*			*		*		*		
7. Chlorine				*									
8. Ethyl Acrylate, Inhibited		*										*	*
9. Ethylene Oxide		*		*	*		*	*					
10. Hydrazine, Anhydrous		*				*					*		
11. Hydrocyanic Acid		*	*	*									
12. Hydrogen, Liquid				*	*						*		
13. Isobutane (LPG)				*							*		
14. Methyl Alcohol		*	*	*									
15. Methyl Bromide				*				*			*		
16. Methylhydrazine			*	*	*						*		
17. Monomethylamine Nitrate													
18. Nitrogen Tetroxide, Liquid		*	*	*	*						*		
19. Oxygen, Liquefied				*	*						*		
20. Propane (LPG)											*		
21. Propylene (LPG)	*	*		*	*								
22. Sodium Hydrosulfide Solution		*					*		*		*		
23. Sodium Hydroxide Solution	*		*	*	*		*						
24. Styrene Monomer, Inhibited	*	*	*		*	*	*						
25. Toluene	*	*		*	*	*							
26. Unsymmetrical Dimethylhydrazine			*	*	*				*				
27. Vinyl Acetate	*	*	*	*	*	*							
28. Vinyl Chloride	*		*	*			*				*		

*Index to type of personal protective clothing required:

1 = Organic Vapor Canister	8 = Slicker Suit
2 = Air-supplied Mask	9 = Rubber Suit
3 = Rubber Gloves	10 = Safety Helmet
4 = Chemical Safety Goggles	11 = Self-contained Breathing Apparatus
5 = Face Splash Shield	12 = Acid Goggles
6 = Plastic Gloves	13 = Impervious Gloves
7 = Rubber Boots	

**Source: USCG, Chemical Hazards Response Information System.

cleanup/disposal work and such equipment has operating limitations. It must also be remembered that there are no universal protective clothing and gear which will keep out all hazardous materials. Manufacturers of such items and the hazardous materials manufacturers can provide the best advice on what should be worn in working with particular hazardous materials. Both EPA and the Coast Guard are supporting development of protective suits (Coast Guard -- butyl rubber maximum protection; and EPA -- lightweight butyl rubber suit).

Before undertaking any cleanup/disposal work, the team needs to have standard operating procedures. Utilizing checklists in conjunction with SOP's can do much to assure compliance and give an added measure of protection to personnel.

The scene, containers and personnel must be continually monitored during cleanup/disposal operations. (See Section 5.3.4)

The number of persons engaged in cleanup/disposal operations should be the minimum required to do the job.

Unless there are some compelling, unique circumstances, cleanup/disposal operations should not be initiated until the situation has stabilized and it has been determined to be safe to do so. Even if the situation appears to have been stabilized, the cleanup/disposal operations should be planned and conducted to assure maximum protection to those involved, in the event a new release occurs, other trouble arises.

Judicious decisions and handling of the incident in the early stages of emergency response (e.g., proper diking or limited use of water) can reduce the quantity of material that has to be cleaned up, thus reducing the overall potential for exposure of the cleanup/disposal team.

5.3.6 Selection of Guidelines, Tools, Equipment, Materials and Receiving Containers

The primary consideration in selecting any of these items is that they must be compatible with the particular hazardous materials which has been spilled. Only non-sparking tools should be used whenever flammable hazardous materials are involved. Also because of the fire/explosion hazard, all equipment (e.g., pumps, and machinery) that will be operating at the scene must be of a design which is safe to operate in the presence of flammable vapors. Separate lists of equipment, pipes, fittings,

valves, containers, personal protective clothing, breathing apparatus, absorbent materials, neutralizing chemicals and sources should be prepared for each HM that the cleanup/disposal team will be handling. In order to accomplish this, the team should prepare representative spill scenarios and schematic drawings of the treatment systems. From these, the team can list the types and quantities of materials, hardware, and equipment needed. Some spare parts and extra amounts of materials should be included in the lists as should auxiliary equipment for really critical items.

Sample calculations should be provided for determining how much of a particular chemical reactant (e.g., neutralizing agent) will be required and instructions should be given for using these chemicals (e.g., how to mix solutions, rate of application, expected behavior and how to handle the reaction products).

If the HM or reaction product is to be transported off-site, containers should meet DOT specifications so that subsequent transfer into other containers will be unnecessary. It is also essential that the containers are easily moved to the location where they are to be filled and be safely moved out after filling. The decision to use a tank car, tank motor vehicle, portable tank or other container, is governed by location, hazardous materials involved and quantity.

The cleanup/disposal team needs to obtain the situation details at the earliest possible time and keep current on changes, so that arrangements may be made for timely delivery of all items and materials which are going to be needed, but which the team does not carry with them. The same is true for obtaining necessary support such as earth-moving equipment.

Hazardous materials manufacturers can be of assistance for determining which type of equipment and hardware are compatible with the individual materials, safe handling methods and neutralizing methods. The chlorine manufacturers, through the Chlorine Institute, have CHLOREP teams located at several points around the country to perform emergency repairs to leaking chlorine containers and on-scene product transfer and cleanup/disposal.

"A Survey of Personnel Protective Equipment and Respiratory Apparatus for Use by Coast Guard Personnel in Response to Discharge of Hazardous Chemicals" is available from the National Technical

Information Service (ADA 010-110). This is a useful document.

The EPA has worked out elaborate procedures for the disposal of a large number of chemicals[5], of which (acetone cyanohydrin, acrylonitrile, ammonia, chlorine, hydrazine, hydrogen cyanide, nitrogen dioxide, sodium hydrosulfide, sodium hydroxide, styrene, toluene and vinyl acetate) are among those involved in this study. However, these are for water spills and the chemicals and propellants are treated as dilute aqueous solutions. Nevertheless, the overall guidelines with respect to decisions on spill handling generally have aplication to land spills. To the extent land spills involve water, the procedures would be directly applicable.

The EPA manual goes into great detail on the factors to consider, duties and responsibilities, equipment sources, the design, construction and operation of an on-site treatment system for the spilled hazardous materials. Table 5-3 is reproduced from the manual to show limiting factors for treatment system design. Table 5-4 gives properties of commercially available plastics. The manual (pgs. 399-403) gives examples of how to calculate the amount of chemicals needed for treatment processing. Some of materials are included on page 423 of the EPA manual.

5.3.7 Treatment Options

The purpose of treating spilled material remaining in the damaged container is to control the hazards and render the product harmless. Once it has been decided that the HM must be treated, the decision must be made as to what treatment method and material should be used. Acids may be neutralized with bases and vice versa. When performed out in the open in a remote location in a suitable pit, it may be possible to react essentially concentrated chemicals directly. For example, liquid chlorine may be added directly to caustic soda at a controlled rate. Reactions can be violent, so this has to be done remotely. Heat released from the reaction also tends to vaporize unreacted chlorine. Dilution of reactants and HM with water may be used, but this approach can create complications.

Because the Coast Guard and EPA have been so extensively involved in treating spills of HM in water, their technology stresses the neutralization treatment of dilute aqueous solutions. Of course, reactions can be better controlled when concentrations of reactants are low. Or if dilution is sufficient, no reaction may be necessary. At higher concentrations violent reactions may occur. However, the quantities of diluted HM and reactants can be enormous, thus presenting several problems. There must be an ample supply of water. There must be enough storage capacity to handle the HM until they can be treated and the products to be disposed can be fed into a sewer or body of water at an allowable rate. If dilution is utilized and transport costs could be prohibitive.

Dilution is a quick, simple way to reduce flammable and perhaps toxic hazards on the short term period, but it may not be judicious in the long run because it significantly spreads the HM and increases the size of the spill to be disposed. Every effort must be made to contain runoff and only the minimum amount of water necessary should be used.

In very dry areas there may automatically be limits on product dilution because of the unavailability of water.

Whether or not to use the dilution technique requires a judgmental decision based upon an assessment of all the facts, alternatives and potential impacts. The cleanup/disposal team can provide good advice and should be involved in the decision making process.

When selecting a neutralizing agent one should choose those whose reaction products will be non-hazardous or least hazardous so that one solves a problem and doesn't create another one. Whether treatment is direct or conducted in a diluted condition must be determined on an individual case basis. Again, it depends upon the particular HM, quantity, remoteness of the area, topography and other influencing factors.

5.3.8 Disposal Options

If the bulk of the spilled/leaking HM can be recovered, the disposal problem has been greatly reduced and should not be a big problem. The same is true if the contents of damaged containers can be transferred to sound ones. Disposal may involve venting/flaring a flammable/toxic gas to reduce the internal pressure of the container and cool the contents through the evaporative effect. This may have to be repeated and should only be done under strictly controlled conditions and it has been determined that it is safe to rig for this operation and perform it. It may also be necessary under some circumstances to mix nitrogen with venting vapors to prevent ignition. Purging of essentially empty containers

TABLE 5-3. LIMITING FACTORS IN TREATMENT SYSTEM DESIGN

TIME:

    Immediate Danger
    Meteorological Conditions
    Local Political Considerations

SITE CONSIDERATIONS:

    Safe Proximity to the Spill
    Accessibility by Vehicles
    Clear Area
    Flat Area
    Firm Ground
    Number of Setups Required
    Proximity to Residences
    Restriction to Civilian Vehicular Traffic

MATERIAL AVAILABILITY:

    Sufficient Tankage
    Sufficient Pump Transfer Capacity
    Media Availability
    Chemical Availability
    Special Equipment Availability

PROCESS RESTRICTIONS:

    Long Detention Time in Sedimentation
    Difficulty in Desludging
    Long Contact Times Required in Columns
    Large Volumes of Sludge Obtained

MANPOWER LIMITATIONS:

    Sufficient Skilled Labor for Construction
    Sufficient Labor for Operation

MISCELLANEOUS PROBLEMS:

    Degree of Contaminant
    Available Hauling Capacity

TABLE 5-4. PROPERTIES OF COMMERCIALLY AVAILABLE PLASTICS

Material	Acids		Alkalies		Organic Solvents	Water Absorption, %/24 hr	Oxygen and Ozone	High Vacuum	Ionizing Radiation	Temperature Resistance	
	Weak	Strong	Weak	Strong						High	Low
Thermoplastics											
Fluorocarbons	Inert	Inert	Inert	Inert	Inert	0.0	Inert	-	P	550	G-275
Methyl Methacrylate	R	A-O	R	A	A	0.2	R	decomp.	P	180	-
Nylon	G	A	R	R	R	1.5	SA	-	F	300	G-70
Polyether (chlorinated)	R	A-O	R	R	G	0.01	R	-	-	280	G
Polyethylene (low density)	R	A-O	R	R	G	0.15	A	F	F	140	G-80
Polyethylene (high density)	R	A-O	R	R	G	0.1	A	F	G	160	G-100
Polypropylene	R	A-O	R	R	R	0.01	A	F	G	300	P
Polystyrene	R	APO	R	R	A	0.04	SA	P	G	160	P
Rigid Polyvinyl Chloride	R	R	R	R	A	0.10	R	-	P	150	P
Vinyls (chloride)	R	R	R	R	A	0.45	R	P	P	160	-
Thermosetters											
Epoxy (cast)	R	SA	R	R	G	0.1	SA	-	G	400	L
Phenolics	SA	A	SA	A	SA	0.6	-	-	G	400	L
Polyesters	SA	A	A	A	SA	0.2	A	-	G	350	L
Silicones	SA	SA	SA	SA	A	0.15	R	?	F	550	L
Ureas	A	A	R	A	R	0.6	A	-	P	170	L

NOTE: R = resistant, A = attacked, SA = slight attack, A-O = attacked by oxidizing acids, G = good, F = fair, P = poor, L = little change.

to remove the last HM vapors is also advisable (e.g., if any air has entered or the container is going to a repair facility).

If the HM product has been too badly contaminated for economic/safe recovery, it may need to be disposed of on-site. If it is flammable and the combustion products are not harmful, controlled burning is a possible method.

Oxygen might best be allowed to evaporate. A very important caution is that oxygen can saturate clothing and, if there is a static spark or other ignition source encountered, the clothing will burn like a torch. Therefore, the area must be secured for a sufficient distance and be constantly monitored to prevent such exposure.

Under carefully controlled conditions, nitrogen tetroxide may be burned in a pit with kerosene. Meteorological conditions and exclusion distances must be adequate and feed rate be low enough to assure the concentration of combustion products does not exceed allowable air pollution limits, because some unreacted oxidizer and other toxic gaseous reaction products will result. Nitrogen tetroxide is a very strong oxidizer and can ignite with certain organic/inorganic materials upon contact. Containers must be especially cleaned before being filled with the oxidizer. Impurities sometimes cause violent reaction. Therefore, it is unwise to put contaminated nitrogen tetroxide in containers. Only fully-qualified experts should dispose of this oxidizer. There is a need for development work on improved direct disposal methods for N_2O_4 and the other chemicals and propellants which will speed up the disposal operation, to assure safety and reduce time and costs.

Venting/flaring may also be used to dispose of larger quantities of certain chemicals and propellants. Depending upon the particular HM involved (e.g., hydrogen), it may be bubbled through water and burned at the water surface; be diluted with nitrogen to make it non-flammable. This latter method usually involves a very large amount of nitrogen which presents a logistics problem and high cost, so it has limited application. Possibly carbon dioxide (e.g., dry ice) might be used in certain instances, be cheaper and be easier to use or be burned. In any event, the venting/flaring system must be designed to preclude flash-back to the source. The vent/flare location must be a sufficient distance and direction from the source so that combustion products are directed away from the scene and populated areas.

Chemical neutralization or other chemical reactions may be utilized. For example, caustic soda is commonly used for on-site neutralization of chlorine. What HM may be treated in this manner depend upon the circumstances at the scene. The simplest system is where reaction takes place in an open pit. In other cases it may be necessary to construct an elaborate system such as is used by the Coast Guard and EPA to process large quantities of aqueous solutions resulting from spills in waterways. Whatever, the treatment method used, it should be performed a safe distance away from the spill point. The reaction products must be dealt with.

In some instances it may be possible to delete the HM sufficiently that it can be run into a stream or into a sewer. Flow rates and concentrations must be carefully monitored and controlled.

There is often the danger of rain which could run into the catchment and cause it to overflow. Care should be taken to prevent such an unintended disposal. Divert water away from the catchment.

Burying is a possible disposal method, if it can be proven that no unsafe concentrations of the HM would reach the atmosphere or migrate through the earth to present a hazard and there will be natural reaction with the earth to render the HM harmless. This would normally have to be in an area which would be under surveillance and be monitored.

Some HM may have to be disposed off-site. This requires prearrangements and authorization. It is essential that the disposal operations are done by fully-qualified, reputable organizations.

Table 5-5 is a rough matrix which shows USCG recommended cleanup/disposal procedures for 25 of the chemicals and propellants. Table 5-6 indicates response definitions. Cleanup/disposal procedures for Aerozine-50, liquefied hydrogen and monomethylamine nitrate are not given.

5.3.9 Handling Unspilled Material

In the case of liquids with relatively low vapor pressure (e.g., hydrazine), some product may remain in the container because the puncture was in the ullage space or in the side of the

TABLE 5-5. U.S. COAST GUARD CAUTIONARY AND CORRECTIVE RESPONSE INDEX*

#		Cautionary Response (A-F)						Corrective Response (G-R)										
		A	B	C	D	E	F	G**	H	I	J	K	L	M	N	O	P	Q	R
1.	Acetone	x	x					x	●					x				●		
2.	Acetone Cyanohydrin	x		x	x	x	x	x	●	x	x							●		x
3.	Acrylonitrile	x	x	x	x	x	x	x	●	x	x							●	x	x
4.	Aerozine-50	x	x	x	x	x	x	x	x								x			
5.	Ammonia, Anhydrous	x		x	x			x	●									●		
6.	Butadiene, Inhibited	x	x	x		x			●		x				x		x			
7.	Chlorine	x		x	x	x	x		●								x			
8.	Ethyl Acrylate, Inhibited	x	x		x		x		x	x	x						x			x
9.	Ethylene Oxide	x	x	x				x	x								x			
10.	Hydrazine, Anhydrous	x	x	x	x	x	x	x	x								x			
11.	Hydrocyanic Acid	x	x	x	x	x	x	x	x								x			
12.	Hydrogen, Liquefied																			
13.	Isobutane	x	x	x		x		x							x		x			
14.	Methyl Alcohol	x	x					x	x								x			
15.	Methyl Bromide	x		x	x			x	x								x			
16.	Methylhydrazine	x	x	x	x	x	x	x	x								x			
17.	Monomethylamine Nitrate																			
18.	Nitrogen Tetroxide	x		x	x	x	x	x	x								x			
19.	Oxygen, Pressurized Liquid	x	x	x					x								x			
20.	Propane (LPG)	x	x	x					x						x		x			
21.	Propylene (LPG)	x	x	x					x						x		x			
22.	Sodium Hydrosulfide Solution	x		x	x	x	x	x	x								x			
23.	Sodium Hydroxide Solution	x		x	x	x	x	x	x								x			
24.	Styrene	x	x	x		x			x	x	x						x		x	x
25.	Toluene	x	x	x					x	x	x				x		x		x	x
26.	Dimethylhydrazine, Unsymmetrical	x	x	x	x	x	x	x	x								x			
27.	Vinyl Acetate	x	x	x	x				x	x		x					x		x	x
28.	Vinyl Chloride	x	x	x	x				x	x							x			

Index to USCG-Cautionary and Corrective Response Index***

A = Restrict Access	G = Dilute and Disperse	M = Burn
B = Restrict Ignition	H = Stop Discharge	N = Neutralize
C = Evacuate	I = Contain	O = Absorption
D = Restrict Human Use	J = Skim	P = Other Treatments (state-
E = Restrict Farm Use	K = Pump	(of-the-art not well
F = Restrict Industrial Use	L = Dredge	developed)
		Q = Clean Shore Line
		R = Salvage Waterfowl

*   Source: USCG, <u>Chemical Hazards Response Information System</u>.
** Dilute and disperse only when other corrective methods cannot be used.
*** Response index key defining response options is located in Table 5-6.

TABLE 5-6. RESPONSE DEFINITIONS

CAUTIONARY RESPONSES (A-F)

A. RESTRICT ACCESS - This response is invoked when appreciable danger arises from a
    flammable or toxic spill, and the general public (spectators) should be kept from
    the spill area.   Access is restricted if ignition is considered possible
    (restrict ignition), or if evacuation is recommended.

B. RESTRICT IGNITION - This response is invoked when chemicals are involved which
    create flammable vapors.

C. EVACUATE - This response is invoked when there is a very real danger that a
    highly flammable or toxic spill may spread, or develop a detrimental reaction
    with water.   This category includes flammable chemicals and extremely toxic
    chemicals, e.g. poisonous gases.

D. RESTRICT HUMAN USE - This response is invoked when mostly soluble substances or
    those which are exceptionally toxic are involved in a spill. The primary danger
    is that of ingesting the chemicals in drinking water.

E. RESTRICT FARM USE - This response is invoked when a toxic chemical contaminant is
    spilled in water used for irrigation or animals.

F. RESTRICT INDUSTRIAL USE - This response is invoked when the spill contains
    chemicals which could corrode machinery, or if the possiblity of ignition from
    highly flammable organics is developed. Those chemicals which upon heating could
    release poisonous gases could also cause this response to be invoked; as could
    those which might form an insulating film on internal boiler surfaces.

CORRECTIVE RESPONSES (G-R)

    It is possible that several responses may be appropriate for a particular
chemical spill. On-site conditions will dictate which responses are required. Also,
a chemical could exist in more than one physical form and thus requires several
ameliorated responses.   In cases where multiple responses are checked, "dilute and
disperse" should be the last response implemented.

G. DILUTE AND DISPERSE - This response is invoked to handle spills primarily
    involving dissolved species which are dangerous in a concentrated state.   The
    situation can be ameliorated by water jets, propellors, or similar means of
    agitation spreading and mixing.

TABLE 5-6 (cont'd)

I. CONTAIN - This response is invoked to contain spills involving insoluble species which form surface slicks. Slicks having vapors of very low flammability may be contained near ships, piers, etc., but highly flammable materials should only be confined in areas which are remote from ignition sources. Explosion-proof equipment should be employed. Corrosivity with respect to materials should also be considered.

J. SKIM - This response is invoked to handle insoluble species which float and form surface slicks. Corrosivity with respect to homes and pumps should be considered.

K. PUMP - This response is invoked to handle insoluble species which sink (particularly liquids or finely divided solids), but which may be pumped directly from the spill. Again, corrosivity should be considered.

L. DREDGE - This response is invoked to handle insoluble species which sink (solids and some liquids).

M. BURN - This response is invoked to handle highly flammable floating chemicals. Even though there is an ignition danger, the "contain" category is checked. Containment may have to be accomplished by air barriers, herders, or expendable booms since few booms are fire-resistant.

N. NEUTRALIZE - This response is invoked to handle acids, bases, oxidants, or reductants. Calcium hypochlorite or caustic soda is often used in neutral-izaton. This response action is largely confined to still or confined non-flowing waters.

O. ABSORPTION - This response is invoked to handle chemical species which can be absorbed or adsorbed. These species which form surface slicks (float) and include: oil-like chemicals, solvents, toxic compounds (e.g. pesticides and halogenated hydrocarbons). Treatment by ion exchange is also possible for miscible chemicals. Materials for sorption include hay, paper, styrofoam, plastic, glass beads, charcoal and ion exchange resins.

P. OTHER TREATMENTS - This response is invoked to handle oils and other floating materials by specialized methods. These treatments include the use of emulsifiers, dispersants, sinking agents, coagulants and flocculants. Biological degradation is also included in this category.

Q. CLEAN SHORE LINE - This response is invoked to handle insolubles (especially oils) with high surface tensions.

R. SALVAGE WATERFOWL - This response is invoked when it is deemed feasible to salvage waterfowl that have been exposed to an oil discharge.

container. It may also be true that evaporative cooling could slow down the overall evaporation rate and result in some residual liquid product. Such products may or may not be contaminated or capable of being recovered.

Whether to neutralize or dilute the produce in the original container or remove it at a controlled rate, to treat or burn it will depend upon the particular hazardous material, the quantitiy of hazardous material, the relative amount of freeboard space; and ease of access to the interior for adding the neutralizer or diluent. In most instances the quantity would be too great to permit treatment in the original container, so the product would have to be removed at a controlled rate either in a transfer operation or to a flare or neutralization/dilution tank or pit.

Hopefully, the container can be patched and sealed before the transfer, cleanup and disposal phases take place, thus reducing the flammable/toxic vapor hazard and enabling controlled flow of the residual product. Essentially the removal of residual product is a transfer operation and the same approach and conditions apply. The physical setups and procedures will be somewhat different only if the product is not being placed in receiving containers for shipment. If disposal is to take place on-site, the controlled transfer will be to a dilution tank or pond/neutralizer/flare/burning pit. Generrlly speaking, the less the material that has to be disposed of, the simpler the overall problem.

Non-availability of suitable transport containers in an economical time-frame might dictate that disposal at the site would be preferable to delays that would be encountered in shipping the produce off-site.

5.3.10 Handling Spilled Material

The hydroscopic, water-soluble chemicals and propellants are those which would be expected to remain for the longest time, be absorbed by the ground and require processing. Ammonia, the three hydrazines and possibly nitrogen tetroxide fall into this category. If water is used to control the vapors, the volume of the resulting aqueous solutions could be substantial and, if contained as a pool, would contaminate a substantially greater quantity of soil than the hazardous materials themselves would.

Providing the rate of ammonia release from contaminated soil is not sufficient to present a fire or toxic hazard, it should not be detrimental to leave it there, because ammonia is applied directly to the soil as a fertilizer.

When one is faced with a monstrous quantity of aqueous solution or contaminated ground which must be treated and disposed of, the importance of making every reasonable effort at the outset to properly contain the material and utilize water judiciously becomes very clear.

UDMH has the lowest boiling point of the three hydrazines, thus is the most volatile and is the most toxic, as well. The fire hazard is removed, if these propellants are diluted with at least 10 volumes of water. The toxic and corrosive hazards still dictate the use of full protective clothing and gear, including self-contained breathing apparatus for those persons handling even the diluted solutions.

A decision has to be made as to whether neutralization should be attempted or the aqueous solution placed in containers. Leaving a large pool of an aqueous hydrazine solution around (i.e., while material is slowly released into a body of water, a sewer or the like) does not appear to be a viable alternative.

Deliberate ignition and burning of the spilled hydrazine, MMH or UDMH is a possible action which would certainly require very solid justification and would have to be conducted far enough away and in a direction so no one would be jeopardized by the unburned vapors or the combustion products.

Because nitrogen tetroxide boils at 70.1^0F, it undergoes self-cooling and a pool will tend to freeze over, thaw, refreeze in a cyclic pattern once it has contacted/reacted and stabilized with respect to the ground. It is likely that the pool will remain for a while and a substantial amount can be pumped into containers. Use of water on the liquid can speed up evaporation, so water application should be confined to knocking down vapors away from the pool. Nitrogen tetroxide is a very strong oxidizer so it can ignite certain organic and inorganic fuels spontaneously upon contact. Reaction can be violent with basic chemicals. If such materials are present on the ground where the N_2O_4 is spilled, the resulting heat will substantially increase the evaporation rate.

Large pools of oxygen are known to persist because moisture is condensed from the air to form a large ice cake which slows evaporation. Extreme care must be used around oxygen vapors because clothing and other materials become saturated and, if near an ignition source, ignite like a torch. If adequate safeguards can be taken, allowing the oxygen to evaporate may be the best disposal method.

Propane will not remain very long and does not contaminate the ground per se. Hydrogen is similar and boils at a lower temperature than propane. Both are easily ignited and, in a massive spill, a conflagration is almost a certainty.

Butadiene, being a hydrocarbon gas, would not be expected to contaminate the ground per se and any spill would tend to evaporate quickly, with the principal hazard being its flammability. It is conceivable, but not very likely, that it might encounter some catalytic material which would tend to polymerize it. Vinyl chloride might be more apt to polymerize, which would give off a large amount of heat which might be sufficient to ignite any pool. Toxicity is the other concern with this hazardous material. The safety group from the Society of Plastic Industries has expertise available to advise on the proper handling of vinyl chloride.

Ethylene oxide is very unstable and decomposition may be triggered by a number of metallic oxides, etc., which may well be found in the ground where a spill has occurred. This reaction gives off an enormous amount of heat and can be violent. Vapors can detonate (6% to 24% by volume in air) and the flammability range is 3% to 100%.

Handling of spilled chlorine should be left to a CHLOREP team.

Ammonia and the three hydrazines are bases, so aqueous solutions must be treated as basic solutions. Substantial dilution is normally required before neutralization is attempted to keep the reaction under control. Direct neutralization or other reaction could be extremely violent. The huge volumes and cumbersome aspects of aqueous solutions and the potential violence of the direct reactions both indicate that it is preferable, easier, if possible, to capture the spilled material for recovery or controlled burning than to attempt neutralization.

Chlorine and nitrogen tetroxide are acidic materials but the same complications abide with them as with the bases. Nitrogen tetroxide can be burned in a pit with a fuel such as kerosene.

Chlorine can be neutralized by sodium bicarbonate or caustic soda in a bulk pit operation such as was done at Crestview, Florida. Special precautions are required for both.

The liquid oxygen (LO_2), liquid hydrogen (LH_2) and propane do not require neutralization, just precautions against their flammable hazards, and they do not contaminate the ground per se.

Vinyl chloride, butadiene, and ethylene oxide do not permanently contaminate the ground either. They can be dangerous if placed in containers, when contaminated, due to the possibility of polymerization or decomposition. Therefore, the best disposal is controlled burning. Spills of acrylonitrile, hydrocyanic acid, isobutane and propylene shold be allowed to burn off. Spills involving acetone, acetone cyanohydrin, ethyl acrylate, methanol, sodium hydrosulfide, soidum hydroxide, styrene, toluene, and vinyl acetate should be taken up with sand or another noncombustible absorbent material.

5.3.11 Recovery Versus Disposal

When practical, recovery of spilled HM is usually preferable to disposal. Among the factors which must be considered in making this decision are the following:

- Safety of the personnel who will perform recovery or cleanup/disposal operation (e.g. potential for exposure).

- Complexity of the recovery versus disposal process.

- Time to set-up and perform operation.

- Preference of the shipper.

- Opinions of the carrier.

- Relative hazard(s) to the other emergency personnel, the public and the environment.

- The HM involved and quantity(ies).

- Environmental conditions (present and forecasted).

- Comparative economics.

- Environmental protection and transporation regulations.

- Availability (or not) of an appropriate disposal site.

- Distance to disposal site(s).

- Availability of equipment and materials.

- The physical orientation and condition of the container(s).

- Potential liability.

Such decisions need to be backed up with analyses. Therefore, it is vital that the OSC, shipper and carrier representatives get with the potential product transfer, cleanup/disposal in-house or contractor teams as early as possible so the latter may be able to start working up the preliminary plan(s) and analysis(es), which can be updated as new facts became available. This approach makes good use of these team members' times and should result in the OSC and other officials having the information for making a decision on which course to follow, when the choice has to be made.

Having schematics of typical transfer, cleanup and disposal operations, lists of equipment, hardware, and other materials, their sources, costs and availability should assist in preparing analyses, and can be prepared ahead of time. The bottom line is that a safety management decision must be made and it is important that the information upon which the decision is made be realistic and as complete as possible. The consideration factors listed could be expressed in matrix form with some rough weighting values for preliminary comparison. More detailed breakdowns could be utilized if the choice were not rather obvious from the preliminary analysis.

5.3.12 Waste Collection

Waste collection must be considered at the very outset of emergency response action at the scene. The spilled/leaking HM must be contained to limit spread and pollution (water, air and ground) as much as possible. Damming, diking, ditching and entrapment are some of the techniques employed. The surfaces upon which the HM spills may vary considerably in porosity (e.g., sand, clay, concrete, railroad ballast, black top or water), so penetration and ease of collection will also vary. Vigorous reaction might occur with certain HM. If it is possible to construct or find a material with less porosity, even better be able to line it with a compatible material, leaks and possibly certain spills (e.g., a pool) could be diverted into such containment for easier collection for cleanup/disposal.

If the porous soil is not deep and is underlayed with rather non-porous earth, it might be possible to put a catch pit lower than the interface and drain the HM into it. Depending upon what HM is involved and the purity, the product may be pumped into containers for shipment, reacted or burned. Of course, if the product is spilled on a non-porous surface and can be contained therein, they can be picked up directly into containers.

Contaminated soil at varying depths and points around the spill needs to be analyzed to see if the degree is above acceptable limits. If the concentration is within acceptable limits, it can be left to undergo natural degradation and no further effort will be necessary to collect the HM. If it exceeds the allowable limit, the contaminated soil must be treated. If treatment in place is not practical, the soil will have to be collected for treatment or shipment by digging it up. Cleanup and disposal teams frequently use vacuum trucks for sucking up liquids. Certain types of contaminated soil might also be handled this way, providing the vacuum equipment and containers are so designed. Small amounts of contaminated soil usually are handled by shovel. Large amounts may have to be scooped up with a high-loader or backhoe. However, depending upon containers to be used, if shipment is intended, it may still be necessary to fill the containers using a shovel. If the spilled HM has soaked into the soil but the settling rate is slow enough it may be possible to move the contaminated soil onto a covered surface or prepared pit with outlet which will allow controlled drainage and collection of HM.

The method of collection will ultimately depend upon the particular HM involved, the quantity, the terrain and what disposal method is contemplated. In any event, waste collection operations should be conducted only by a fully-qualified cleanup/disposal team properly protected and monitored. If transport is contemplated, collection is made so that the amount to be shipped is kept as small as practical. The Coast Guard and EPA have detailed instructions on waste collection as related to water spills. These generally would apply to land spills to the extent these involve the HM getting into waterways.

5.3.13 Waste Removal

If it is not possible to dispose of the spilled/otherwise contaminated HM on-site, such waste must be moved off-site to an authorized treatment facility/disposal site. Usually cleanup contractors obtain the necessary approvals and handle the transport of the waste. In any case, they must be obtained before shipment. Such transport must be in accordance with DOT regulations for interstate shipments and State regulations for intrastate shipments. In addition to removing any of the HM, all the remaining contaminated soil, absorbents, debris and reaction products, must be removed, so that the concentration of any residual HM is within acceptable limits and the area is safe for normal use.

Tank trucks and drums are the most frequently used containers for shipping hazardous wastes. However, if large quantities of contaminated earth had to be moved, suitably covered lined dump trucks/rail cars might be usable. It should be recognized that vibration from transportation could possibly cause the liquid to migrate and concentrate (e.g., in the bottom of the container), so the lining of the container is important to prevent leakage. Barges also might be suitable for hauling very large quantities of contaminated earth.

REFERENCES

1. Deborah K. Shaver, Erskine E. Harton Jr., Robert L. Berkowitz and T. James Rudd. Post-Accident Procedures for Chemical and Propellants, April 1981 Contract. Report No. F04611-80-C-0046. Prepared for Air Force Rocket Propulsion Laboratory, Edwards AFB, CA.

2. Al Smith Jr. Managing Hazardous Substances Accidents. McGraw-Hill Book Company, 1981 (this information is provided contingent upon approval of the publisher).

3. Code of Federal Regulations Part 40 Section 109 "A Guide for State Contingency Plans."

4. 40 C.F.R. Part 1510 National Oil and Hazardous Substances Pollution Contingency Plan (1510 Plan), 1972.

5. U.S. Environmental Protection Agency, Oil and Hazardous Materials Spill Branch. Manual for the Control of Hazardous Material Spills, Volume I: Spill Assessment and Water Treatment Techniques. EPA-600/2-77-227. November 1977.

6. U.S. Department of Transportation, Research and Special Programs Administration, Materials Transportation Bureau. 1980 Emergency Response Guidebook. DOT P-5800.2.

7. U.S. Coast Guard. Chemical Hazards Response Information System. Volumes I-IV. April 1974.

8. Association of American Railroads, Bureau of Explosives. Emergency Handling of Hazardous Materials in Surface Transportation. B.E. Pamphlet No. 1-4.

9. NTSB Recommendation R-78-57

10. Shell Development Company, Westhollow Research Center. Mitigation of Chemical Spills: An Evaporation/Air Dispersion Model for Chemical Spills on Land. M.T. Fleischer. December 1980.

11. Lewis C. Dixon, Technical Basis for Design of the DDESB Downwind Chemical Hazards Slide Rule, Naval Surface Weapons Center for DOD Explosives Safety Board, March 1977.

12. R.L. Miller and F.H. Miller, Diffusion Forecasting for Titan II Operations, Air Weather Service (MATS), USAF, 10 February 1964.

13. Association of American Railroads, 19th and L St., NW, Washington, D.C., 20036. Car and Locomotive Cyclopedia.

14. W. Rossnagel. Handbook of Rigging., 3rd Edition, New York, McGraw-Hill Book Company, 1964.

15. DOT/FRA Special Safety Inquiry- Lifting Lugs Requirements, October 31, 1978.

16. Buschman, C.H., "Experiments on the Dispersion of Heavy Gases and Abatement of Chlorine Clouds", Fourth International Symposium on Transport of Hazardous Cargoes by Sea and Inland Waterways, National Academy of Sciences, 1975.

17. USEPA Contract 68-03-2478, "Evaluation/Development of Foams for Mitigating Air Pollution From Hazardous Spills", 1976.

18. Norman, E.C.., et al., "The Use of Foams to Control Vapor Emissions From Hazardous Materials Spills", Proceedings of 1978 National Conference on Control of Hazardous Materials Spills, April 1978.

19. Kaiser, G.B., "Accidental Release of Vapors", Proceedings of Gastech 79, November 1979.

20. "The Use of Foams to Control the Vapor Hazards from Liquefied Gas Spills" R.H. Hiltz and S.S. Gross, MSA. Research.

21. ORI, INC., Report No. DOT/RSPA/MTB-79/A, "Risk Assessment of Air Versus Other Transportation Modes for Explosives and Flammable Cryogenic Liquids, Volume II: Supporting Documentation".

22. Baker, W.E. "Workbook for Predictory Pressure Wave and Fragment Effects of Exploding Propellant Tanks and Gas Storage Vessals," Minutes of the Seventeenth Explosives Safety Seminar, Volume II, Department of Defense, Explosives Safety Board, September 1976. The Workbook is by Baker, et al and is NASA Report CR-134906, November 1975.

23. Hokason, J.C. and Wenzel, A.B., "Explosive/Flammability Characteristics of Vinyl Chloride Momomer (VCM) - Air - Water Vapor Mixtures", Minutes of the Seventeenth Explosives Safety Seminar, Volume I, Department of Defense, Explosives Safety Board, September 1976.

24. Jones, George P., et al, "Risk Analysis in Hazardous Materials Transportation", Volume 1, Final Report", Report No. TES-20-73-4 for U.S. Department of Transportation, March 1973.

25. Bowen, James A., "Hazard Considerations relating to Fuel-Air Explosive Weapon", Fourteenth Explosives Safety Seminar, Minutes of Dept. of Defense Explosives Safety Seminar, November 1972.

26. The Accident Performance of Tank Car Safeguards, National Transportation Safety Board Report NTSB-H2M-80-1, 1980.

27. Tank Car Structural Integrity After Derailment, National Transportation Safety Board Report, NTSB-SIR-80-1, 1980.

28. Derailment of Louisville and Nashville Railroad Company's Train No. 584 and Subsequent Rupture of Tank Car Containing Liquefied Petroleum Gas, Waverly, Tennessee, February 22, 1978, National Transportation Safety Board Report, NTSB-RAR-79-1, 1979.

29. Kelly, M.P. and Pollock, A.A., Some Examples of Acoustic Emission Monitoring of Pressurized Components, Acoustic Emission Monitoring of Pressurized Systems, ASTM STP 697. W.F. Hartman and J.W. McElroy, Eds., American Society for Testing and Materials, 1979, pp. 60-70.

30. Hutton, P.H., Acoustic Emission Applied Outside of the Laboratory, Acoustic Emission, ASTM STP 505, American Society for Testing and Materials, 1972, pp. 114-128.

31. Liptai, R.G., Harris, D.O., and Tatro, An Introduction to Acoustic Emission, Acoustic Emission, ASTM STP 505, American Society for Testing and Materials, 1972, pp. 3-10.

32. Schofield, B.H., Why Acoustic Emission -- Why Not?, Monitoring Structural Integrity by Acoustic Emission, ASTM STP 571, American Society for Testing and Materials, 1975, pp. 3-10.

33. Spanner, J.C., Acoustic Emission -- Some Examples of Increasing Industrial Maturity, Acoustic Emission Monitoring of Pressurized Systems, ASTM STP 697. W.F. Hartman and J.W. McElroy, Eds., American Society for Testing and Materials, 1979, pp. 2-34.

34. Takahashi, H., Khan, M.A., Kikuchi, M., and Suzuki, M., Acoustic Emission Crack Monitoring in Fracture-Toughness Tests for A151, 4340 and 5A533B Steels, Experimental Mechanics, Vol. 90, 1981, pp. 89-99.

35. Kishi, T., and Mori, Y., Evaluating the Severity of Rocket Motor Case During Burst Test Using Acoustic Emission, Acoustic Emission Monitoring of Pressurized Systems, ASTM STP 697. W.F. Hartman and J.W. McElroy, Eds., American Society for Testing and Materials, 1979, pp. 131-148.

36. Williams, R.S., Modeling of Elastoplastic Fracture Behavior Using Acoustic Emission Methods, Closed Loop, The Magazine of Materials Testing, Vol. 10, No. 2, 1980, pp. 15-23.

37. Keledy, F.C. and Hartman, W.F., Some Examples of Evaluating Structural Integrity by Acoustic Emission Monitoring During Pressure Testing, Acoustic Emission Monitoring of Pressurized Systems, ASTM STP 697j. W.F. Hartman and J.W. McElroy, Eds., American Society for Testing and Materials, 1979, pp. 35-46.

38. Smith, J.R., Rao, G.V. and Gopal, R., Acoustic Monitoring for Leak Detection in Pressurized Water Reactors, Acoustic Emission Monitoring of Pressurized Systems, ASTM STP 697. W.F. Hartman and J.W. McElroy, Eds., American Society for Testing and Materials, 1979, pp. 177-204.

39. Votava, E. and Jax, P., Inspection of Nuclear Reactors by Means of Acoustic Emission During Hydrostatic Test, Acoustic Emission Monitoring of Pressurized Systems, ASTM STP 697. W.F. Hartman and J.W. McElroy, Eds., American Society for Testing and Materials, 1979, pp. 149-164.

40. Morcais, C.F. and Green, A.T., Establishing Structural Integrity Using Acoustic Emission, Monitoring Structural Integrity Using Acoustic Emission, ASTM STP 571, American Society for Testing and Materials, 1975, pp. 184-199.

41. Carlyle, J.M., Imminent Fracture Detection in Graphite/Epoxy Using Acoustic Emission, Experimental Mechanics, Vol. 18, 1978, pp. 191-195.

42. Federal Emergency Management Agency, Planning Guide and Checklist for Hazardous Materials - Contingency Plans, FEMA-10, July 1981.

– APPENDIX A –

PHYSICAL AND CHEMICAL PROPERTIES OF SELECTED MATERIALS

Hazardous Material	Flammable Limits in Air (Percent)	Color	TLV-ICGIH (ppm)	Odor Threshold (ppm)	Short-Term Inhalation Limits (ppm-30 min.)	Specific Gravity (liquid)	Vapor (Gas) Specific Gravity	Critical Pressure (atm)	Critical Temperature (°F)	Flash Point (°F)
Acetone	2.6-12.8	Colorless	1,000	100	1,000	0.791	2.0	46.4	455	0
Acetone Cyanohydrin	2.2-12	Colorless	NA**	NA	NA	0.925	–	–	–	165
Acrylonitrile	3.05-17	Colorless to Light Yellow	20	21.4	40	0.8075	1.8	45	505	32
Aerozine-50 (UDMH)	2-95	Colorless	0.5	6-14	50	0.791	2.1	53.5	480	34
Anhydrous Ammonia	15.5-27	Colorless	25	46.8	50 (5 min.)	0.682	0.6	111.3	271	–
Butadiene, Inhibited	2-11.5	Colorless	1,000	4 mg/m³	NA	0.621	1.9	42.7	306	-105
Chlorine	–	Greenish Yellow	1	3.5	3 (5 min.)	1.424	2.4	76.05	291	–
Ethyl Acrylate, Inhibited	1.8-9.5	Colorless	25	0.00024	50 (5 min.)	0.923	–	37	534	60
Ethylene Oxide	3-100	Colorless	50	50	200	0.869	1.5	71	385	0
Hydrazine, Anhydrous	4.7-100	Colorless	0.1	3-4	0.1	1.008	–	145	716	99
Hydrocyanic Acid	5.6-40	Colorless	10	1 mg/m³	20	0.689	0.9	50	362.3	0
Hydrogen, Liquefied	4-75	Colorless	–	–	–	0.071	0.067	12.8	-400	–

* Source: 1980 Hazardous Chemicals Data Book, Noyes Data Corporation, Park Ridge, NJ.

** Data Not Available.

Hazardous Material	Flammable Limits in Air (Percent)	Color	TLV-ICGIH (ppm)	Odor Threshold (ppm)	Short-Term Inhalation Limits (ppm-30 min.)	Specific Gravity (liquid)	Vapor (Gas) Specific Gravity	Critical Pressure (atm)	Critical Temperature (°F)	Flash Point (°F)
Isobutane (LPG)	1.8-8.4	Colorless	NA	NA	NA	0.557	2.0	36	275	-117
Methyl Alcohol	6-36.5	Colorless	200	100	260 mg/m³ (60 min.)	0.792	1.1	77.7	464	52
Methyl Bromide	10-15	Colorless	15	Odorless	20 (5 min.)	1.68	3.3	-	376	-
Methylhydrazine	2.5-98	Colorless	0.2	1-3	30	0.878	1.59	81.3	594	17
Monomethyl-amine Nitrate	NA	NA	NA	NA	NA	NA	NA	NA	NA	NA
Nitrogen Tetroxide, Liquid	-	Red-Brown	5	5	25 (5 min.)	1.45	3.2	100	317	-
Oxygen, Liquefied	-	Light Blue	-	-	-	1.14	1.1	50.1	-180	-
Propane (LPG)	2.1-9.5	Colorless	1,000	5,000-20,000	NA	0.590	1.5	41.94	-142.01	-156
Propylene (LPG)	2-11	Colorless	4,000	NA	NA	0.609	1.4	45.6	197.2	-162
Sodium Hydrosulfide Solution	-	Light Yellow to Red	NA	0.0047	NA	1.3	-	-	-	-
Sodium Hydroxide Solution	-	White	-	-	-	2.13	-	-	-	-
Styrene Monomer, Inhibited	1.1-6.1	Colorless to Light Yellow	100	0.148	100	0.906	-	39.46	703	90
Toluene	1.27-7	Colorless	100	0.17	600	0.867	-	40.55	605.4	40
Dimethyl-hydrazine, Unsymmetrical	2-95	Colorless	0.5	6-14	50	0.791	2.1	53.5	480	34
Vinyl Acetate	2.6-13.4	Colorless	10	0.12	NA	0.934	-	42	486	18
Vinyl Chloride	4-26	Colorless	200	260	500 (5 min.)	0.969	2.2	52.7	317.1	-110

— APPENDIX B —
PARTIAL LISTING OF SOURCES OF INFORMATION/
ASSISTANCE FOR HAZARDOUS MATERIAL SPILLS

Information Source	Type of Organization	Type of Information Assistance*	Access
EPA Oil and Hazardous Materials - Technical Assistance Data System (OHMTADS)	Federal	2-A	EPA Regional Office, University of Indiana (24-hour on-line capability)
Coast Guard Chemical Hazards Response Information System (CHRIS)	Federal	2-A	National Response Center through OSC. Regional Response Centers District Offices: (see Appendix E)
Coast Guard National Strike Team	Federal	1	National Response Center (800/424-8802)
U.S. Army Technical Escort Center Chemical Emergency Response Team	Federal	1	Dept. of Army Operation Center (703/521-2185)
Chemical Transportation Emergency Center (CHEMTREC)	Industry sponsored	2,3	Through CHEMTREC 800/424-9300 (in Washington, D.C. 202/483-7616)
Pesticides Safety Team Network	Industry sponsored	1,2,3	Through CHEMTREC 800/424-9300 (in Washington, D.C. 202/483-7616)
Transportation Emergency Assistance Plan (TEAP)	Canadian, privately sponsored	1,2,3	Each regional Control Center has a 24 hour number:

1. Hooker Chemicals Division, Vancouver, British Columbia 604/929-3441; Geographic location: British Columbia

2. Celanese Canada Ltd., Edmonton, Alberta, 403/477-8339; Geographic location: Prairie Provinces

3. Canadian Industries Ltd., Copper Cliff, Ontario, 705/682-2881 Geographic location: Northern Ontario

* 1. Respond to scene with trained personnel if required.
2. Provide information on identity, hazards, or what to do.
3. Refer to knowledgeable contact.

A. On-line computer available.

Information Source	Type of Organization	Type of Information Assistance	Access
			4. Dow Chemical of Canada, Ltd., Sarnia, Ontario 519/339-3711; Geographic location: Central Ontario
			5. Cyanamid of Canada, Ltd., Niagara Falls, Ontario, 416/356-8310 Geographic location: Eastern Ontario
			6. DuPont of Canada, Ltd., Maitland, Ontario, 613/348-3616 Geographic location: Western Ontario
			7. Allied Chemical Canada, Ltd., Valleyfield, Quebec, 514/373-8330 Geographic location: Quebec, south of St. Lawrence
			8. Gulf Oil Canada, Ltd., Shawinigan, Quebec, 819/537-1123 Geographic location: Quebec, north of St. Lawrence
Chlorine Emergency Plan (CHLOREP)	Privately sponsored	1,2,3	Through CHEMTREC - 800/424-9300 (in Washington, D.C. 202/483-7616)

— APPENDIX C —
TYPICAL ON-LINE INFORMATION RETRIEVAL SYSTEMS

Information Source	On-line computer System	Contact
Lockheed Information Systems	yes	408/742-4321 Ext. 45635
Illinois Department of Energy & Natural Resources Environmental Quality Library	no	312/793-3870
NIOSH Technical Information Center	yes	301/443-4220
National Technical Information Service	yes	703/487-4650
Environmental Emergency Center	yes	819/997-3742
National Emergency Equipment Locator System (NEELS-Canadian)		
National Analysis of Trends in Emergencies System (NATES-Canadian)		
NASA - Scientific & Technical Information Office	yes	202/755-3548
NASA - Industrial Applications Centers:		
Univ. of Conn., Storrs, CT	yes	203/486-4533
Univ. of Pittsburg, PA	yes	412/624-5211
Indiana Univ., Bloomington, IN	yes	812/335-8884
Univ. of N. Mexico, Albuquerque, NM	yes	505/277-3622
Univ. of S. California, Los Angeles, CA	yes	213/746-6132
Global Engineering Documentation Services	no	714/540-9870 213/624-1216
National Bureau of Standards Fire Technology Library	no	301/921-3249
NASA - Aerospace Safety Research & Research & Data Institute	no	216/443-4000 Ext. 285
Chemical Abstract Service Ohio State Univ.	no	614/421-6940
Fire Research Section Southwest Research Institute	no	512/684-5111 Ext. 2415
Environmental Engineering Division Texas A&M Univ.	no	713/845-3011
Toxicology Data Bank National Library of Medicine	no	301/496-1131

— APPENDIX D —
SELECTED HAZARDOUS MATERIAL REFERENCES

OHMTADS Data Sheets	US EPA Office of Hazardous Materials, Washington, D.C. 20400.
CHRIS Manuals 1-4 (CG-446-1-4)	US Gov't Printing Office, Wash. D.C. 20402
Regional Contingency Plan	US EPA, Regional Environmental Emergency Section.

Regulation for Shipping Hazardous Materials

49 CFR-Code of Federal Regulations, Transportation Vol.49, Parts 100-199.	US Dept. of Transportation Office of Hazardous Materials
FAR 103-Federal Aviation Regulations Vol. VI, Part 103.	US Dept. Federal Aviation
CAB 82-Official Air Transport Restricted Articles Tariff No. 6-D	
IATA-International Air Transport Association Restricted Articles Regulations	

EPA Field Detection and Damage Assessment Manual for Oil and Hazardous Materials Spills	US EPA, Division of Oil and Hazardous Materials Washington, D.C. 20400
Official Motor Freight Directory	
Official Railway Guide	
Dangerous Properties of Industrial Materials, by N. Irving Sax	Van Nostrand Reinhold Co., 450 W. 33rd Street, New York, NY 10001
Chemical Transportation and Handling Guide	RSMA, 181 E. Lake Shore Drive, Chicago, IL 60611
Laboratory Waste Disposal Manual	Manufacturing Chemists Association (now Chemical Manufacturing Association) 1825 Connecticut Ave., N.W., Wash., D.C. 20009.
Recommended Methods of Reduction, Neutralization, Recovery or Disposal of Hazardous Waste (Vol. 1-16) by TRW Systems Group	Government Reports NTIS U.S. Dept. of Commerce Springfield, VA 22151
Hazardous Chemicals Data Noyes Data Corp.	National Fire Protection Association 470 Atlanta Ave. Boston, MA 02110
Merck Index Perry, Merck & Co., Inc.	Chemical Engineers' Handbook, John H., et al, eds. & 5th ed., 1973, Rahway, NJ

Chemical Rubber Corporation
Handbook of Chemistry and Physics
CRC Press

Handbook of Chemistry - Handbook
Publishers Inc. by NA Lange

Behavior of Organic Chemicals in
the Aquatic Environment - Part 1 -
A Literature Critique, Manufacturing
Chemist's Association

Behavior of Organic Chemicals in
the Aquatic Environment - Part 2 -
Behavior in Dilute Solutions,
Manufacturing Chemists'
Association, April 1968

1963 Census of Manufacturers -
Location of Manufacturing
Plants by Industry,
County, and Employment Size

Chemical Data Guide for Bulk
Shipment by Water, US Coast
Guard 1966

Hygienic Guide Series, American
Industrial Hygiene Association

Pesticide Poisoning of Pond Lake,
Ohio, Investigation and Resolution
(for the EPA, Ryckman, Edgerly,
Tomlinson and Associates, Inc.)

Proceedings of the 1972 National
Conference on Control of Hazardous
Materials Spills (For the EPA)
University of Houston, Houston, TX

Spill Prevention Techniques for
Hazardous Polluting Substances,
(For the EPA), Arthur D. Little Co.

Standard Methods for the Examina-
tion of Water and Wastewater,
American Public Health Association,
American Public Water Works, and
Water Pollution Control Federation

Water Quality Criteria, McKee, J.E.
and H.W. Wolf, the Resources Agency
of California, State Water Quality
Control Board

Water Quality Criteria - Report of
the National Technical Advisory
Committee to the Secretary of the
Interior, April 1, 1968, F.W.P.C.A.,
Wash.

Pollution and Marine Ecology, Olson,
T.A., and R.J. Burgess, 1967

Chemical Safety Data Sheets (SD-1-D-96),
Manufacturing Chemists' Association

Handbook of Analytical Toxicology, Sunshine,
I., ed., Chemical Rubber Co., 1969

MCA Chem-Card Manual

Mineral Facts and Problems, US Bureau of
Mines Bull. 630, 1965

Organic Chemistry, Morrison, R.T., and R.N.
Boyd, 2nd ed., 1966

Orsanco Quality Monitor, July 1970

The Pesticide Review, US Dept. of Agriculture,
1970

Railroad Accident Report-Southern Railway
Company Train 154 Derailment with Fire &
Explosion, Laurel, MS., Jan. 25, 1969

Safety Guides (SG-1-SG-19) Manufacturing
Chemists' Association Spillages of Hazardous
Chemicals (Chart)

Water Pollution Abatement Manual, Manuals
Sheets W-1, W-2, W-3, W-4 & W-6,
Manufacturing Chemists' Association

Control of Spillage of Hazardous Polluting
Substances, 15090 FOZ (for the EPA), Battelle
Memorial Institute

Dangerous Articles Emergency Guide, Bureau of
Explosives, Association of American Railroads

Explosives and Other Dangerous Articles,
Bureau of Explosives, Association of American
Railroads

Fire Protection for Chemicals, Bahme, C.W.,
National Fire Protection Association

— APPENDIX E —
UNITED STATES COAST GUARD AND
ENVIRONMENTAL PROTECTION AGENCY REGIONAL OFFICES

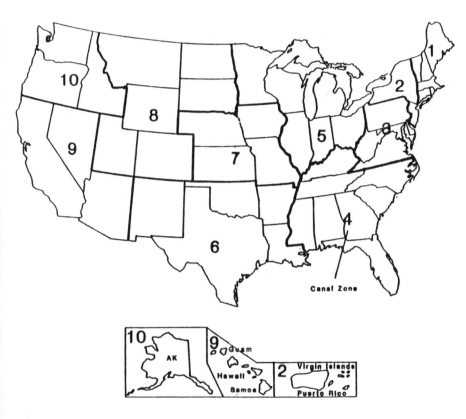

U.S. EPA REGIONS

EPA REGIONAL EMERGENCY RESPONSE OFFICES

REGION 1

Chief, Oil & Hazardous Materials Section
Surveillance and Analysis Division
60 Westview Street
Lexington, MA   02173
(617) 861-6700

REGION 2

Chief, Emergency Response and Hazardous
  Materials
Inspection Branch
Environmental Services Division
Edison, NJ   08837
(201) 321-6657

REGION 3

Chief, Environmental Emergency Branch
6th & Walnut Streets
Curtis Building 3ES30
Philadelphia, PA   19106
(215) 597-9075

REGION 4

Chief, Emergency Remedial & Response
  Branch
345 Courtland Street, NE
Atlanta, GA   30365
(404) 881-3931

REGION 5

Chief, Superfund, Oil & Hazardous
  Materials Coordinator
Environmental Services Division
5SEES
536 South Clark Street
Chicago, IL   60605
(315) 353-9773

REGION 6

Chief, Emergency Response Branch
6ESE, 1201 Elm Street
First International Building
Dallas, TX   75270
(214) 767-2720

REGION 7

Chief, Emergency Planning & Response
  Branch
Environmental Services Division
25 Funston Road
Kansas City, KS   66115
(816) 374-4482

REGION 8

Chief, Emergency Response Branch
Environmental Services Division
1860 Lincoln Street
Denver, CO   80295
(303) 837-2468

REGION 9

Chief, Emergency Response Section
T-3-3
Compliance & Response Branch
Toxic & Waste Management Division
215 Fremont Street
San Francisco, CA   94105
(415) 974-8132

REGION 10

Chief, Environmental Emergency Response
  Team
Environmental Services Division
1200 6th Avenue
Seattle, WA   98101
(206) 442-1295

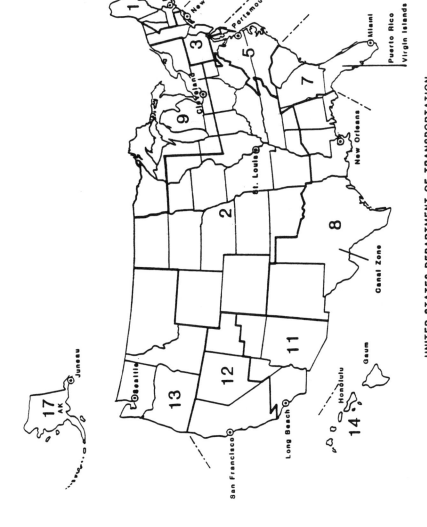

UNITED STATES DEPARTMENT OF TRANSPORTATION

U.S. COAST GUARD DISTRICTS

DEPARTMENT OF TRANSPORTATION, U.S. COAST GUARD DISTRICTS

1st Coast Guard District, 150 Causeway Street, Boston, MA 02114, Duty Officer:
(617) 223-6978.

2nd Coast Guard District, 1430 Olive Street, St. Louis, MO 63101, Duty Officer:
(314) 353-7110.

3rd Coast Guard District, Governors Island, New York, NY 10004, Duty Officer:
(212) 668-7298.

5th Coast Guard District, Federal Buidling, 431 Crawford Street, Portsmouth, VA
23705, Duty Officer: (804) 398-6231.

7th Coast Guard District, Room 1018, Federal Building, 51 SW 1st Avenue, Miami, FL
33130, Duty Officer: (305) 350-5611.

8th Coast Guard District, Hale Boggs Federal Building, 500 Camp Street, New Orleans,
LA 70130, Duty Officer: (504) 589-6298.

9th Coast Guard District, 1240 East 9th Street, Cleveland, OH 44199, Duty Officer:
(216) 522-3984.

11th Coast Guard District, Union Bank Building, 400 Oceangate Boulevard, Long Beach,
CA 90822, Duty Officer: (213) 590-2315.

12th Coast Guard District, 630 Sansome Street, San Francisco, CA 94126, Duty
Officer: (415) 273-7611.

13th Coast Guard District, 915 2nd Avenue, Seattle, WA 98174, Duty Officer:
(206) 442-5886.

14th Coast Guard District, Prince Kalanianaole Federal Building, 300 Ala Moana,
Honolulu, HI 96850, Duty Officer: (808) 546-2170 (commercial only), AUTOVON -
(315) 430-0111.

17th Coast Guard District, P.O. Box 3-5000, Juneau, AK 99802, Duty Officer:
(907) 586-7340 (commercial only), AUTOVON - (317) 388-7340.

STATE SOLID WASTE MANAGEMENT AGENCIES

Alabama

Director
Division of Solid Waste and Vector
  Control
State Department of Public Health
State Office Building
Montgomery, Alabama 36104
(205) 834-1303

Alaska

Solid Waste Program Coordinator
Department of Environmental Conservation
State of Alaska
Pouch O
Juneau, Alaska 99801
(907) 465-2660

American Samoa

Department of Public Works
Government of American Samoa
Pago Pago, American Samoa
Overseas Operator (Commercial Call)

Arizona

Division of Sanitation
Environmental Health Services
Arizona State Department of Health
1740 W. Adams Street
Phoenix, Arizona 85017
(602) 255-1156

Arkansas

Chief
Division of Solid Waste
Arkansas Department of Pollution Control
  and Ecology
P.O. Box 9583
8001 National Drive
Little Rock, Arkansas 72209
(501) 562-7444

California

Chief, Hazardous Waste Mgmt Program
Vector Control Bureau
State Department of Public Health
744 P Street
Sacramento, California 95814
(916) 322-2337

Colorado

State Department of Health
4210 East Eleventh Avenue
Denver, Colorado 80220
(303) 320-8333

Connecticut

Solid Waste Management Programs
Department of Environmental Protection
State of Connecticut
122 Washington Street
Hartford, Connecticut 06106
(203) 566-3672

Delaware

Chief, Solid Waste Section
Delaware Department of Natural Resources
  and Environmental Control
Edward Tatnall Building
Dover, Delaware 19901
(302) 736-4781

District of Columbia

Director, Solid Waste Administration
Department of Environmental Sciences
415 12th Street, N.W., Room 307
Washington, D.C. 20004
(202) 629-4581

Florida

Administrator
Solid Waste Management Section
Division of Environmental Programs
Department of Environmental Regulations
2562 Executive Center Circle, East
Montgomery Building
Tallahassee, Florida 32301
(904) 488-9334

Georgia

Chief, Land Protection Branch
Environmental Protection Division
270 Washington Street, S.W.
Atlanta, Georgia 30334
(404) 656-2833

Guam

Administrator, Guam, EPA
P.O. Box 2999
Agana, Guam 96910
Overseas Operator (Commercial Call)
749-2486

Hawaii

Director, State Department of Health
P.O. Box 3378
Honolulu, Hawaii 96801
(808) 548-6505

Idaho

Chief, Solid Waste Management Section
Environmental Services Division
Idaho Department of Health & Welfare
State House
Boise, Idaho   83720
(208) 334-4059

Illinois

Division of Land/Noise Pollution Control
Illinois Environmental Protection Agency
2200 Churchill Drive
Springfield, Illinois   62706
(217) 782-6760

Indiana

Chief, Solid Waste Section
Division of Sanitary Engineering
Indiana State Board of Health
1330 West Michigan Street
Indianapolis, Indiana   46207
(317) 633-0100

Iowa

Director, Land Quality Division
Department of Environmental Quality
3920 Delaware Avenue
P.O. Box 3326
Des Moines, Iowa   50316
(515) 281-8690

Kansas

Chief, Solid Waste Management Section
Department of Health and Environment
Topeka, Kansas   66620
(913) 862-9360

Kentucky

Director, Division of Solid Waste
State Department for Natural Resources
  and Environmental Protection
275 East Main Street
Frankfort, Kentucky   40601
(502) 564-6716

Louisiana

Louisiana Health and Human Resources
  Administration
State Office Building
P.O. Box 60630
New Orleans, Louisiana   70160
(504) 568-5521

Maine

Chief, Division of Oil and Hazardous
  Materials Management
Department of Environmental Protection
State House
Augusta, Maine   04330
(207) 289-2651

Maryland

Acting Chief
Division of Solid Waste Control
Maryland State Department of Health and
  Mental Hygiene
201 West Preston Street
Baltimore, Maryland   21201
(301) 383-2770/1/2

Massachusetts

Division of Water Pollution Control
Department of Environmental Quality
  Engineering
110 Tremont Street
Boston, Massachusetts   02108
(617) 292-5673

Michigan

Chief, Resource Recovery Division
Environmental Protection Branch
Department of Natural Resources
3500 Logan Street
Lansing, Michigan   48914
(517) 373-1220

Minnesota

Director
Minnesota Pollution Control Agency
Division of Solid Waste
1935 West County Road, B-2
Roseville, Minnesota   55113
(612) 296-7373

Mississippi

Director
Division of Solid Waste Management and
  Vector Control
Mississippi State Board of Health
P.O. Box 1700
Jackson, Mississippi   39205
(601) 354-6612

Missouri

Director, Solid Waste Management Program
Department of Natural Resources
2010 Missouri Boulevard
Jefferson City, Missouri   65101
(314) 751-4422

NOTE: Address all mail to:
        P.O. Box 1368
        State Office Building
        Jefferson City, Missouri   65101

Montana

Chief, Solid Waste Management Bureau
Montana State Department of Health and
  Environmental Sciences
1424 9th Avenue
Helena, Montana   59601
(406) 449-2544

Nebraska

Chief, Solid Waste Division
Department of Environmental Control
State House Station, Box 94653
Lincoln, Nebraska 68509
(402) 471-2186

Nevada

Department of Human Resources
Environmental Protection Service
Capitol Complex
Carson City, Nevada 89701
(702) 885-4740

New Hampshire

Bureau of Solid Waste
Department of Health and Welfare
Hazen Drive
Concord, New Hampshire 03301
(603) 224-5500

New Jersey

Department of Environmental Protection
Solid Waste Administration
P.O. Box 2807
Trenton, New Jersey 08625
(609) 292-9120

New Mexico

Chief, Environmental Improvement Agency
General Sanitation Division, Room 517
P.O. Box 2348, P.E.R.A. Building
Santa Fe, New Mexico 87501
(505) 984-0020

New York

Director, Division of Solid Waste Mgmt
New York State Department of
  Environmental Conservation
50 Wolf Road
Albany, New York 12201
(518) 474-2121

North Carolina

Branch Head
Solid Waste and Vector Control Branch
Department of Human Resources
Divsion of Health Services
P.O. Box 2091
Raleigh, North Carolina 27602
(919) 733-6407

North Dakota

Assistant Director
Division of Water Supply and Pollution
  Control - State Capital
State Department of Health
Bismark, North Dakota 58501
(701) 224-2354

Ohio

Office of Land Pollution Control
Ohio Environmental Protection Agency
P.O. Box 1049
Columbus, Ohio   43216
(614) 466-8934

Oklahoma

Chief, Sanitation Service
State Department of Health
10th and Stonewall
Oklahoma City, Oklahoma 73105
(405) 271-5600

Oregon

Director, Solid Waste Mgmt Division
Oregon State Department of Environmental
  Quality
1234 S.W. Morrison Street
Portland, Oregon 97201
(503) 229-5913

Pennsylvania

Director
Division of Solid Waste Management
Department of Environmental Resources
8th Floor Fulton Building
P.O. Box 2063
Harrisburg, Pennsylvania 17120
(717) 787-9697

Puerto Rico

Environmental Quality Board
Office of the Governor
Box 11488
Santurce, Puerto Rico 00910
(809) 725-5140 Ext. 226

Rhode Island

Department of Health
204 Health Building
Davis Street
Providence, Rhode Island 02908
(401) 277-2231

South Carolina

Director, Solid Waste Mgmt Division
Department of Health and Environmental
  Control
J. Marion Sims Building
2600 Bull Street
Columbia, South Carolina 29201
(803) 776-6194

South Dakota

Division of Air Quality and Solid Waste
South Dakota Department of Water and
  Natural Resources
Office Building No. 2
Pierre, South Dakota 57501
(605) 773-3153

Tennessee

Director
Division of Solid Waste Management
Bureau of Environmental Management
  and Quality Assurance
State Department of Public Health
Capitol Hill Building, Suite 320
Nashville, Tennessee 37219
(615) 741-3657

Texas

Department of Water Resources
Water Quality Section
P.O. Box 13246
Austin, Texas 78711
(512) 475-3454

Trust Territories

Chief, Department of Health Services
Office of High Commission
Trust Territory of the Pacific Islands
Saipan, Marianas 96950
Overseas Operator (Commercial Call)

Utah

Utah State Division of Environmental
  Health
44 Medical Drive
Salt Lake City, Utah 84113
(801) 533-6163

Vermont

Air and Solid Waste Programs
Agency of Environmental Conservation
P.O. Box 489
Montpelier, Vermont 05602
(802) 828-3395

Virgin Islands

Assistant Director
Division of Utilities and Sanitation
Department of Public Works
Government of the Virgin Islands
Charlotte Amalie
St. Thomas, Virgin Islands 00801
(809) 774-7970

Virginia

Director
Bureau of Solid Waste and Vector Cont.
Virginia State Department of Health
James Madison Building
109 Govenor Street
Richmond, Virginia 23219
(804) 786-5271

Washington

Division Chief
Solid Waste and Resource Recovery
  Division
Department of Ecology
Olympia, Washington 98501
(206) 459-6000

West Virginia

Director, Solid Waste Program
State Department of Health
1800 Washington Street, E.
Charleston, West Virginia 25305
(304) 348-2971

Wisconsin

Chief, Solid Waste Management Section
Division of Environmental Protection
Department of Natural Resources
Box 450
Madison, Wisconsin 53701
(608) 266-5848

Wyoming

SW Program Supervisor
Wyoming Department of Environmental
  Quality
State Office Building West
Cheyenne, Wyoming 82002
(307) 777-7937

— APPENDIX F —
LOCATION OF HAZARDOUS WASTE DISPOSAL SITES

BFI - Chemical Services Division
Mobile, Alabama
(205) 666-5724

Services:	Collection/haulage, processing/treatment, storage, lab analysis, recovery, reclamation, disposal
Waste Handled:	Most wastes considered
Processing:	Chemical fixing, neutralization, oxidation/reduction
Disposal:	Landfill

Chancellor and Ogden, Inc.
3031 East I Street
Wilmington, California 90744
(213) 432-8461

Services:	Collection/hauling, lab analysis, storage, disposal
Waste Handled:	Most wastes considered
Disposal:	Secure landfill (CA, Class I)

County of Los Angeles Site
1955 Workman Mill Road
P.O. Box 4998
Whitter, California 90607
(213) 699-7411

Palos Verdes Landfill

Services:	Disposal, lab analysis
Wastes Handled:	Oil wastes, various wastes considered
Wastes Excluded:	Highly flammable, mixed loads, magnesium, wastes with 4-11pH range
Disposal:	Secure landfill (Class I)

Calabasa Landfill

Wastes Handled:	Caustics, drummed wastes
Wastes Excluded:	Magnesium, conc. acids, alkali
Disposal:	Secure landfill (Class I)

---

*Source: U.S. Environmental Protection Agency, Hazardous Waste Management Facilities in the United States - 1977, EPA/530/SW-146.3.

Omar Rendering Company
P.O. Box 1236
Chula Vista, California
(619) 421-8600

    Services: Collection, hauling, processing/treatment, disposal, storage

    Wastes Handled: Acids, caustics, solvents, etchants–liquids only

    Processing: Evaporation

    Disposal: Open pit, lagoons

Richmond Sanitary Service
1224 Nevin Avenue
Richmond, California
(415) 236-8000

    Services: Collection/hauling, disposal

    Wastes Handled: Acids, refinery wastes, lead sludge, pesticide containers

    Wastes Excluded: Pending analysis

    Disposal: Lagoons, landfill

San Diego County Site
5555 Overland Road
San Diego, California
(714) 565-5703

    Services: Disposal, storage

    Wastes Handled: Pesticides, chemical

    Wastes Excluded: Cyanides

    Disposal: Secure landfill

Zero Waste System, Inc.
2928 Poplar St.
Oakland, California 94608
(415) 893-8257

    Services: Wastes utilization and waste exchange program, disposal

    Wastes Handled: Most waste considered, lab chemicals

    Disposal: Off-site landfills

```
Rollins Environmental Services
(Main Office) One Rollins Plaza
Wilmington, Delaware   19803
(302) 429-2700
```

Services:	Collection/haulage, storage, processing/treatment, lab analysis, disposal
Wastes Handled:	All wastes considered
Processing/Treatment:	Chemical Degradation (neutralization, oxidation, reduction), incineration, biological
Disposal:	Landfill, incineration (rotary kiln), ocean disposal

```
Complete Refuse Removal Service
P.O. Box 488
Smyrna, Georgia   30081
(404) 433-2421
```

Services:	Collection/haulage, processing, storage, disposal
Wastes Handled:	Most wastes considered
Processing:	Chemical solidifications, latex treatment

```
Envirosafe Services of Idaho
P.O. Box 936
Melton Home, Idaho   83647
(208) 587-8433
```

Services:	Disposal
Wastes Handled:	Pesticides, most wastes considered
Disposal:	Secure burial

```
Services Corporations of America, Inc.
11700 Stony Island Avenue
Chicago, Illinois   60617
(312) 646-5700
```

Services:	Processing/treatment, storage, lab analysis, disposal, reclamation/recycling
Wastes Handled:	Most materials considered
Processing:	Chemical neutralization, electrochemical oxidation, biological activated sludge
Disposal:	Incinerator (rotary kiln)

```
U.S. Ecology
Box 7246 Louisville, KY   40207
(Site) Sheffield, Illinois
(815) 454-2376
```

Wastes Handled:	Radioactive, pesticides, heavy metals, organics
Wastes Excluded:	Reactive sodium and potassium
Disposal:	Secure landfill

Waste Management, Inc. 3003 Butterfield Road Oak Brook, Illinois 60521 (312) 654-8800	Also: Chem Waste Management, Inc. 138 Calumet Expressway Calumet City, Illinois 60409 (312) 891-1500
Services:	Collection/hauling, storage, processing/treatment, lab analysis, disposal reclamation/recovery
Wastes Handled:	Acids, caustics, solvents, heavy metals
Wastes Excluded:	Cyanides, pesticides, herbicides
Processing:	Chemical neutralization, precipitation
Disposal:	Landfill, sludge farming

U.S. Scrap Company
11507 South Michigan Avenue
Chicago, Illinois

Services:	Collection/haulage, reclamation/recycling, disposal
Wastes Handled:	Solvents, oily wastes, sludges
Wastes Excluded:	Cyanide, arsenic
Disposal:	Landfill

Advanced Industrial Maintenance
4645 West 138th Street
Crestwood, Illinois   60445
(312) 396-1810

Services:	Collection/hauling, storage, processing/treatment, lab analysis, reclamation/recovery, disposal
Wastes Handled:	Most wastes considered
Processing:	Chemical fixings, neutralization, oxidation/reduction
Disposal:	Landfill

Rollins Environmental Services
(Main Office) Wilmington, Delaware   19803
Baton Rouge, Louisiana
(504) 778-1234

Services:	Collection/hauling, processing/treatment, storage, lab analysis, disposal, reclamation/recycling
Wastes Handled:	All materials considered
Processing:	Chemical degradation, neutralization, precipitation
Disposal:	Incineration, landfill

BFI - Chemical Services Div. Also: Lake Charles Disposal Site
Baton Rouge, LA   (318) 527-6857
(504) 293-4571

  Services: Collection/hauling, processing/treatment,
             reclamation, disposal

  Wastes Handled: Most wastes considered

  Processing: Neutralization, chemical solidification

  Disposal: Landfill

Robb Tyler, Inc.   (Subsidiary of BFI)
Baltimore, Maryland
(301) 686-6161

  Services: Collection/haulage, processing/treatment, storage,
             lab analysis, reclamation, disposal

  Waste Handled: Most wastes considered

  Processing: Chemical fixing, neutralization, oxidation -
             reduction

  Disposal: Landfill

Chem Met Service
18550 Allen Road
Wyandotte, Michigan
(313) 282-9250

  Services: Collection/hauling, processing/treatment, disposal,
             storage

  Wastes Handled: Most wastes considered

  Wastes Excluded: Arsenic

  Processing: Chemical neutralization, chemical fixation

  Disposal: Landfill

Prenco Manufacturing Co.
2601 West 14 Mile
Royal Oak, Michigan 48073
(313) 399-6262

  Services: Lab analysis, processing/treatment, disposal

  Wastes Handled: Most wastes considered, some explosives

  Disposal: Incineration of liquids and solids

Systech Waste Treatment Center
3030 Wood Street
Mushegon Heights, Michigan 49444
(616) 733-1444
Business Office: (513) 298-6614

  Services: Collection/haulage, treatment processing, storage,
             disposal

  Wastes Handled: Most wastes considered

  Processing: Chemical and biological

Conservation Chemical Company
5201 Johnson Drive
Mission, Kansas 66205
(816) 483-4222
(Plants): St. Louis, Missouri
          Gary, Indiana

    Services: Collection/haulage, processing/treatment, lab
                                      analysis, disposal, storage, recycling/recovery

    Wastes Handled: Acids, caustics, arsenicals, cyanide, phenols,
                                        heavy metal solutions

    Wastes Excluded: Pending analysis

    Processing: Distillation, neutralization recombination,
                                      flouride recovery, sedimentation

Wheeling Disposal Service Co., Inc.
1805 South 8th Street
St. Joseph, Missouri 64503
(816) 279-0815
Site: Andrew County, Missouri

    Services: Disposal, storage

    Wastes Handled: Most waste considered, including pesticides

    Disposal: Soil incorporation, landfill

Big 3 Enterprises
10,000 E. Girmingham Rd.
Kansas City, Missouri 64161
(816) 741-4466

    Services: Collection/haulage, disposal

    Wastes Handled: O:ganic chemicals, liquid and some solids

    Disposal: Incineration

Atlantic Marine Industrial Services
235 Forrest St.
Metuchuy, New Jersey 08840
(201) 549-1788

    Services: Collection/hauling, processing/treatment, disposal,
                                      lab analysis, storage

    Wastes Handled: Petro-based, chemical

    Processing: Chemical neutralization

    Disposal: Landfill

Browning - Ferris Industries, Inc.
Pedricktown, New Jersey
(609) 299-0835

    Services: Collection/hauling, processing/treatment,
                                      reclamation, lab analysis, disposal

    Wastes Handled: Most wastes considered

    Processing: Chemical fixation, neutralization

    Disposal: Landfill

Rollins Environmental Services
Bridgeport, New Jersey (Logan Township)
(609) 467-3100
(Main Office) Wilmington, Delaware 19803
(Main Office) (302) 429-2700

Services:	Collection/hauling, processing/treatment, reclamation/recycling, lab analysis, storage, disposal
Wastes Handled:	All wastes considered
Processing:	Chemical degradation, flocculation, trickling filter, neutralization, precipitation
Disposal:	Landfill, incineration (rotary kiln)

Solvent Recovery Service of New Jersey
1200 Sylvan Street
Linden, New Jersey 07036
(201) 862-2000

Services:	Collection/haulage, processing/treatment, storage, lab analysis, disposal, recovery
Wastes Handled:	Liquid organic wastes, other wastes considered
Processing:	Distillation, neutralization
Disposal:	Incineration, landfill

Frontier Chemical Wastes Process, Inc.
4626 Royal Avenue
Niagra Falls, New York 14303
(716) 285-8208

Services:	Collection/hauling, processing/treatment, consulting, recycling/reclamation, storage, brokerage, lab analysis, disposal
Wastes Handled:	All materials considered
Processing:	Chemical degradation, catalysis, pyrolysis
Disposal:	Landfill

Services Corporations of America
P.O. Box 200, 1550 Balner Road
Model City, New York 14107
(716) 754-8231

Services:	Collection/hauling, recycling/reclamation, processing/treatment, lab analysis, storage, disposal
Wastes Handled:	Most wastes considered
Processing:	Chemical degradation (patented neutralization process), chemical fixation, distillation, centrifuging, (resource recovery)
Disposal:	Secure landfill, incineration

Radiac Research Corporation
261 Kent Avenue
Brooklyn, New York   11211
(212) 963-2233

    Services: Collection/haulage, treatment, transfer to ultimate
disposal operations

    Wastes Handled: Most wastes considered

Systech Corporation   Also: Hilliard, Ohio
Systech Waste Treatment Center   (614) 876-1186
245 N. Valley Road
Xenia, Ohio   45385
(513) 372-8077

    Services: Storage, process/treatment, disposal, lab analysis

    Wastes Handled: Acids, caustics, plating wastes, organic wastes
(combustibles)

    Wastes Excluded: Pending lab analysis

    Processing: Chemical neutralization, reduction, flocculation,
precipitation

    Disposal: Incineration (fluid bed), landfill

Browning - Ferris of Ohio
P.O. Box 2907
530 Glenwood Avenue
Youngston, Ohio   44511
(216) 747-4433

    Services: Collection/haulage, lab analysis,
treatment/processing, storage, disposal, recovery

    Wastes Handled: Most wastes considered

    Processing: Neutralization, chemical fixing

    Disposal: Incineration, landfill

Ecological Services, Inc.
East Palestine, Ohio
(216) 426-4171

    Services: Collection/hauling, processing/treatment, lab
analysis, disposal

    Wastes Handled: Most wastes considered

    Processing: Chemical fixing, neutralization

    Disposal: Landfill

Ross Incineration Services, Inc.
394 Giles Road
Grafton, Ohio
(216) 748-2171

    Services: Disposal

    Wastes Handled: Most burnable wastes considered

    Disposal: Incineration

Pottstown Disposal Service
Route 20 Sell Road
Pottstown, Pennsylvania   19464
(215) 326-6050

Services:	Disposal, lab analysis
Wastes Handled:	All material considered
Disposal:	Sanitary landfill

Browning - Ferris, Inc.
(Main Office)
14701 St. Mary's
Houston, Texas   77079
(713) 870-8100

Services:	Collection/hauling, processing/treatment, reclamation/recovery, lab analysis, storage, disposal
Wastes Handled:	Most materials considered
Processing:	Chemical degradation, biochemical
Disposal:	Landfill, incineration, encapsulation

Rollins Environmental Services
Houston, Texas
(713) 479-6001

Services:	Collection/hauling, storage, lab analysis, processing/treatment, disposal
Wastes Handled:	Most wastes considered
Processing:	Neutralization, oxidation/reduction
Disposal:	Incineration, landfill

Texas Ecologists, Inc.   Subsidiary of: Nuclear Engineering Co.
Robstown, Texas
(512) 387-3518

Services:	Collection/hauling, processing, treatment, disposal
Wastes Handled:	Most wastes considered
Wastes Excluded:	Cyanide
Processing:	Chemical neutralization, evaporation
Disposal:	Secure landfill, incineration

Chemical Processors, Inc.
5501 Airport Way South
Seattle, Washington   96108
(206) 767-0350

Services:	Collection/hauling, processing/treatment, storage, reclamation, lab analysis
Wastes Handled:	All wastes considered; solvents, oil
Processing:	Distillation, evaporation

Western Processing Company
7215 South 196th
Kent, Washington   98031
(206)   872-8075

Services:	Processing/treatment, lab analysis, recycling/reclamation
Wastes Handled:	Most wastes considered
Wastes Excluded:	Beryllium
Processing:	Chemical detoxification for reclamation

— APPENDIX G —
DOT-HAZARDOUS MATERIALS
EMERGENCY RESPONSE GUIDE

DOT RESPONSE GUIDE 13
HYDROCYANIC ACID - UN 1051

Fire or Explosion
- Some of these materials are extremely flammable.
- May be ignited by heat, sparks and flames.
- Flammable vapor may spread away from spill.
- Container may explode in heat of fire.
- Vapor explosion and poison hazardous indoors, outdoors or in sewers.

Health Hazards
- Poison; extremely hazardous.
- May be fatal if inhaled or absorbed through skin.
- Vapors non-irritating, deaden sense of smell.
- Runoff from fire control or dilution water may cause pollution.

EMERGENCY ACTION

- Keep unnecessary people away.
- Stay upwind; keep out of low areas.
- Isolate hazard area and deny entry.
- Wear positive pressure breathing apparatus and special protective clothing.
- Evacuate area endangered by gas (See Isolation and Evacuation Table in back of guidebook; find the material by name).
- **Isolate for 1/2 mile in all directions if tank or tank car is involved in fire.**
- FOR EMERGENCY ASSISTANCE CALL CHEMTREC (800) 424-9300.

Fire
- Let burn unless leak can be stopped immediately.
- **Small Fires:** Dry chemical or CO2.
- **Large Fires:** Water spray, fog or foam.
- Move container from fire area if you can do it without risk.
- Stay away from ends of tanks.
- Cool container with water using unmanned device until well after fire is out.
- Isolate area until gas has dispersed.

Spill or Leak
- Do not touch spilled material.
- No flares, smoking or flames in hazard area.
- Stop leak if you can do it without risk.
- Use water spray to reduce vapors.
- Isolate area until gas has dispersed.

First Aid
- Move victim to fresh air; call emergency medical care.
- If not breathing, give artificial respiration.

143

DOT RESPONSE GUIDE 13 (continued)
HYDROCYANIC ACID - UN 1051

- If breathing is difficult, give oxygen.
- Remove and isolate contaminated clothing and shoes.
- In case of contact with material, immediately flush skin or eyes with running water for at least 15 minutes.
- Keep victim quiet and maintain normal body temperature.
- Effects may be delayed, keep victim under observation.

DOT RESPONSE GUIDE 15

ANHYDROUS AMMONIA - UN 1005

Health Hazards

- Poison (if inhaled may be fatal).
- Contact may cause burns to skin and eyes.
- Contact with liquid may cause frostbite.
- Runoff from fire control or dilution water may cause pollution.

Fire or Explosion

- Some of these materials may burn, but do not ignite readily.
- Container may explode in heat of fire.

EMERGENCY ACTION

- Keep unnecessary people away.
- Stay upwind; keep out of low areas.
- Isolate hazard area and deny entry.
- Wear positive pressure breathing apparatus and full protective clothing.
- FOR EMERGENCY ASSISTANCE CALL CHEMTREC **(800) 424-9300** (in case of water pollution call local authorities).

Fire

- **Small Fires:** Dry chemical or CO2.
- **Large Fires:** Water spray, fog or foam.
- Move container from fire area if you can do it without risk.
- Stay away from ends of tanks.
- Cool containers that are exposed to flames with water from the side until well after fire is out.
- Isolate area until gas has dispersed.

Spill or Leak

- Stop leak if you can do it without risk.
- Use water spray to reduce vapors.

First Aid

- Move victim to fresh air; call emergency medical care.
- If not breathing, give artificial respiration.
- If breathing is difficult, give oxygen.
- Remove and isolate contaminated clothing and shoes.
- In case of contact with material, immediately flush skin or eyes with running water for at least 15 minutes.
- Keep victim quiet and maintain normal body temperature.
- Effects may be delayed, keep victim under observation.

DOT RESPONSE GUIDE 17
BUTADIENE, INHIBITED - UN 1010
VINYL CHLORIDE - UN 1086

Fire or Explosion
- Extremely flammable.
- May be ignited by heat, sparks and flames.
- Flammable vapor may spread away from spill.
- Container may explode violently in heat of fire.
- Vapor explosion hazard indoors, outdoors or in sewers.

Health Hazards
- If inhaled, may be harmful.
- Vapors may cause dizziness or suffocation.
- Contact may irritate or burn skin and eyes.
- Contact with liquid may cause frostbite.
- Fire may produce irritating or poisonous gases.

EMERGENCY ACTION
- Keep unnecessary people away.
- Stay upwind; keep out of low areas.
- Isolate hazard area and deny entry.
- Wear self-contained breathing apparatus and full protective clothing.
- **Isolate for 1/2 mile in all directions if tank or tank car is involved in fire.**
- FOR EMERGENCY ASSISTANCE CALL CHEMTREC (800) 424-9300.

Fire
- Let burn unless leak can be stopped immediately.
- **Small Fires:** Dry chemical or CO2.
- **Large Fires:** Water spray, fog or foam.
- Move container from fire area if you can do it without risk.
- Stay away from ends of tanks.
- For massive fire in cargo area, use unmanned hose holder or monitor nozzles.
- If this is impossible, withdraw from area and let fire burn.
- Withdraw immediately in case of rising sound from venting safety device or discoloration of tank.
- Cool container with water using unmanned device until well after fire is out.

Spill or Leak
- No flares, smoking or flames in hazard area.
- Stop leak if you can do it without risk.
- Use water spray to reduce vapors.
- Isolate area until gas has dispersed.

First Aid
- Move victim to fresh air; call emergency medical care.
- If not breathing, give artificial respiration.
- If breathing is difficult, give oxygen.
- In case of frostbite, thaw frosted parts with water.
- Keep victim quiet and maintain normal body temperature.

DOT RESPONSE GUIDE 20
CHLORINE - UN 1017
NITROGEN TETROXIDE - UN 1067

Health Hazards

- Poison.
- If inhaled, may be fatal.
- Vapors may cause dizziness or suffocation.
- Contact may cause burns to skin and eyes.
- Contact with liquid may cause frostbite.
- Runoff from fire control or dilution water may cause pollution.

Fire or Explosion

- May ignite combustibles (wood, paper, oil, etc.).
- Mixture with fuels may explode.
- Container may explode in heat of fire.
- Vapor explosion hazard indoors, outdoors or in sewers.

EMERGENCY ACTION

- Keep unnecessary people away.
- Stay upwind; keep out of low areas.
- Isolate hazard area and deny entry.
- Wear positive pressure breathing apparatus and full protective clothing.
- Evacuate area endangered by gas (See Isolation and Evacuation Table in back of guidebook; find the material by name).
- FOR EMERGENCY ASSISTANCE CALL CHEMTREC (800) 424-9300. Also, in case of water pollution, call local authorities.

Fire

- **Small Fires:** Dry chemical or CO2.
- **Large Fires:** Water spray, fog or foam.
- Move container from fire area if you can do it without risk.
- Stay away from ends of tanks.
- Cool containers that are exposed to flames with water from the side until well after fire is out.
- For massive fire in cargo area, use unmanned hose holder or monitor nozzles.
- If this is impossible, withdraw from area and let fire burn.

Spill or Leak

- Keep combustibles (wood, paper, oil, etc.) away from spilled material.
- Stop leak if you can do it without risk.
- Use water spray to reduce vapors but **do not** put water on leak area.
- Isolate area until gas has dispersed.

First Aid

- Move victim to fresh air; call emergency medical care.
- If not breathing, give artificial respiration.
- If breathing is difficult, give oxygen.
- Remove and isolate contaminated clothing and shoes.
- In case of contact with material, immediately flush skin and eyes with running water for at least 15 minutes.

DOT RESPONSE GUIDE 20 (continued)
CHLORINE - UN 1017
NITROGEN TETROXIDE - UN 1067

● Keep victim quiet and maintain normal body temperature.
● Effects may be delayed, keep victim under observation.

DOT RESPONSE GUIDE 22
ISOBUTANE - UN 1075
PROPYLENE - UN 1075
HYDROGEN, LIQUEFIED - UN 1966
PROPANE/LPG - UN 1075

Fire or Explosion

- Extremely flammable.
- May be ignited by heat, sparks and flames.
- Flammable vapor may spread away from spill.
- Container may explode in heat of fire.
- Vapor explosion hazard indoors, outdoors or in sewers.

Health Hazards

- Vapors may cause dizziness or suffocation.
- Contact will cause severe frostbite.
- Fire may produce irritating or poisonous gases.

EMERGENCY ACTION

- Keep unnecessary people away.
- Stay upwind; keep out of low areas.
- Isolate hazard area and deny entry.
- Wear positive pressure breathing apparatus and full protective clothing.
- **Isolate for 1/2 mile in all directions if tank or tank car is involved in fire.**
- FOR EMERGENCY ASSISTANCE CALL CHEMTREC (800) 424-9300.

Fire

- Let burn unless leak can be stopped immediately.
- **Small Fires:** Dry chemical or CO2.
- **Large Fires:** Water spray, fog or foam.
- Move container from fire area if you can do it without risk.
- Stay away from ends of tanks.
- Cool containers that are exposed to flames with water from the side until well after fire is out.
- For massive fire in cargo area, use unmanned hose holder or monitor nozzles.
- If this is impossible, withdraw from area and let fire burn.
- Withdraw immediately in case of rising sound from venting safety device or discoloration of tank.

Spill or Leak

- No flares, smoking or flames in hazard area.
- Do not touch spilled material.
- Stop leak if you can do it without risk.
- Use water spray to reduce vapors.
- Isolate area until gas has dispersed.

First Aid

- Move victim to fresh air; call emergency medical care.
- If not breathing, give artificial respiration.
- If breathing is difficult, give oxygen.
- In case of frostbite, thaw frosted parts with water.
- Keep victim quiet and maintain normal body temperature.

DOT RESPONSE GUIDE 23

OXYGEN, PRESSURIZED LIQUID - UN 1073

Fire or Explosion
- May ignite combustibles (wood, paper, oil, etc.).
- Mixture with fuels may explode.
- Container may explode in heat of fire.
- Vapor explosion hazard indoors, outdoors or in sewers.

Health Hazards
- Vapors may cause dizziness or suffocation.
- Contact will cause frostbite.
- Fire may produce irritating or poisonous gases.

EMERGENCY ACTION
- Keep unnecessary people away.
- Isolate hazard area and deny entry.
- Stay upwind; keep out of low areas.
- Wear self-contained breathing apparatus and full protective clothing.
- **Isolate for 1/2 mile in all directions if tank or tank car is involved in fire.**
- FOR EMERGENCY ASSISTANCE CALL CHEMTREC **(800) 424-9300.**

Fire
- **Small Fires:** Dry chemical or CO_2.
- **Large Fires:** Water spray, fog or foam.
- Move container from fire area if you can do it without risk.
- Stay away from ends of tanks.
- Cool containers that are exposed to flames with water from the side until well after fire is out.
- For massive fire in cargo area, use unmanned hose holder or monitor nozzles.
- If this is impossible, withdraw from area and let fire burn.

Spill or Leak
- Keep combustibles (wood, paper, oil, etc.) away from spilled material.
- Do not touch spilled material.
- Stop leak if you can do it without risk.
- Isolate area until gas has dispersed.

First Aid
- Move victim to fresh air; call emergency medical care.
- Remove and isolate contaminated clothing and shoes.
- In case of frostbite, thaw frosted parts with water.
- Keep victim quiet and maintain normal body temperature.

DOT RESPONSE GUIDE 26
ACETONE — UN 1090
VINYL ACETATE — UN 1301

Fire or Explosion

- Will burn. May be ignited by heat, sparks and flames.
- Flammable vapor may spread away from spill.
- Container may explode in heat of fire.
- Vapor explosion hazard indoors, outdoors or in sewers.
- Runoff to sewer may create fire or explosion hazard.

Health Hazards

- Vapors may cause dizziness or suffocation.
- Contact may irritate or burn skin and eyes.
- Fire may produce irritating or poisonous gases.
- Runoff from fire control or dilution water may cause pollution.

EMERGENCY ACTION

- Keep unnecessary people away.
- Stay upwind; keep out of low areas.
- Isolate hazard area and deny entry.
- Wear self-contained breathing apparatus and full protective clothing.
- **Isolate for 1/2 mile in all directions if tank or tank car is involved in fire.**
- FOR EMERGENCY ASSISTANCE CALL CHEMTREC (800) 424-9300.
- Also, in case of water pollution, call local authorities.

Fire

- **Small Fires:** Dry chemical, CO_2, water spray or alcohol foam.
- **Large Fires:** Water spray, fog or alcohol foam.
- Move container from fire area if you can do it without risk.
- Stay away from ends of tanks.
- Cool containers that are exposed to flames with water from the side until well after fire is out.
- For massive fire in cargo area, use unmanned hose holder or monitor nozzles.
- Withdraw immediately in case of rising sound from venting safety device or discoloration of tank.

Spill or Leak

- No flares, smoking or flames in hazard area.
- Stop leak if you can do it without risk.
- Use water spray to reduce vapors.
- **Small Spills:** Take up with sand, or other noncombustible absorbent material, then flush area with water.
- **Large Spills:** Dike far ahead of spill for later disposal.

First Aid

- Move victim to fresh air; call emergency medical care.
- If not breathing, give artificial respiration.
- If breathing is difficult, give oxygen.
- In case of contact with material, immediately flush skin and eyes with running water for at least 15 minutes.
- Remove and isolate contaminated clothing and shoes.

DOT RESPONSE GUIDE 27
ETHYL ACRYLATE, INHIBITED — UN 1917
STYRENE MONOMER, INHIBITED — UN 2055
TOLUENE — UN 1294

Fire or Explosion

● Will burn. May be ignited by heat, sparks and flames.
● Flammable vapor may spread away from spill.
● Container may explode in heat of fire.
● Vapor explosion hazard indoors, outdoors or in sewers.
● Runoff to sewer may create fire or explosion hazard.

Health Hazard

● Vapors may cause dizziness or suffocation.
● Contact may irritate or burn skin and eyes.
● Fire may produce irritating or poisonous gases.
● Runoff from fire control or dilution water may cause pollution.

EMERGENCY ACTION

● Keep unnecessary people away.
● Stay upwind; keep out of low areas.
● Isolate hazard area and deny entry.
● Wear self-contained breathing apparatus and full protective clothing.
● Isolate for 1/2 mile in all directions if tank or tank car is involved in fire.
● FOR EMERGENCY ASSISTANCE CALL CHEMTREC (800) 424-9300.
● Also, in case of water pollution, call local authorities.

Fire

● Small Fires: Dry chemical, CO2, water spray or foam.
● Large Fires: Water spray, fog or foam.
● Move container from fire area if you can do so without risk.
● Stay away from ends of tanks.
● Cool containers that are exposed to flames with water from the side until well after fire is out.
● For massive fire in cargo area, use unmanned hose holder or monitor nozzles.
● If this is impossible, withdraw from area and let fire burn.
● Withdraw immediately in case of rising sound from venting safety device or discoloration of tank.

Spill or Leak

● No flares, smoking or flames in hazard area.
● Stop leak if you can do it without risk.
● Use water spray to reduce vapors.
● Small Spills: Take up with sand, or other noncombustible absorbent material, then flush area with water.
● Large Spills: Dike far ahead of spill for later disposal.

First Aid

● Move victim to fresh air; call emergency medical care.
● If not breathing, give artificial respiration.
● If breathing is difficult, give oxygen.

DOT RESPONSE GUIDE 27 (continued)
ETHYL ACRYLATE, INHIBITED — UN 1917
STYRENE MONOMER, INHIBITED — UN 2055
TOLUENE — UN 1294

- In case of contact with material, immediately flush skin or eyes with running water for at least 15 minutes.
- Remove and isolate contaminated clothing and shoes.

DOT RESPONSE GUIDE 28
METHYL ALCOHOL - UN 1230
METHYL HYDRAZINE - UN 1244
DIMETHYL HYDRAZINE, UNSYMMETRICAL - UN 1163
HYDRAZINE, ANHYDROUS - UN 2029

Fire or Explosion

- Will burn. May be ignited by heat, sparks and flames.
- Flammable vapor may spread away from spill.
- Container may explode in heat of fire.
- Vapor explosion and poison hazardous indoors, outdoors or in sewers.
- Runoff to sewer may create fire or explosion hazard.

Health Hazards

- Poison.
- May be fatal if inhaled, swallowed or absorbed through skin.
- Contact may cause burns to skin and eyes.
- Runoff from fire control or dilution water may cause pollution.

EMERGENCY ACTION

- Keep unnecessary people away.
- Isolate hazard area and deny entry.
- Stay upwind; keep out of low areas.
- Wear positive pressure breathing apparatus and special protective clothing.
- **Isolate for 1/2 mile in all directions if tank or tank car is involved in fire.**
- FOR EMERGENCY ASSISTANCE CALL CHEMTREC (800) 424-9300.
- Also, in case of water pollution, call local authorities.

Fire

- **Small Fires:** Dry chemical, CO2, water spray or foam.
- **Large Fires:** Water spray, fog or foam.
- Move container from fire area if you can do it without risk.
- Stay away from ends of tanks.
- Cool containers that are exposed to flames with water from the side until well after fire is out.
- Withdraw immediately in case of rising sound from venting safety device or discoloration of tank.

Spill or Leak

- No flares, smoking or flames in hazard area.
- Do not touch spilled material.
- Stop leak if you can do it without risk.
- Use water spray to reduce vapors.
- **Small Spills:** Take up with sand, or other noncombustible absorbent material, then flush area with water.
- **Large Spills:** Dike far ahead of spill for later disposal.

First Aid

- Move victim to fresh air; call emergency medical care.
- If not breathing, give artificial respiration.
- If breathing is difficult, give oxygen.
- Remove and isolate contaminated clothing and shoes.

DOT RESPONSE GUIDE 28 (continued)
METHYL ALCOHOL - UN 1230
METHYL HYDRAZINE - UN 1244
DIMETHYL HYDRAZINE, UNSYMMETRICAL - UN 1163
HYDRAZINE, ANHYDROUS 2029

- In case of contact with material, immediately flush skin or eyes with running water for at least 15 minutes.
- Keep victim quiet and maintain normal body temperature.
- Effects may be delayed, keep victim under observation.

DOT RESPONSE GUIDE 30
ACRYLONITRILE, INHIBITED — 1093
ETHYLENE OXIDE — UN 1040

Health Hazards

- Poison.
- May be fatal if inhaled, swallowed or absorbed through skin.
- Contact may cause burns to skin and eyes.
- Runoff from fire control or dilution water may cause pollution.

Fire or Explosion

- Will burn. May be ignited by heat, sparks and flames.
- Flammable vapor may spread away from spill.
- Container may explode in heat of fire.
- Vapor explosion and poison hazardous indoors, outdoors or in sewers.
- Runoff to sewer may create fire or explosion hazard.

EMERGENCY ACTION

- Keep unnecessary people away.
- Isolate hazard area and deny entry.
- Stay upwind; keep out of low areas.
- Wear positive pressure breathing apparatus and special protective clothing.
- **Isolate for 1/2 mile in all directions if tank or tank car is involved in fire.**
- FOR EMERGENCY ASSISTANCE CALL CHEMTREC (800) 424-9300.
- Also, in case of water pollution, call local authorities.

Fire

- **Small Fires:** Dry chemical, CO2, water spray or foam.
- **Large Fires:** Water spray, fog or foam.
- Stay away from ends of tanks.
- Do not get water inside container.
- Cool containers that are exposed to flames with water from the side until well after fire is out.
- For massive fire in cargo area, use unmanned hose holder or monitor nozzles.
- If this is impossible, withdraw from area and let fire burn.
- Withdraw immediately in case of rising sound from venting safety device or discoloration of tank.

Spill or Leak

- No flares, smoking or flames in hazard area.
- Do not touch spilled material.
- Stop leak if you can do it without risk.
- Use water spray to reduce vapors.
- **Small Spills:** Flush area with flooding amounts of water.
- Do not get water inside containers.
- **Large Spills:** Dike far ahead of spill for later disposal.

First Aid

- Move victim to fresh air; call emergency medical care.
- If not breathing, give artificial respiration.

DOT RESPONSE GUIDE 30 (continued)
ACRYLONITRILE, INHIBITED — UN 1093
ETHYLENE OXIDE — UN 1040

- If breathing is difficult, give oxygen.
- Remove and isolate contaminated clothing and shoes.
- In case of contact with material, immediately flush skin or eyes with running water for at least 15 minutes.
- Keep victim quiet and maintain normal body temperature.
- Effects may be delayed, keep victim under observation.

DOT RESPONSE GUIDE 32
MONOMETHYLAMINE NITRATE SOLUTION*

Fire or Explosion

- Will burn. May be ignited by heat, sparks and flames.
- May burn rapidly with flare-burning effect.

Health Hazards

- Little immediate health hazard.
- Fire may produce irritating or poisonous gases.
- Contact may cause burns to skin and eyes.
- Runoff from fire control or dilution water may cause pollution.

EMERGENCY ACTION

- Keep unnecessary people away.
- Stay upwind; keep out of low areas.
- Isolate hazard area and deny entry.
- Wear self-contained breathing apparatus and full protective clothing.
- FOR EMERGENCY ASSISTANCE CALL CHEMTREC (800) 424-9300.
- Also, in case of water pollution, call local authorities.

Fire

- **Small Fires:** Dry chemical, sand, water spray or foam.
- **Large Fires:** Water spray, fog or foam.
- Move container from fire area if you can do it without risk.
- Cool containers that are exposed to flames with water from the side until well after fire is out.
- For massive fire in cargo area, use unmanned hose holder or monitor nozzles.
- If this is impossible, withdraw from area and let fire burn.
- **Magnesium Fires:** Use dry sand, Met-L-X powder or G-1 graphite powder; do not use water.

Spill or Leak

- No flares, smoking or flames in hazard area.
- Do not touch spilled material.
- **Small Dry Spills:** Shovel into dry containers and cover; move containers; then flush area with water.
- **Large Spills:** Wet down with water and dike for later disposal.

First Aid

- Move victim to fresh air; call emergency medical care.
- In case of contact with material, immediately flush skin or eyes with running water for at least 15 minutes.
- Remove and isolate contaminated clothing and shoes.

---

*At the time that shipments of monomethylamine nitrate solution was terminated in August 1974 this material was classified as a flammable solid.

DOT RESPONSE GUIDE 55
ACETONE CYANOHYDRIN - UN 1541
METHYL BROMIDE - UN 1062

Health Hazards

- Poison.
- May be fatal if inhaled, swallowed or absorbed through skin.
- Contact may cause burns to skin and eyes.
- Runoff from fire control or dilution water may cause pollution.

Fire or Explosion

- Some of these materials may burn but do not ignite readily.
- Cylinder may explode in heat of fire.

EMERGENCY ACTION

- Keep unnecessary people away.
- Isolate hazard area and deny entry.
- Wear positive pressure breathing apparatus and special protective clothing.
- FOR EMERGENCY ASSISTANCE CALL CHEMTREC (800) 424-9300.
- Also, in case of water pollution, call local authorities.

Fire

- **Small Fires:** Dry chemical, CO2, water spray or foam.
- **Large Fires:** Water spray, fog or foam.
- Move container from fire area if you can do it without risk.
- Fight fire from maximum distance.

Spill or Leak

- Do not touch spilled material.
- Stop leak if you can do it without risk.
- Use water spray to reduce vapors.
- **Small Spills:** Take up with the sand, or other noncombustible absorbent material, then flush area with water.
- **Large Spills:** Dike far ahead of spill for later disposal.

First Aid

- Move victim to fresh air; call emergency medical care.
- If not breathing, give artificial respiration.
- If breathing is difficult, give oxygen.
- In case of contact with material, immediately flush skin or eyes with running water for at least 15 minutes.
- Speed in removing material from skin is of extreme importance.
- Remove and isolate contaminated clothing and shoes.
- Keep victim quiet and maintain normal body temperature.
- Effects may be delayed, keep victim under observation.

DOT RESPONSE GUIDE 59
SODIUM HYDROSULFIDE SOLUTION-UN 2922

Health Hazards

- Poison.
- Poisonous if inhaled or swallowed.
- Skin contact poisonous.
- Contact may cause burns to skin and eyes.
- Fire may produce irritating or poisonous gases.
- Runoff from fire control or dilution water may cause pollution.

Fire or Explosion

- Some of these materials may burn but do not ignite readily.
- Some of these materials may ignite combustibles (wood, paper, oil, etc.).

EMERGENCY ACTION

- Keep unnecessary people away.
- Stay upwind; keep out of low areas.
- Isolate hazard area an deny entry.
- Wear positive pressure breathing apparatus and special protective clothing.
- FOR EMERGENCY ASSISTANCE CALL CHEMTREC (800) 424-9300.
- Also, in case of water pollution, call local authorities.

Fire

- Some of these materials may react violently with water.
- **Small Fires:** Dry chemical, CO2, water spray or foam.
- **Large Fires:** Water spray, fog or foam.
- Move container from fire area if you can do it without risk.
- Cool containers that are exposed to flames with water from the side until well after fire is out.

Spill or Leak

- Do not touch spilled material.
- Stop leak if you can do so without risk.
- Use water spray to reduce vapors.
- **Small Spills:** Take up with sand, or other noncombustible absorbent material, then flush area with water.
- **Large Spills:** Dike for later disposal and dilute with large amounts of water.

First Aid

- Move victim to fresh air; call emergency medical care.
- If not breathing, give artificial respiration.
- If breathing is difficult, give oxygen.
- In case of contact with material, immediately flush skin or eyes with running water for at least 15 minutes.
- Remove and isolate contaminated clothing and shoes.
- Keep victim quiet and maintain normal body temperature.
- Effects may be delayed, keep victim under observation.

DOT RESPONSE GUIDE 60
SODIUM HYDROXIDE SOLUTION - UN 1824

Health Hazards

- Contact may cause burns to skin and eyes.
- If inhaled, may be harmful.
- Fire may produce irritating or poisonous gases.
- Runoff from fire control or dilution water may cause pollution.

Fire or Explosion

- Some of these materials may burn but do not ignite readily.
- Explosive concentrations of gas may accumulate in tanks.
- Some of these materials may ignite combustibles (wood, paper, oil, etc.).

EMERGENCY ACTION

- Keep unnecessary people away.
- Stay upwind; keep out of low areas.
- Isolate hazard area and deny entry.
- Wear positive pressure breathing apparatus and full protective clothing.
- FOR EMERGENCY ASSISTANCE CALL CHEMTREC (800) 424-9300.
- Also, in case of water pollution, call local authorities.

Fire

- Some of these materials may react violently with water.
- **Small Fires:** Dry chemical, CO_2, water spray or foam.
- **Large Fires:** Water spray, fog or foam.
- Move container from fire area if you can do it without risk.
- Cool containers that are exposed to flames with water from the side until well after fire is out.

Spill or Leak

- Do not touch spilled material.
- Stop leak if you can do it without risk.
- **Small Spills:** Take up with sand, or other noncombustible absorbent material, then flush area with water.
- **Small Dry Spills:** Shovel into dry containers and cover; move containers; then flush area with water.
- **Large Spills:** Dike far ahead of spill for later disposal.

First Aid

- Move victim to fresh air; call emergency medical care.
- Remove and isolate contaminated clothing and shoes.
- In case of contact with material, immediately flush skin or eyes with running water for at least 15 minutes.
- Keep victim quiet and maintain normal body temperature.

DOT ISOLATION AND EVACUATION DISTANCES*

| | Small Spill or Leak | Large Spill | | |
| | | First | Then Evacuate in a Downwind Direction | |
Material	Initial Isolation (feet)	Isolate in All Directions (feet)	width miles	length miles
Acrylonitrile	30	60	0.1	0.2
Ammonia, Anhydrous	100	200	0.4	0.7
Chlorine	250	520	1.3	2.0
Ethylene Oxide	40	70	0.2	0.2
Hydrocyanic Acid	90	190	0.5	0.7
Methyl Bromide	50	90	0.2	0.3
Nitrogen Tetroxide	110	220	0.5	0.8

* These recommended distances to ISOLATE or EVACUATE people from spill areas are only for the initial phase of an accident involving volatile, hazardous liquids or gases shipped in bulk or multiple container loads. Continuing reassessment will be necessary since there may be a change in circumstances, such as a change in wind direction. Good judgment must be used in evacuation procedures to avoid placing people in greater danger.

If a hazardous materials cloud goes between several tall buildings or down a valley, the cloud may affect people much farther away than is specified in the table and the evacuation distances should be increased in the downwind direction. It is important to note at this point that the occupants of the upper floors of any tall buildings in the evacuation sector may be safer remaining where they are if the heating and air-handling equipment can be shut down so that the hazardous vapors or gases will not be circulated in the building. A short-term spill cloud also may be deflected or reflected by such a building and pass by it without affecting the occupants or the equipment within it.

If a fire begins to involve the spilled material, the poisonous effect of gases on the population may be reduced considerably as may the evacuation distances. On the other hand, if undamaged containers are involved in a fire, the potential fragmentation hazards would require isolation in all directions for one-half mile which may be more or less than the distance suggested in the table.

— APPENDIX H —
AAR-EMERGENCY HANDLING OF HAZARDOUS MATERIALS IN SURFACE TRANSPORTATION

ACETONE
FLAMMABLE LIQUID
STCC 4908105
UN 1090

Acetone is a clear, colorless liquid with a pleasant odor. It is used to make other chemicals, in paint and nail polish removers, as a solvent. It is quite volatile and has a flash point of 0 deg. F. It is lighter than water and soluble in water. Its vapors are heavier than air.

If Material On Fire or Involved in Fire
- Do not extinguish fire unless flow can be stopped
- Use water in flooding quantities as fog
- Solid streams of water may be ineffective
- Cool all affected containers with flooding quantities of water
- Apply water from as far a distance as possible
- Use 'alcohol' foam, carbon dioxide or dry chemical

If Material Not on Fire and Not Involved in Fire
- Keep sparks, flames, and other sources of ignition away
- Keep material out of water sources and sewers
- Build dikes to contain flow as necessary
- Attempt to stop leak if without hazard
- Use water spray to disperse vapors and dilute standing pools of liquid

Personnel Protection
- Avoid breathing vapors
- Keep upwind
- Wear boots, protective gloves, and safety glasses
- Do not handle broken packages without protective equipment
- Wash away any material which may have contacted the body with copious amounts of water or soap and water

Evacuation
- If fire becomes uncontrollable or container is exposed to direct flame - evacuate for a radius of 1500 feet
- If material leaking (not on fire), downwind evacuation must be considered

ACETONE CYANOHYDRIN
POISON B, COMBUSTIBLE
ENVIRONMENTALLY HAZARDOUS SUBSTANCE (RQ-10/4.54)
STCC 4921401
UN 1541

Acetone cyanohydrin is a colorless liquid. It has a flash point of 165 deg. F. It slowly dissociates to acetone, a flammable liquid, and hydrogen cyanide, a flammable poisonous gas, under normal storage and transportation conditions. , The rate of dissociation is increased by contact with alkalis and/or heat. It is lethal by inhalation and less readily by skin absorption. It is lighter than water and is soluble in water. Its vapors are heavier than air. Toxic oxides of nitrogen are produced during combustion of this material.

If Material on Fire or Involved in Fire
- Do not extinguish fire unless flow can be stopped
- Use water in flooding quantities as fog
- Solid streams of water may be ineffective
- Cool all affected containers with flooding quantities of water
- Apply water from as far a distance as possible
- Use "alcohol" foam, carbon dioxide or dry chemical

If Material Not on Fire and Not Involved in Fire
- Keep sparks, flames, and other sources of ignition away
- Keep material out of water sources and sewers
- Build dikes to contain flow as necessary
- Attempt to stop leak if without hazard
- Use water spray to disperse vapors and dilute standing pools of liquid

Personnel Protection
- Avoid breathing vapors
- Keep upwind
- Wear self-contained breathing apparatus
- Avoid bodily contact with the material
- Do not handle broken packages without protective equipment
- Wash away any material which may have contacted the body with copious amounts of water or soap and water

Evacuation
- If material leaking (not on fire), downwind evacuation must be considered

Environmental Considerations - Land Spill
- Dig a pit, pond, lagoon, holding area to contain liquid or solid material
- Dike surface flow using soil, sand bags, foamed polyurethane, or foamed concrete
- Absorb bulk liquid with fly ash or cement powder

Environmental Considerations - Water Spill
- Use natural barriers or oil spill control booms to limit spill motion
- Use surface active agent (e.g., detergent, soaps, alcohols) to compress and thicken spilled material
- If dissolved, apply activated carbon at ten times the spilled amount in region of 10 ppm or greater concentration
- Adjust pH to neutral (pH=7)
- Use mechanical dredges or lifts to remove immobilized masses of pollutants and precipitates

ACRYLONITRILE
FLAMMABLE LIQUID, POISONOUS POLYMERIZABLE
ENVIRONMENTALLY HAZARDOUS SUBSTANCE (RQ-100/45.4)
STCC 4906420
UN 1093

Acrylonitrile is a clear colorless liquid with a strong, pungent odor. It is used in insecticides and to make plastics, fibers and other chemicals. It has a flash point of 32 deg. F. It may polymerize if contaminated with strong bases or if the container is subject to heat, as in fire conditions. Prolonged exposure to the vapors or skin contact may result in death. It is lighter than water and is soluble in water. The vapors are heavier than air. Toxic oxides of nitrogen are produced during combustion of this material.

If Material on Fire or Involved in Fire

- Do not extinguish fire unless flow can be stopped
- Use water in flooding quantities as fog
- Solid streams of water may be ineffective
- Cool all affected containers with flooding quantities of water
- Apply water from as far a distance as possible
- Use "alcohol" foam, carbon dioxide or dry chemical

If Material Not on Fire or Not Involved in Fire

- Keep sparks, flames, and other sources of ignition away
- Keep material out of water sources and sewers
- Build dikes to contain flow as necessary
- Attempt to stop leak if without hazard
- Use water spray to disperse vapors and dilute standing pools of liquid

Personnel Protection

- Avoid breathing vapors
- Keep upwind
- Wear self-contained breathing apparatus
- Avoid bodily contact with the material
- Wear full protective clothing
- Do not handle broken packages without protective equipment
- Wash away any material which may have contacted the body with copious amounts of water or soap and water

Evacuation

- If fire becomes uncontrollable or container is exposed to direct flame – evacuate for a radius of 2500 feet
- If material is leaking (not on fire), downwind evacuation must be considered

Environmental Considerations - Land Spill

- Dig a pit, pond, lagoon, holding area to contain liquid or solid material
- Dike surface flow using soil, sand bags, foamed polyurethane, or foamed concrete
- Absorb bulk liquid with fly ash, cement powder, sawdust, or commercial sorbents
- Apply "universal" gelling agent to immobilize spill

ACRYLONITRILE (continued)
FLAMMABLE LIQUID, POISONOUS POLYMERIZABLE
ENVIRONMENTALLY HAZARDOUS SUBSTANCE (RQ-100/45.4)
STCC 4906420
UN 1093

Environmental Considerations - Water Spill

- Use natural barriers or oil spill control booms to limit spill motion
- Use surface active agent (e.g., detergent, soaps, alcohols) to compress and thicken spilled material
- Inject "universal" gelling agent to solidify encircled spill and increase effectiveness of booms
- Add calcium hypochlorite
- If dissolved, apply activated carbon at ten times the spilled amount in region of 10 ppm or greater concentration
- Use mechanical dredges or lifts to remove immobilized masses of pollutants and precipitates

Environmental Considerations - Air Spill

- Apply water spray or mist to knock down vapors
- Combustion products include corrosive or toxic vapors

ANHYDROUS AMMONIA
NONFLAMMABLE GAS, CORROSIVE
ENVIRONMENTALLY HAZARDOUS SUBSTANCE (RQ-100/45.4)
STCC 4904210
UN 1005

Anhydrous ammonia is a clear colc.less gas with a characteristic odor. It is used as a fertilizer, as a refrigerant, and in the manufacture of other chemicals. Although it is classed as a nonflammable gas, it will burn within certain vapor concentration limits, and it will increase fire hazard in the presence of oil or other combustible materials. Its "combustibility" is definitely not a common problem in the event of leakage. It is shipped as a liquid under pressure. Contact with the liquid can cause frostbite. It is soluble in water forming a corrosive liquid. Although ammonia is lighter than air, the vapors from a leak initially hug the ground. It weighs 5.7 pounds per gallon.

If Material Involved in Fire

- Extinquish fire using agent suitable for type of surrounding fire (Material itself does not burn or burns with difficulty.)
- Cool all affected containers with flooding quantities of water
- Apply water from as far a distance as possible
- Use water spray to absorb vapors

If Material Not Involved in Fire

- Keep material out of water sources and sewers
- Attempt to stop leak if without hazard
- Use water spray to knock-down vapors

Personnel Protection

- Avoid breathing vapors
- Keep upwind
- Wear self-contained breathing apparatus
- Avoid bodily contact with the material
- Wear boots, protective gloves, and safety glasses
- Do not handle broken packages without protective equipment
- Wash away material which may have contacted the body with copious amounts of water or soap and water
- If contact with the material anticipated, wear full protective clothing

Evacuation

- If material leaking (not on fire), downwind evacuation must be considered

BUTADIENE, INHIBITED (Butadiene from Petroleum)
FLAMMABLE GAS
STCC 4905704
UN 1010

Butadiene, inhibited is a colorless gas with an aromatic odor. It is shipped as a liquefied gas under its vapor pressure. Contact with the liquid can cause frostbite. It must be shipped inhibited as butadiene is liable to polymerization. If polymerization were to take place in a cylinder or tank car, the cylinder or tank car may violently rupture. It is easily ignited. Its vapor is heavier than air and a flame can flash back to the source of leak very easily. It can asphyxiate by the displacement of air. Under fire conditions the cylinders or tank cars may violently rupture and rocket.

If Material on Fire or Involved in Fire
- Do not extinguish fire unless flow can be stopped
- Use water in flooding quantities as fog
- Cool all affected containers with flooding quantities of water
- Apply water from as far a distance as possible

If Material Not on Fire and Not Involved in Fire
- Keep sparks, flames, and other sources of ignition away
- Keep material out of water sources and sewers
- Attempt to stop leak if without hazard
- Use water spray to knock-down vapors

Personnel Protection
- Avoid breathing vapors
- Keep upwind
- Wear protective gloves and safety glasses
- Do not handle broken packages without protective equipment
- Approach fire with caution

Evacuation
- If fire becomes uncontrollable or container is exposed to direct flame - evacuate for a radius of 2500 feet
- If material leaking (not on fire), downwind evacuation must be considered

CHLORINE
NONFLAMMABLE GAS, POISONOUS
ENVIRONMENTALLY HAZARDOUS SUBSTANCE (RQ-10/4.54)
STCC 4904120
UN 1017

Chlorine is a greenish yellow gas with a pungent suffocating odor. It is used to purify water, bleach woodpulp, and to make other chemicals. It is toxic by inhalation. It is soluble in water. It reacts explosively or forms explosive compounds with many common chemicals. It is normally shipped as a liquid in cylinders or tank cars. Contact with liquid should be avoided as it can cause frostbite; the liquid does readily vaporize to gas. The vapors are much heavier than air and tend to settle in low areas. It weighs 13.0 pounds per gallon.

If Material Involved in Fire

- Extinguish fire using agent suitable for type of surrounding fire (Material itself does not burn or burns with difficulty.)
- Cool all affected containers with flooding quantities of water
- Apply water from as far a distance as possible
- Use water spray to absorb vapors

If Material Not Involved in Fire

- Keep material out of water sources and sewers
- Attempt to stop leak if without hazard
- Use water spray to knock-down vapors

Personnel Protection

- Avoid breathing vapors
- Keep upwind
- Wear self-contained breathing apparatus
- Avoid bodily contact with the material
- Wear full protective clothing
- Do not handle broken packages without protective equipment
- Wash away material which may have contacted the body with copious amounts of water or soap and water

Evacuation

- If material leaking (not on fire), evacuate for a radius of 2500 feet

ETHYL ACRYLATE, INHIBITED
FLAMMABLE LIQUID, POLYMERIZABLE
STCC 4907215
UN 1917

Ethyl acrylate is a clear colorless liquid with an acrid odor. It is used to make paints and plastics. It has a flash point of 60 deg. F. If the material is subjected to heat for prolonged periods or becomes contaminated it is subject to polymerization with evolution of heat. If the polymerization takes place inside a container the container may violently rupture. The material is lighter than water and slightly soluble in water. The vapors are heavier than air.

If Material on Fire or Involved in Fire

- Do not extinguish fire unless flow can be stopped
- Use water in flooding quantities as fog
- Solid streams of water may spread fire
- Cool all affected containers with flooding quantities of water
- Apply water from as far a distance as possible
- Use "alcohol" foam, carbon dioxide or dry chemical

If Material Not on Fire and Not Involved in Fire

- Keep sparks, flames and other sources of ignition away
- Keep material out of water sources and sewers
- Build dikes to contain flow as necessary
- Attempt to stop leak if without hazard
- Use water spray to disperse vapors and dilute standing pools of liquid

Personnel Protection

- Avoid breathing vapors
- Keep upwind
- Wear boots, protective gloves, and safety glasses
- Do not handle broken packages without protective equipment
- Wash away any material which may have contacted the body with copious amounts of water or soap and water

Evacuation

- If fire becomes uncontrollable or container is exposed to direct flame - evacuate for a radius fo 2500 feet
- If material leaking (not on fire), downwind evacuation must be considered

ETHYLENE OXIDE
FLAMMABLE LIQUID, CORROSIVE
THERMALLY UNSTABLE
STCC 4906610
UN 1040

Ethylene oxide is a clear, colorless, volatile liquid with an ethereal odor. It has a flash point of less than 0 deg. F, and is flammable over a wide vapor-air concentration range. The material has to be diluted on the order of 24 to 1 with water before the liquid loses its flammability. If contaminated it may polymerize violently with evolution of heat and rupture of its container. The vapors may burn inside a container. The vapors are irritating to the eyes, skin, and respiratory system. Prolonged contact with the skin may result in delayed burns. It is lighter than water and soluble in water. The vapors are heavier than air.

If Material on Fire of Involved in Fire

- Do not extinguish fire unless flow can be stopped
- Use water in flooding quantities as fog
- Solid streams of water may be ineffective
- Cool all affected containers with flooding quantities of water
- Apply water from as far a distance as possible
- Use "alcohol" foam, carbon dioxide or dry chemical

If Material Not On Fire and Not Involved in Fire

- Keep sparks, flames, and other sources of ignition away
- Keep material out of water sources and sewers
- Build dikes to contain flow as necessary
- Attempt to stop leak if without hazard
- Use water spray to disperse vapors and dilute standing pools of liquid

Personnel Protection

- Avoid breathing vapors
- Keep upwind
- Wear self-contained breathing apparatus
- Avoid bodily contact with the material
- Wear full protective clothing
- Do not handle broken packages without protective equipment
- Wash away material which may have contacted the body with copious amounts of water or soap and water

Evacuation

- If fire is prolonged and material is confined in the container - evacuate for a radius of 5000 feet
- If fire becomes uncontrollable or container is exposed to direct flame - evacuate for a radius of 5000 feet

HYDRAZINE, ANHYDROUS
FLAMMABLE LIQUID, POISONOUS, CORROSIVE
THERMALLY UNSTABLE
STCC 4906225
UN 2029

Hydrazine, anhydrous is a colorless, fuming oily liquid with an ammonia like odor. It has a flash point of 99 deg. F. It can ignite spontaneously on contact with oxidizers, and may ignite spontaneously on contact with porous materials such as earth, wood and cloth. It is toxic by inhalation and by skin absorption. It is corrosive to tissue. Toxic oxides of nitrogen are produced during combustion of this material.

If Material on Fire or Involved in Fire
- Do not extinguish fire unless flow can be stopped
- Use water in flooding quantities as fog
- Solid streams of water may be ineffective
- Cool all affected containers with flooding quantities of water
- Apply water from as far a distance as possible
- Use "alcohol" foam, carbon dioxide or dry chemical

If Material Not On Fire and Not Involved in Fire
- Keep sparks, flames, and other sources of ignition away
- Keep material out of water sources and sewers
- Build dikes to contain flow as necessary
- Attempt to stop leak if without hazard
- Use water spray to disperse vapors and dilute standing pools of liquid

Personnel Protection
- Avoid breathing vapors
- Keep upwind
- Wear self-contained breathing apparatus
- Avoid bodily contact with the material
- Wear full protective clothing
- Do not handle broken packages without protective equipment
- Wash away material which may have contacted the body with copious amounts of water or soap and water

Evcuation
- If fire becomes uncontrollable or container is exposed to direct flame – evacuate for a radius of 2500 feet
- If material leaking (not on fire), downwind evacuation must be considered

HYDROCYANIC ACID LIQUEFIED
POISON A, FLAMMABLE
ENVIRONMENTALLY HAZARDOUS SUBSTANCE (RQ-10/4.54)
STCC 4920125
NA 1051

Hydrocyanic acid liquefied is a colorless gas with a faint aromatic odor. It is shipped as a liquefied gas under its vapor pressure and it must be stabilized to avoid polymerization; it is easily ignited. The vapor is just lighter than air but a flame can travel back to the source of leak very easily. It can polymerize from contact with alkali. Lethal amounts may be absorbed through the skin as well as by inhalation. It may be shipped in cylinders or tank cars. Prolonged exposure to fire or heat may cause the cylinder or tank car to violently rupture and rocket. It weighs 5.7 pounds per gallon.

If Material on Fire or Involved in Fire

- Do not extinguish fire unless flow can be stopped
- Use water in flooding quantities as fog
- Cool affected containers with flooding quantities of water
- Apply water from as far a distance as possible
- Solid streams of water may be ineffective
- Use "alcohol" foam, carbon dioxide or dry chemical

If Material Not on Fire and Not Involved in Fire

- Keep sparks, flames, and other sources of ignition away
- Keep material out of water sources and sewers
- Build dikes to contain flow as necessary
- Attempt to stop leak if without hazard
- Use water spray to knock-down vapors

Personnel Protection

- Avoid breathing vapors
- Keep upwind
- Wear self-contained breathing apparatus
- Avoid bodily contact with the material
- Wear full protective clothing
- Do not handle broken packages without protective equipment
- Wash away any material which may have contacted the body with copious amounts of water or soap and water

Evacuation

- If fire becomes uncontrollable or container is exposed to direct flame - evacuate for a radius of 2500 feet
- If material leaking (not on fire), evacuate for a radius of 2500 feet

Environmental Considerations - Land Spill

- Use natural barriers or oil spill control booms to limit spill motion
- Dig a pit, pond, lagoon, holding area to contain liquid or solid material
- Dike surface flow using soil, sand bags, foamed polyurethane, or foamed concrete
- Absorb bulk liquid with fly ash or cement powder

Environmental Considerations - Water Spill

- Neutralize with agricultural lime (slaked lime), crushed limestone, or sodium bicarbonate

HYDROCYANIC ACID SOLUTION (continued)
POISON A, FLAMMABLE
ENVIRONMENTALLY HAZARDOUS SUBSTANCE (RQ-10/4.54)
STCC 4920125
NA 1051

Environmental Considerations - Air Spill

- Apply water spray or mist to knock-down vapors
- Vapor knock-down water is corrosive or toxic and should be diked for containment

HYDROGEN
FLAMMABLE GAS
STCC 4905746
UN 1049

Hydrogen is a colorless, odorless gas. It is easily ignited. It is lighter than air, but a flame can flash back to the source of the leak very easily. It is flammabe over a wide range of vapor air concentrations. It may be shipped in cylinders and special tank cars. Under fire conditions the cylinders may violently rupture and rocket.

If Material on Fire or Involved in Fire

- Do not extinguish fire unless flow can be stopped
- Use water in flooding quantities
- Apply water from as far a distance as possible

If Material Not on Fire and Not Involved in Fire

- Keep sparks, flames, and other sources of ignition away
- Keep material out of water sources and sewers
- Attempt to stop leak if without hazard
- Use water spray to knock-down vapors

Personnel Protection

- Avoid breathing vapors
- Keep upwind
- Wear protective gloves and safety glasses
- Do not handle broken packages without protective equipment
- Approach fire with caution

Evacuation

- If fire becomes uncontrollable or container is exposed to direct flame — evacuate for a radius of 1500 feet
- If material leaking (not on fire), downwind evacuation must be considered

ISOBUTANE
FLAMMABLE GAS
STCC 4905747
UN 1075

Isobutane is a colorless gas with a faint petroleum-like odor. It is shipped as a liquefied gas under its vapor pressure. Contact with the liquid can cause frostbite. It is easily ignited. Its vapor is heavier than air and a flame can flash back to the source of leak very easily. The leak can either be a liquid or vapor leak. It can asphyxiate by the displacement of air. Under fire conditions the cylinders or tank car may violently rupture and rocket.

If Material on Fire of Involved in Fire

- Do not extinguish fire unless flow can be stopped
- Use water in flooding quantities as fog
- Cool all affected containers with flooding quantities of water
- Apply water from as far a distance as possible

If Material Not on Fire and Not Involved in Fire

- Keep sparks, flames, and other sources of ignition away
- Keep material out of water sources and sewers
- Attempt to stop leak if without hazard
- Use water spray to knock down vapors

Personnel Protection

- Avoid breathing vapors
- Keep upwind
- Wear protective gloves and safety glasses
- Do not handle broken packages without protective equipment
- Approach fire with caution

Evacuation

- If fire becomes uncontrollable or container is exposed to direct flame – evacuate for a radius of 2500 feet
- If material leaking (not on fire), downwind evacuation must be considered

```
METHYL ALCOHOL
FLAMMABLE LIQUID
STCC 4909230
UN 1230
```

Methyl alcohol is a clear, colorless liquid. It is used to make other chemicals, to remove water from automotive and aviation fuels, as an antifreeze, and as a solvent for various paints and plastics. It has a flash point of 52 deg. F. It is lighter than water and soluble in water. Its vapors are heavier than air.

If Material on Fire or Involved in Fire

- Do not extinguish fire unless flow can be stopped
- Use water in flooding quantities as fog
- Solid streams of water may be ineffective
- Cool all affected containers with flooding quantities of water
- Apply water from as far a distance as possible
- Use "alcohol" foam, carbon dioxide or dry chemical

If Material Not on Fire and Not Involved in Fire

- Keep sparks, flames, and other sources of ignition away
- Keep material out of water sources and sewers
- Build dikes to contain flow as necessary
- Attempt to stop leak if without hazard
- Use water spray to disperse vapors and dilute standing pools of liquid

Personnel Protection

- Avoid breathing vapors
- Keep upwind
- Wear boots, protective gloves, and safety glasses
- Do not handle broken packages without protective equipment
- Wash away any material which may have contacted the body with copious amount of water or soap and water

METHYL BROMIDE, LIQUID (INCLUDING
UP TO 2% CHLOROPICRIN)
POISON B
STCC 4921440
UN 1062

Methyl bromide is colorless liquid with a chloroform-like odor. Under most circumstances it is noncombustible. It is very slightly soluble in water. It is toxic by inhalation. Prolonged or repeated skin contact can cause severe burns and possible absorption of toxic quantities of the material.

If Material Involved in Fire

- Extinguished fire using agent suitable for type of surrounding fire (Material itself does not burn or burns with difficulty.)
- Use water in flooding quantities as fog
- Cool all affected containers with flooding quantities of water
- Use foam, carbon dioxide or dry chemical

If Material Not Involved in Fire

- Keep material out of water sources and sewers
- Build dikes to contain flow as necessary
- Attempt to stop leak if without hazard
- Use water spray to knock down vapors

Personnel Protection

- Avoid breathing vapors
- Keep upwind
- Wear self-contained breathing apparatus
- Avoid bodily contact with the material
- Wear full protective clothing
- Do not handle broken packages without protective equipment
- Wash away any material which may have contacted the body with copious amounts of water or soap and water

Evacuation

- If material leaking (not on fire), downwind evacuation must be considered

METHYL HYDRAZINE
FLAMMABLE LIQUID, POISONOUS, CORROSIVE
THERMALLY UNSTABLE
STCC 4906230
UN 1244

Methyl hydrazine is a colorless liquid with an ammonia like odor. It has a flash point of 17 deg. F. It is flammable over a wide range of vapor air concentrations. It may ignite spontaneously in contact with porous materials such as earth, wood, cloth, etc., and with oxidizing materials. It is toxic and the vapors attack the eyes and respiratory system. It is also corrosive to the skin. It is lighter than water and slightly soluble in water. The vapors are heavier than air. Prolonged exposure of the containers of the material to fire or heat may result in spontaneous decomposition of the material and violent rupture of the container. Toxic oxides of nitrogen are produced during combustion of this material.

If Material on Fire or Involved in Fire

- Do not extinguish fire unless flow can be stopped
- Use water in flooding quantities as fog
- Solid streams of water may be ineffective
- Cool all affected containers with flooding quantities of water
- Apply water from as far a distance as possible
- Use "alcohol" foam, carbon dioxide or dry chemical

If Material Not on Fire and Not Involved in Fire

- Keep sparks, flames, and other sources of ignition away
- Keep material out of water sources and sewers
- Build dikes to contain flow as necessary
- Attempt to stop leak if without hazard
- Use water spray to disperse vapors and dilute standing pools of liquid

Personnel Protection

- Avoid breathing vapors
- Keep upwind
- Wear self-contained breathing apparatus
- Avoid bodily contact with the material
- Wear full protective clothing
- Do not handle broken packages without protective equipment
- Wash away material which may have contacted the body with copious amounts of water or soap and water

Evacuation

- If fire becomes uncontrollable or container is exposed to direct flame - evacuate for a radius of 5000 feet
- If material leaking (not on fire), downwind evacuation must be considered

NITROGEN TETROXIDE, LIQUID
POISON A, OXIDIZING
STCC 4920360
NA 1067

Nitrogen tetroxide liquid is a reddish-brown colored gas which becomes a yellowish-brown liquid on cooling or compressing. It is shipped as a liquefied gas under its vapor pressure. Its vapor is heavier than air. It dissolves in water forming nitric acid, a corrosive material. It is noncombustible, but will accelerate the burning of combustible materials. It is toxic by inhalation and by skin absorption. The cylinders and "ton container" tank cars may not be equipped with a safety relief device. Prolonged exposure to fire or heat can cause the violent rupturing and rocketing of the cylinders and "ton container" tank cars, and the possible violent rupturing and rocketing of the single unit tank car.

If Material Involved in Fire

- Do not use carbon dioxide
- Extinguish fire using agent suitable for type of surrounding fire (Material itself does not burn or burns with difficulty.)
- Use water in flooding quantities as fog
- Cool all affected containers with flooding quantities of water
- Apply water from as far a distance as possible
- Use "alcohol" foam, carbon dioxide or dry chemical

Personnel Protection

- Avoid breathing vapors
- Keep upwind
- Wear self-contained breathing apparatus
- Avoid bodily contact with the material
- Wear full protective clothing
- Do not handle broken packages without protective equipment
- Wash away material which may have contacted the body with copious amounts of water or soap and water

Evacuation

- If material leaking (not on fire) evacuate for a radius of 2500 feet

OXYGEN, PRESSURIZED LIQUID
NONFLAMMABLE GAS, OXIDIZING
STCC 4904360
UN 1073

Oxygen, pressurized liquid is an odorless, colorless to light blue liquid. It is noncombustible but it will actively support the burning of combustible material. Contact with liquid make many normally hard to burn materials readily combustible. When the liquid contacts combustible or oxidizable materials, an explosion may result. Contact with the liquid will cause frostbite. Leaked or spilled material will readily vaporize to the gaseous state. It may only be shipped in cylinders.

If Material Involved in Fire

- Dangerously explosive
- Cool all affected containers with flooding quantites of water
- Do not use water on material itself
- Apply water from as far a distance as possible

If Material Not Involved in Fire

- Keep sparks, flames, and other sources of ignition away
- Attempt to stop leak if without hazard
- Do not use water on material itself

Personnel Protection

- Wear boots, protective gloves, and safety glasses
- Do not handle broken packages without protective equipment
- Approach fire with caution

Evacuation

- If fire becomes uncontrollable or container is exposed to direct flame — evacuate for a radius of 1500 feet

```
PROPANE
FLAMMABLE GAS
STCC 4905781
UN 1075
```

Propane is a colorless gas with a faint petroleum like odor. It is shipped as a liquefied gas under its vapor pressure. For transportation it may be stenched. Contact with the liquid can cause frostbite. It is easily ignited. Its vapors are heavier than air and a flame can flash back to the source of leak very easily. This leak can be either a liquid or vapor leak. It can asphyxiate by the displacement of air. Under fire conditions the cylinders or tank cars may violently rupture and rocket.

If Material on Fire or Involved in Fire
- Do not extinguish fire unless flow can be stopped
- Use water in flooding quantites as fog
- Cool all affected containers with flooding quantites of water
- Apply water from as far a distance as possible

If Material Not On Fire and Not Involved in Fire
- Keep sparks, flames, and other sources of ignition away
- Keep material out of water sources and sewers
- Attempt to stop leak if without hazard
- Use water spray to knock-down vapors

Personnel Protection
- Avoid breathing vapors
- Keep upwind
- Wear protective gloves and safety glasses
- Do not handle broken packages without protective equipment
- Approach fire with caution

Evacuation
- If fire becomes uncontrollable or container is exposed to direct flame - evacuate for a radius of 2500 feet
- If material leaking (not on fire), downwind evacuation must be considered

PROPYLENE
FLAMMABLE GAS
STCC 4905782
UN 1075

Propylene is a colorless gas with a faint petroleum like odor. It is used to make other chemicals. It is shipped as a liquefied gas under its own vapor pressure. For transportation it may be stenched. Contact with the liquid can cause frostbite. It is easily ignited. Its vapors are heavier than air, and a flame can flash back to the source of leak very easily. This leak can be either a liquid or vapor leak. It can asphyxiate by the displacement of air. Under fire conditions the cylinders or tank cars may violently rupture and rocket.

If Material on Fire or Involved in Fire

- Do not extinguish fire unless flow can be stopped
- Use water in flooding quantities as fog
- Cool all affected containers with flooding quantities of water
- Apply water from as far a distance as possible

If Material Not on Fire and Not Involved in Fire

- Keep sparks, flames, and other sources of ignition away
- Keep material out of water sources and sewers
- Attempt to stop leak if without hazard
- Use water spray to knock-down vapors

Personnel Protection

- Avoid breathing vapors
- Keep upwind
- Wear protective gloves and goggles
- Do not handle broken packages without protective equipment
- Approach fire with caution

Evacuation

- If fire becomes uncontrollable or container is exposed to direct flame - evacuate for a radius of 2,500 feet
- If material leaking (not on fire), downwind evacuation must be considered

SODIUM HYDROSULFIDE SOLUTION
CORROSIVE MATERIAL, BASIC
ENVIRONMENTALLY HAZARDOUS SUBSTANCE (RQ-5000/2270)
STCC 4935268
NA 2922

Sodium hydrosulfide in solution is a colorless to light yellow colored liquid. It is used in paper pulping, manufacturing dyes and dehairing hides. It is soluble in water. It is corrosive to metals and tissue.

If Material on Fire of Involved in Fire

- Extinguish fire using agent suitable for type of surrounding fire (Material itself does not burn or burns with difficulty)
- Use water in flooding quantities as fog
- Apply water from as far a distance as possible

If Material Not on Fire and Not Involved in Fire

- Keep material out of water sources and sewers
- Build dikes to contain flow as necessary

Personnel Protection

- Avoid breathing vapors or dusts
- Avoid bodily contact with the material
- Wear boots, protective gloves, and goggles
- Do not handle broken packages without protective equipment
- Wash away any material which may have contacted the body with copious amounts of water or soap and water
- If contact with the material anticipated, wear full protective clothing

Environmental Considerations - Land Spill

- Dig a pit, pond, lagoon, holding area to contain liquid or solid material
- Dike surface flow using soil, sand bags, foamed polyurethane, or foamed concrete
- Absorb bulk liquid with fly ash or cement powder

Environmental Considerations - Water Spill

- Add soda ash
- Allow to aerate
- Use mechanical dredges or lifts to remove immobilized masses of pollutants and precipitates

Environmental Considerations - Air Spill

- Apply water spray or mist to knock down vapors
- Evolves flammable hydrogen sulfide gas on contact with acids

SODIUM HYDROXIDE LIQUID
CORROSIVE MATERIAL, BASIC
ENVIRONMENTALLY HAZARDOUS SUBSTANCE (RQ-1000/454)
STCC 4935240
UN 1824

Sodium hydroxide liquid is the water solution of sodium hydroxide. It is used in chemical manufacturing, petroleum refining, paper making, cleaning compounds, and for many other uses. The concentrated solutions will dissolve in additional water with the evolution of heat. It is corrosive to metals and tissue.

If Material Involved in Fire

- Extinguish fire using agent suitable for type of surrounding fire (Material itself does not burn or burns with difficulty)
- Use water in flooding quantities as fog
- Apply water from as far a distance as possible

If Material Not Involved in Fire

- Keep material out of water sources and sewers
- Build dikes to contain flow as necessary

Personnel Protection

- Avoid breathing vapors or dusts
- Avoid bodily contact with the material
- Wear boots, protective gloves and safety glass
- Do not handle broken packages without protective equipment
- Wash away any material which may have contacted the body with copious amounts of water or soap and water
- If contact with the material anticipated, wear full protective clothing

Environmental Considerations - Land Spill

- Dig a pit, pond, lagoon, holding area to contain liquid or solid material
- Dike surface flow using soil, sand bags, foamed polyurethane, or foamed concrete
- Absorb bulk liquid with fly ash or cement powder
- Neutralize with vinegar or other dilute acid

Environmental Considerations - Water Spill

- Neutralize with dilute acid or removable strong acid

Environmental Considerations - Air Spill

- Apply water spray or mist to knock down vapors

```
STYRENE MONOMER INHIBITED
FLAMMABLE LIQUID, POLYMERIZABLE
ENVIRONMENTALLY HAZARDOUS SUBSTANCE (RQ-1000/454)
STCC 4907265
UN 2055
```

Styrene monomer inhibited is a clear colorless liquid with an aromatic odor. It is used to make plastics, paints, and synthetic rubber, and to make other chemicals. It has a flash point of 90 deg. F. Its vapors are irritating to the eyes and mucous membranes. If it becomes contaminated or is sujected to heat, it may polymerize. If the polymerization takes place inside a container, the container is subject to violent rupture. It is lighter than water and insoluble in water. Its vapors are heavier than air.

If Material on Fire or Involved in Fire

- Do not extinguish fire unless flow can be stopped
- Use water in flooding quantities as fog
- Solid streams of water may spread fire
- Cool all affected containers with flooding quantities of water
- Apply water from as far a distance as possible
- Use "alcohol" foam, carbon dioxide or dry chemical

If Material Not on Fire and Not Involved in Fire

- Keep sparks, flames, and other sources of ignition away
- Keep material out of water sources and sewers
- Build dikes to contain flow as necessary
- Attempt to stop leak if without hazard
- Use water spray to knock down vapors

Personnel Protection

- Avoid breathing vapors
- Keep upwind
- Wear boots, protective gloves and safety glasses
- Do not handle broken packages without protective equipment
- Wash away any material which may have contacted the body with copious amounts of water or soap and water

Evacuation

- If fire becomes uncontrollable or container is exposed to direct flame - evacuate for a radius of 2500 feet
- If material leaking (not on fire), downwind evacuation must be considered

Environmental Considerations - Land Spill

- Dig a pit, pond, lagoon, holding area to contain liquid or solid material
- Dike surface flow using soil, sand bags, foamed polyurethane, or foamed concrete
- Absorb bulk liquid with fly ash, cement powder, sawdust, or commercial sorbents
- Apply "universal" gelling agent to immobilize spill
- Apply fluorocarbon-water foam to diminish vapor and fire hazard

Environmental Considerations - Water Spill

- Use natural barriers or oil spill control booms to limit spill motion
- Use surface active agent (e.g., detergent, soaps, alcohols) to compress and thicken spilled material

STYRENE MONOMER INHIBITED (continued)
FLAMMABLE LIQUID, POLYMERIZABLE
ENVIRONMENTALLY HAZARDOUS SUBSTANCE (RQ-1000/454)
STCC 4907265
UN 2055

- Inject "universal" gelling agent to solidify encircled spill and increase effectiveness of booms
- If dissolved, apply activated carbon at ten times the spilled amount in region of 10 ppm or greater concentration
- Remove trapped material with suction hoses
- Use mechanical dredges or lifts to remove immobilized masses of pollutants and precipitates

Environmental Considerations - Air Spill
- Apply water spray or mist to knock down vapors

TOLUENE
FLAMMABLE LIQUID
ENVIRONMENTALLY HAZARDOUS SUBSTANCE (RQ-1000/454)
STCC 4909305
UN 1294

Toluene is a clear colorless liquid with a characteristic aromatic odor. It is
used in aviation and automotive fuels, as a solvent for many materials, and to make
other chemicals. It has a flash point of 40 deg. F. It is lighter than water and
insoluble in water. Its vapors are heavier than air.

If Material on Fire or Involved in Fire

- Do not extinguish fire unless flow can be stopped
- Use water in flooding quantities as fog
- Solid streams of water may spread fire
- Cool all affected containers with flooding quantities of water
- Apply water from as far a distance as possible
- Use "alcohol" foam, carbon dioxide or dry chemical

If Material Not on Fire and Not Involved in Fire

- Keep sparks, flames, and other sources of ignition away
- Keep material out of water sources and sewers
- Build dikes to contain flow as necessary
- Attempt to stop leak if without hazard
- Use water spray to knock-down vapors

Personnel Protection

- Avoid breathing vapors
- Keep upwind
- Wear boots, protective gloves, and safety glasses
- Do not handle broken packages without protective equipment
- Wash away any material which may have contacted the body with copious amounts of water or soap and water

Environmental Considerations - Land Spill

- Dig a pit, pond, lagoon, holding area to contain liquid or solid material
- Dike surface flow using soil, sand bags, foamed polyurethane, or foamed concrete
- Absorb bulk liquid with fly ash, cement powder, sawdust, or commercial sorbents
- Apply "universal" gelling agent to immobilize spill
- Apply fluorocarbon-water foam to diminish vapor and fire hazard

Environmental Considerations - Water Spill

- Use natural barriers or oil spill control booms to limit spill motion
- Use surface active agent (e.g., detergent, soaps, alcohols) to compress and thicken spilled material
- Inject "universal" gelling agent to solidify encircled spill and increase effectiveness of booms
- If dissolved, apply activated carbon at ten times the spilled amount in region of 10 ppm or greater concentration
- Remove trapped material with suction hoses
- Use mechanical dredges or lifts to remove immobilized masses of pollutants and precipitates

Environmental Consideration - Air Spill

- Apply water spray or mist to knock-down vapors

VINYL ACETATE
FLAMMABLE LIQUID, POLYMERIZABLE
ENVIRONMENTALLY HAZARDOUS SUBSTANCE (RQ-1000/454)
STCC 4907270
UN 1301

Vinyl acetate is a clear colorless liquid. It is used to make adhesives, paints and plastics. It has a flash point of 18 deg. F. Its vapors are irritating to the eyes and respiratory system. If it is subjected to heat or becomes contaminated it is subject to polymerization. If the polymerization takes place inside a container, the container is subject to violent rupture. It is lighter than water and slightly soluble in water. Its vapors are heavier than air.

If Material on Fire or Involved in Fire

- Do not extinguish fire unless flow can be stopped
- Use water in flooding quantities as fog
- Solid streams of water may spread fire
- Cool all affected containers with flooding quantities of water
- Apply water from as far a distance as possible
- Use "alcohol" foam, carbon dioxide or dry chemical

If Material Not on Fire and Not Involved in Fire

- Keep sparks, flames, and other sources of ignition away
- Keep material out of water sources and sewers
- Build dikes to contain flow as necessary
- Attempt to stop leak if without hazard
- Use water spray to disperse vapors and dilute standing pools of liquid

Personnel Protection

- Avoid breathing vapors
- Keep upwind
- Wear boots, protective gloves, and safety glasses
- Do not handle broken packages without protective equipment
- Wash away any material which may have contacted the body with copious amounts of water or soap and water

Evacuation

- If fire becomes uncontrollable or container is exposed to direct flame - evacuate for a radius of 2500 feet
- If material leaking (not on fire), downwind evacuation must be considered

Environmental Considerations - Land Spill

- Dig a pit, pond, lagoon, holding area to contain liquid or solid material
- Dike surface flow using soil, sand bags, foamed polyurethane, or foamed concrete
- Absorb bulk liquid with fly ash, cement powder, sawdust, or commercial sorbents
- Apply "universal" gelling agent to immobilize spill
- Apply fluorocarbon-water foam to diminish vapor and fire hazard

Environmental Considerations - Water Spill

- Use natural barriers or oil spill control booms to limit spill motion
- Use surface active agent (e.g., detergent, soaps, alcohols) to compress and thicken spilled material

VINYL ACETATE (continued)
FLAMMABLE LIQUID, POLYMERIZABLE
ENVIRONMENTALLY HAZARDOUS SUBSTANCE (RQ-1000/454)
STCC 4907270
UN 1301

- Inject "universal" gelling agent to solidify encircled spill and increase effectiveness of booms
- If dissolved, apply activated carbon at ten times the spilled amount in region of 10 ppm or greater concentration
- Remove trapped material with suction hoses
- Use mechanical dredges or lifts to remove immobilized masses of pollutants and precipitates

Environmental Considerations - Air Spill

- Apply water spray or mist to knock-down vapors

VINYL CHLORIDE
FLAMMABLE GAS
STCC 4905792
UN 1086

Vinyl chloride is a colorless gas with a sweet odor. It is shipped as a liquefied gas under its vapor pressure. Contact with the liquid can cause frostbite. It is easily ignited. Its vapors are heavier than air and a flame can flash back to the source of leak very easily. This leak may be either a liquid or vapor leak. It can asphyxiate by the displacement of air. Under fire conditions the cylinders or tank cars may violently rupture and rocket. Prolonged exposure of the cylinders or tank cars to heat or fire may cause the material to polymerize with possible container rupture. This material is thought to be a cancer suspect agent on long term exposure to low concentrations. However, this effect has not been demonstrated for single exposures to high concentrations of the material.

If Material on Fire of Involved in Fire
- Do not extinguish fire unless flow can be stopped
- Use water in flooding quantites as fog
- Cool all affected containers with flooding quantites of water
- Apply water from as far a distance as possible

If Material Not On Fire and Not Involved in Fire
- Keep sparks, flames, and other sources of ignition away
- Keep material out of water sources and sewers
- Attempt to stop leak if without hazard
- Use water spray to knock-down vapors

Personnel Protection
- Avoid breathing vapors
- Keep upwind
- Wear self-contained breathing apparatus
- Wear protective gloves and safety glasses
- Do not handle broken packages without protective equipment
- Approach fire with caution

Evacuation
- If fire becomes uncontrollable or container is exposed to direct flame - evacuate for a radius of 2500 feet
- If material leaking (not on fire), downwind evacuation must be considered

— APPENDIX I —

EPA-MANUAL FOR THE CONTROL OF HAZARDOUS SPILLS: VOLUME 1

TABLE I-1. SPILLS ON LAND

Type	Application or Construction Method	Use	Advantages	Disadvantages
Dikes Earthen	Create with bulldozer or earth-moving equipment to compact earth (height depends on earth type)	Flat or sloped surface	1. Material on site 2. Construct with common equipment 3. Construct quickly	1. Natural permeability of soil 2. Seepage through ground 3. Surface composition of soil not suitable in all cases
Foamed Poly-urethane	Use trained personnel to construct	Hard, dry surfaces	1. Hold up to several feet of water (3)	1. Leaks on wet ground 2. Hard to obtain dispersion device
Foamed Concrete	Use trained personnel to construct	Flat ground Slow moving spill	1. Better adhesion to substrates (clay/shale/grass)	1. Hard to obtain foam and dispersion device 2. Must set for a time period. Will not hold high hydraulic heads
Evacua-tion	Bulldozer or earthmoving equipment-line if possible	Soft ground Natural cavitation	1. Material on site 2. Construct with common equipment	1. Move large amounts of material 2. Natural permeability of soil 3. Surface of soil not suitable in all cases
Evacua-tion & Dikes	Bulldozer or earthmoving equipment-line if possible	Soft ground	1. Need less space than separate 2. Material on site 3. Construct with common equipment	1. Move large amounts of material 2. Natural permeability of soil 3. Surface of soil not suitable in all cases

TABLE I-2. SPILLS IN WATER-HEAVIER THAN WATER SPILLS

Type	Application or Construction Method	Use	Advantages	Disadvantages
Natural Excava-tions & Dikes	None	Where a natural barrier exists	No construction needed	Can't control the area which contains the spill
Construc-tion of Excavation & Dikes	Dredges: hydraulic or vacuum pumps Divers with pumps then place concrete or sand bags around to form dike if bottom material is not sufficient	If bottom can be moved	Material is on site	1. Hard to construct 2. Stirred up bottom may cause dispersion and increased turbidity

TABLE I-3.   SPILLS IN WATER-SOLUBLE OR MISCIBLE SPILLS

Type	Application or Construction Method	Use	Advantages	Disadvantages
Sealed booms	Boom Device to anchor	Contain depth limited volumes leaking containers	Contain entire depth of water	1. Deployment difficult 2. Not used for large bodies 3. Difficult to get good seal
Diversion of Uncontaminated	Earthmoving equipment	Special area where topography is right	1. Can put cleaned water into diverted stream 2. Used for flowing water	1. Difficult to move large amounts of earth 2. Clear area needed 3. Impermeability of ground
Diversion of Contaminated Flow	Block entrance with sandbags, sealed booms or dikes	Special area where topography is right	1. Can put clean water back into stream 2. Used for flowing water	1. Difficult to move large amount of earth 2. Clear area needed 3. Impermeability of ground 4. Adverse environmental impact
Gelling Agent	Gels, dispersion devices; use experienced personnel	If small volumes	1. Stop flowing contaminant 2. Stop permeation	1. Hard to obtain 2. Can't use in large area 3. Must haul to dispose
Containment of Entire Waterbody	Diking materials Earthmoving equipment Sandbags, etc. Lining	For entirely contaminated area	1. Can allow containment of a large waterbody 2. Materials on-site 3. Easily constructed	1. Not all waterbodies have containable overflow 2. Permeability 3. May be an unstable condition

TABLE I-4. SPILLS IN WATER-FLOATING SPILLS

Type	Application or Construction Method	Use	Advantages	Disadvantages
Booms	Varies; need deployment device	Not too much current	Used on large area; Many varieties	1. Only in waves less 2-4 feet 2. Current speed less 0.7 knots
Weirs	Weir & Boat	Calm	Not easily clogged; Collects & contains	Not used in rough water
Pneumatic Barriers	Air compressor diffuser deployment method	Only shallow water	Do not create a physical barrier to vessels	1. Not in rough water 2. Only shallow water 3. Only thin layers or materials
Spill Herding Methods	Chemicals on water spray or prop. wash	To protect shore or other facilities	Useful in rough	1. Not easily obtainable 2. Not 100% effective

TABLE I-5.   SPILLS IN AIR

Type	Application or Construction Method	Use	Advantages	Disadvantages
Mist Knock Down	Spray fine mist into air	Water soluble or low lying vapors	Removes hazard from air	Create water pollution problems and must be contained in solution
Fans or Blowers	Disperse air by directing blower toward it	Very calm and sheltered areas	Can direct air away from populated areas	1. Not at all effective if any wind 2. Need large capacity of blowers 3. Hard to control

EPA-SUGGESTED TREATMENT SCHEMES

Hazardous Chemical	Amenable To Biological Trmt. at Municipal STP	Treatment Scheme	Treatment Specifications	Comments
Acetone Cyanohydrin	May require acclimatization	(diagram)	Neutralize with NaOH to pH 8.5 / Adsorb/neutralize to pH 7 / C:10-100 #/# sol. matl.	Raise pH to suppress cyanide gas formation but not greater than pH 9
Acrylonitrile	When diluted/may need to be acclimated	(diagram)	1. Add NaOH to pH 8.5/adsorb/neutralize to pH 7 with HCl / C:10-100 #/# sol. matl. / 2. Add NaOH to pH 10 then add HOCl to a residual react 30 min./discharge to STP	Liquid is flammable and explosive - Careful to avoid HCN evolution or direct contact with NaOH. Option 2 produces cyanates which are less toxic
Chlorine	When reduced and diluted	(diagram)	Add H₂SO₄ to pH 2-3; add Na bisulfite until small or no chlorine residual; neutralize to pH 7	Carbon can be used for low concentration of Cl₂
Nitrogen Dioxide	After neutralization and dilution	(diagram)	Add Ca(OH)₂ to pH 7-8 dilute with water	Beware of flash fire Self-contained breathing apparatus mandatory/lime addition forms nitrates and nitrates require dilution
Sodium Hydrosulfide	When reduced	(diagram)	Add Na₂CO₃ to pH 7 - air to 70% max. DO level	Remove any solids to land fill
Sodium Hydroxide	When neutralized	(diagram)	Add acid to pH 7/ discharge	Be careful not to create strong reaction
Styrene	If diluted	(diagram)	C:10-100 #/# sol. matl.	Skim surface of water body

EPA-SUGGESTED TREATMENT SCHEMES (cont'd)

Hazardous Chemical	Amenable To Biological Trmt. at Municipal STP	Treatment Scheme	Treatment Specifications	Comments
Toluene	When dilute		C: 10-100 #/# sol. matl.	Skim off surface of water body
Vinyl Acetate	When dilute		C: 10-35 #/# sol. matl.	Skim off from water body; light may cause polymerization to solid so dredging may be required
Hydrogen Cyanide (Hydrocyanic Acid)	If acclimated		Add NaOH to pH 8-8.5 then add HOCl to a residual/add 10% XS HOCl/react 1 hr/ neutralize w/H_2SO_4 prior to discharge	Do not allow pH to drop below neutral or NH_4 will be formed/ add large excess HOCl to avoid the liberation of toxic cyanogen chloride

KEY TO TREATMENT SCHEME UNIT OPERATIONS

S   = Solids
CR = Cyanide gas reduction
F   = Filtration
A   = Adsorption
N   = Neutralization
O   = Oxidation
STP = Sewage treatment plant

CHEMICALS

HCl = Hydrochloric Acid
$NaOH$ = Sodium Hydroxide
$HOCl$ = Hypochloric Acid
Na_2CO_3 = Sodium Carbonate
H_2SO_4 = Sulfuric Acid
NH_3 = Ammonia

ACETONE

Synonyms – Dimethyl ketone, beta-ketopropane, 2-propanone

United Nations Number. . . . . __1090__

CHRIS Code . . . . __ACT__

Formula – CH_3COCH_3

Boiling Point. . . . . __56.7__ ^0C __134__ ^0F

Freezing Point . . . . __-95.0__ ^0C __-139__ ^0F

Appearance-Odor – Colorless liquid; sweetish odor

Vapor Pressure 20^0C (68^0F) (mmHg) __180__

Specific Gravity – 0.79

Reid Vapor Pressure (psia). . . . . __7.25__

Chemical Family – Ketone

Vapor Pressure 46^0C (115^0F) (psia) __10.0__

Vapor Density (Air = 1.0). . . . . __2.0__

Applicable Bulk Regulations 46 CFR Subchapter __D__

Solubility in Water. . . . . . . __complete__

FIRE & EXPLOSION HAZARD DATA

Grade – C Flammable liquid
Electrical Group – D

General – Highly flammable. Keep away from heat, sparks, and open flame.

Flash Point (^0F). 15
Flammable Limits 2.5-12.8%
Autoignition Temp. (^0F). 1040
Extinguishing Agents. . . . . CO_2, dry chemical, alcohol foam, water fog
Special Fire Procedures . . . . . . If water is used, large quantities must be applied in order to prevent re-ignition. A
solution of 4% acetone and 96% water has a flash point of 129^0F.

HEALTH HAZARD DATA

Health Hazard Ratings	Odor Threshold (ppm)	TLV (ppm)
1,0,0	200-400	1000

General – Irritant and anaesthetic effects after high concentration exposures.

Symptoms – Drowsiness and throat irritation.

*Short Exposure Tolerance – 10,000 ppm has been reported as endurable for 30-60 minutes without symptoms.

Exposure Procedures – Vapor – remove victim to fresh air, if breathing stops, apply artificial respiration. Skin or eye
contact – remove contaminated clothing and gently flush affected areas with water for 15 minutes. Get medical advice
or attention.

REACTIVITY DATA

Stability – Stable compound

Compatibility – Material. Will dissolve many plastics and rubber.
Cargo. Group 18 of compatibility chart.

SPILL OR LEAK PROCEDURE

If possible: Wear rubber gloves, face shield and protective clothing. Have all purpose canister mask available. Secure
ignition sources. Flush spilled acetone away with water. Do not flush into confined space such as a sewer because of
the danger of explosion. If a spill occurs, call the National Response Center 800-424-8802.

Remarks.

ACETONE CYANOHYDRIN

Synonyms —a-Hydroxyisobutyronitrile
2-Methylacetonitrile

Formula—$(CH_3)_2C(OH)CN$

Appearance-Odor —Colorless liquid; almond odor

Specific Gravity —0.93

Chemical Family —Cyanohydrin

Applicable Bulk Regulations 46 CFR Subchapter ___o___

United Nations Number. . . . . __1541__
CHRIS Code . . . . __ACY__

Boiling Point. . . . . __120__ °C __248__ °F
Freezing Point . . . . __−19__ °C __−2__ °F

Vapor Pressure 20°C (68°F) (mmHg) __0.8__
Reid Vapor Pressure (psia). . . . . . . __0.3__
Vapor Pressure 46°C (115°F) (psia). __0.4__
Vapor Density (Air = 1.0). . . . . __2.9__
Solubility in Water. . . . . . . __complete__

FIRE & EXPLOSION HAZARD DATA

Grade —E: Combustible liquid—Class B poison
Electrical Group—D

General—Gives off flammable and poisonous vapor (cyanide gas) when heated.

Flash Point (°F).   165
Flammable Limits 2.25-11%
Autoignition Temp. (°F).   1270
Extinguishing Agents. . . . . CO_2, alcohol foam, water fog
Special Fire Procedures . . . . . .   DO NOT USE SODA-ACID EXTINGUISHER
       Respiratory protection required for firefighting personnel. Wear full protective, airtight clothing.

HEALTH HAZARD DATA

Health Hazard Ratings	Odor Threshold (ppm)	TLV (ppm)
1,2,4	Unavailable	Unavailable

General—Vapor very poisonous by inhalation. Liquid poisonous by absorption through the skin.

Symptoms —Headache, dizziness, nausea; blueness of lips and fingernails

*Short Exposure Tolerance —Unavailable

Exposure Procedures —Vapor—remove victim to fresh air; if breathing stops, apply artificial respiration. Skin or eye contact—remove contaminated clothing and gently flush affected areas with water for 15 minutes. Keep victim at rest. Get prompt medical attention for liquid or vapor exposure. Wash contaminated clothing including shoes.

REACTIVITY DATA

Stability —When heated, decomposes to form cyanide gas. Must be kept slightly acidified.

Compatibility — Material: Dilution with water causes decomposition with formation of hydrogen cyanide.

SPILL OR LEAK PROCEDURE

If possible, wear long rubber gloves, self contained breathing apparatus, and protective clothing. Eliminate all sources of ignition. Evacuate personnel not equipped with respiratory protection. Do not flush spill where humans or animals may contact.

If a spill occurs, call the National Response Center 800-424-8802.

Remarks: *Decompses at the boiling point.

ACRYLONITRILE (Inhibited)

Synonyms—Cyanoethylene, fumigrain, propenenitrile, ventox, vinyl cyanide

United Nations Number. 1093
CHRIS Code . . . . ACN

Formula—CH_2CHCN

Boiling Point. . . . . 77°C   171 °F
Freezing Point . . . . −85°C −121 °F

Appearance-Odor—Colorless liquid; odor resembles that of peach seed
Specific Gravity—0.81

Vapor Pressure 20°C (68°F) (mmHg) 83
Reid Vapor Pressure (psia). 3.5

Chemical Family—Nitrile

Vapor Pressure 46°C (115°F) (psia). 5.0
Vapor Density (Air = 1.0). 1.8

Applicable Bulk Regulations 46 CFR Subchapter o

Solubility in Water. . . . . . . Moderate

FIRE & EXPLOSION HAZARD DATA

Grade —C Flammable liquid
Electrical Group—D

General—When heated this material may evolve toxic cyanide gas, or explode, or both. Fire may cause violent rupture of tank.
Flash Point (°F). 32
Flammable Limits . . . . 3.0 - 17.0%
Autoignition Temp. (°F). 898
Extinguishing Agents. . . . . . . CO_2, dry chemical, alcohol foam
Special Fire Procedures . . . . . . DO NOT use dry chemical for a large, confined fire. Fire parties must wear respiratory protection and full protective clothing including rubber boots. Keep tank cool with water spray.

HEALTH HAZARD DATA

Health Hazard Ratings   Odor Threshold (ppm)   TLV (ppm)
3.1.3   Unavailable   20
General—Harmful by inhalation and skin absorption. Liquid in shoes causes delayed burns. Penetrates leather.

Symptoms—Eye irritation, headache, nausea, blueness of lips and fingertips. Contact with skin may also cause dermatitis.

*Short Exposure Tolerance—400 ppm for 30 minutes.

Exposure Procedures—Remove victim to fresh air. If he is not breathing, apply artificial respiration. Remove contaminated clothing and wash chemical from skin with a gentle flow of water. Get medical attention. If patient is unconscious, administer vapor of amyl nitrite.

REACTIVITY DATA

Stability—Very reactive; may polymerize explosively in the presence of strong bases. Must be inhibited to prevent polymerization. Polymerization could be initiated by visible light.

Compatibility—Material: Copper and copper alloys are attacked and should not be used. This material penetrates leather, so contaminated leather shoes and gloves should be destroyed. Attacks aluminum in high concentrations.
Cargo: Group 15 of compatibility chart.

SPILL OR LEAK PROCEDURE

If possible, wear long rubber gloves, self-contained breathing apparatus, protective clothing. Avoid contact with liquid. Secure ignition sources. May add excess of strong calcium hypochlorite solution. Scoop up slurry. Wash site of spill with soap solution containing some hypochlorite.

If a spill occurs, call the National Response Center 800-424-8802

Remarks:

AMMONIA (ANHYDROUS)

Synonyms—Ammonia gas

United Nations Number.   1005
CHRIS Code . . . .   AMA

Formula —NH_3

Boiling Point. . . . .   −33 °C   −28 °F
Freezing Point . . . .   −77.7 °C   −107.9 °F

Appearance-Odor—Colorless liquid or gas; pungent, highly
irritating odor
Specific Gravity—0.68 at −33.4°C (liquid)

Vapor Pressure 20°C (68°F) (mmHg)   6477
Reid Vapor Pressure (psia). 211.9

Chemical Family —Ammonia

Vapor Pressure 46°C (115°F) (psia).   266.0
Vapor Density (Air = 1.0). 0.6

Applicable Bulk Regulations 46 CFR Subchapter   O

Solubility in Water. . . . . . .   Appreciable

FIRE & EXPLOSION HAZARD DATA

Grade—Liquefied compressed gas
Electrical Group—D

General —Fire hazard when in high concentrations and at high temperature. Oil or other combustible vapors increase the
fire hazard.

Flash Point (°F). . . . .   indefinite, below 32°F
Flammable Limits . . . .   16 - 25%
Autoignition Temp. (°F).   1204
Extinguishing Agents. . . . .   Stop the flow of gas (lighter than air); cool tanks with water spray.
Special Fire Procedures . . . . . .   Use respiratory and body protection when approaching ammonia-contaminated
atmosphere. Liberal use of water fog, where possible, will reduce vapor concentration.

HEALTH HAZARD DATA

Health Hazard Ratings	Odor Threshold (ppm)	TLV (ppm)
4,2,2	Approx 50	25

General—Vapor extremely irritating. Liquid causes burns.

Symptoms—Coughing; burning sensation, eye irritation or pain. Frozen areas turn white.

*Short Exposure Tolerance—A 2500 ppm (0.25%) concentration of ammonia in air is dangerous for 30 minutes
exposure.

Exposure Procedures—Remove victim to fresh air. Call a physician at once. If not breathing, apply artificial respiration,
oxygen. If breathing is difficult, administer oxygen. Flush affected areas of body with plenty of water for 15 minutes.
DO NOT FLUSH FROZEN AREAS. Remove contaminated clothing and shoes. Get prompt medical attention. Low-
velocity fog is effective for decontaminating the atmosphere.

REACTIVITY DATA

Stability—Normally stable. Reacts with acidic materials.

Compatibility —Material: Corrosive to galvanized surfaces, copper and copper alloys. Iron and steel are suitable for the
construction of containers, fittings and piping.

Cargo: Group 8 of compatibility chart.

SPILL OR LEAK PROCEDURE

Evacuate area in case of large leaks or tank rupture. Shut off leak if without risk. Wear self-contained breathing apparatus.
If necessary to enter spill area, wear full protective clothing including boots. Water spray is extremely effective in
absorbing ammonia gas and should be used around leaks of gas only. DO NOT PUT WATER ON LIQUID AMMONIA.

If a spill occurs, call the National Response Center 800-424-8802.

Remarks:

BUTADIENE (INHIBITED)

Synonyms —Bivinyl, biethylene, 1,3-butadiene, divinyl, pyrrolylene, vinyl ethylene

Formula —C_4H_6

Appearance-Odor —Colorless gas or liquid; mild, aromatic odor

Specific Gravity —0.62

Chemical Family —Unsaturated hydrocarbon

Applicable Bulk Regulations 46 CFR Subchapter ___O___

United Nations Number . . . . ___1010___
CHRIS Code . . . . ___BDI___

Boiling Point . . . . ___−4___ °C ___24___ °F
Freezing Point . . . . ___−109___ °C ___−164___ °F

Vapor Pressure 20°C (68°F) (mmHg) ___982___
Reid Vapor Pressure (psia) . . . . ___61___
Vapor Pressure 46°C (115°F) (psia) ___75___
Vapor Density (Air = 1.0) . . . . ___1.88___
Solubility in Water . . . . ___Negligible___

FIRE & EXPLOSION HAZARD DATA

Grade —Liquefied Flammable Gas (LFG)
Electrical Group —B

General —Unless flow of gas can be stopped, extinguishing a butadiene fire may permit accumulation of an explosive concentration of vapor, and subsequent explosion or re-flash. Fire may cause violent rupture of tank.

Flash Point (°F) . . . .   below 0
Flammable Limits . . . .   2.0 - 11.5%
Autoignition Temp. (°F)   842
Extinguishing Agents . . . .   Stop flow of gas; CO_2, dry chemical, water fog
Special Fire Procedures . . . . . .   Keep burning tank and adjacent tanks cool with a water spray.

HEALTH HAZARD DATA

Health Hazard Ratings	Odor Threshold (ppm)	TLV (ppm)
1,1,1	Above 1000	1100

General —Liquid or cold gas may cause skin or eye injury similar to frost bite.

Symptoms—Inhalation: dizziness, headache; skin contact: frostbitten areas will appear white. Irritating to eyes and respiratory tract.

*Short Exposure Tolerance—8,000 ppm was found endurable for 8 hours with only slight irritation of the eyes and upper respiratory tract.

Exposure Procedures—Vapor—remove victim to fresh air; if breathing stops, apply artificial respiration. Skin or eye contact—remove contaminated clothing and gently flush affected areas with water for 15 minutes. Protect frostbitten areas from abrasions and mechanical damage. Get medical advice or attention.

REACTIVITY DATA

Stability —Must be inhibited to prevent polymerization. Forms unstable peroxides in presence of oxygen and/or iron rust.

Compatibility —Material: Unsafe in acetylide-forming materials such as monel, copper or copper alloys
Cargo: Group 30 of compatibility chart.

SPILL OR LEAK PROCEDURE

Wear rubber gloves, face shield, protective clothing. Have all-purpose canister mask available. Secure ignition sources. Do not extinguish fire unless leak can be secured. In case of a spill, call the National Response Center 800-424-8802.

Remarks:

CAUSTIC SODA SOLUTIONS

Synonyms —Sodium hydroxide, lye

Formula—NaOH

Appearance-Odor —Colorless or gray; syrupy liquid; no odor

Specific Gravity —up to 1.53 (solid dissolved in water)

Chemical Family —Caustic

Applicable Bulk Regulations 46 CFR Subchapter _____O_____

United Nations Number. 1824
CHRIS Code . . . . CSS

	146	298*
Boiling Point.	198 °C	388 °F**
Freezing Point	−41 °C	−41 °F*
	−98	−144 **

Vapor Pressure 20°C (68°F) (mmHg) 1 - 7 at 47%
Reid Vapor Pressure (psia). . . . . . . Unavailable
Vapor Pressure 46°C (115°F) (psia) Unavailable
Vapor Density (Air = 1.0). . . . . Not pertinent
Solubility in Water. . . . . . . _Complete_____

FIRE & EXPLOSION HAZARD DATA

Grade —Corrosive liquid
Electrical Group —NA

General —Non-flammable

Flash Point (°F). . . . .   None
Flammable Limits . . . .   None
Autoignition Temp. (°F). . . . .   None
Extinguishing Agents. . . . . . .   None
Special Fire Procedures . . . . . . Cannot catch fire. Cool exposed tanks with water.

HEALTH HAZARD DATA

Health Hazard Ratings   Odor Threshold (ppm)   TLV (ppm)
0,4,1   No odor   2mg/m³**

General —Causes severe damage to the eyes. On contact with the skin, severe burns with deep ulcerations and ultimate scarring may result.

Symptoms —If the solution splashes onto skin no pain may be felt; but hair and skin touched by caustic will begin to dissolve on contact.

*Short Exposure Tolerance —Unavailable.

Exposure Procedures—Do not delay! Flush affected areas gently with plenty of water for at least 15 minutes. Remove contaminated shoes or clothing. Get medical attention. Wash contaminated clothing including shoes.

REACTIVITY DATA

Stability—Heat of dilution of liquid caustic is considerable and variable, depending upon initial and final caustic concentrations.

Compatibility —Material: Noncorrosive to rubber at atmospheric temperatures. Slowly corrosive to iron, copper and monel metal. Reacts with clothing and a few metals, such as aluminum, tin, lead and zinc, and alloys containing these metals.
            Cargo Group 5 of compatibility charts.

SPILL OR LEAK PROCEDURE

Wear rubber gloves, large face shield, and protective clothing. Avoid contact with the liquid. Neutralize with weak acid and mop, or, at dock, flush with excess water.

If a spill occurs, call the National Response Center 800-424-8802

Remarks   *50 per cent solution
           **73 per cent solution
           ***in the form of a fine mist or spray.

CHLORINE

Synonyms—Chlorine gas

United Nations Number.   1017
CHRIS Code   CLX

Formula—Cl_2

Boiling Point. . . . .   −34 °C   −29 °F
Freezing Point . . . .   −101 °C   −150 °F

Appearance-Odor—Greenish-yellow gas; choking odor

Specific Gravity—1.56

Chemical Family—Halogen

Applicable Bulk Regulations 46 CFR Subchapter ___O___

Vapor Pressure 20°C (68°F) (mmHg)   4590
Reid Vapor Pressure (psia).   155
Vapor Pressure 46°C (115°F) (psia).   180
Vapor Density (Air = 1.0). 2.4
Solubility in Water. . . . . . .   at 60°F   1.0%

FIRE & EXPLOSION HAZARD DATA

Grade—Nonflammable compressed gas
Electrical Group—NA

General—Chlorine is non-explosive and non-flammable. However, it can support combustion of certain substances.

Flash Point (°F). . . . .   None
Flammable Limits . . . .   None
Autoignition Temp. (°F). . . . .   None
Extinguishing Agents. . . . .   None
Special Fire Procedures . . . . . .   Chlorine tanks exposed to fire should be cooled with a water spray to decrease the buildup of pressure. If leak seems likely, emergency personnel should carry self-contained breathing apparatus so that facepiece may be donned without delay.

HEALTH HAZARD DATA

Health Hazard Ratings	Odor Threshold (ppm)	TLV (ppm)
4,2,4	3.5	1

General—Gas is primarily a respiratory irritant; severe exposure can be fatal. Liquid or high concentrations of gas in contact with skin or eyes will cause local irritation or burns.

Symptoms—Vapor: coughing, choking, burning sensation in eyes and throat, and shortness of breath. Liquid: severe irritation or blistering. Frostbite can also result.

*Short Exposure Tolerance—Exposure to vapor concentration of 1000 ppm for 10 minutes has caused death.

Exposure Procedures—Remove victim to fresh air. If breathing stops, apply artificial respiration. Oxygen, administered by trained personnel, is often helpful. If eyes are effected, wash gently with water for 15 minutes. If liquid chlorine has spilled onto the skin, remove contaminated clothing and flood the exposed area gently with water for 15 minutes. Get medical attention promptly.

REACTIVITY DATA

Stability—Will react with many inorganic and organic compounds, usually with an evolution of heat.

Compatibility—Material: Below 230 degrees F, copper, iron, lead, nickel, platinum, silver, steel and tantalum are chemically resistant to dry chlorine gas or liquid. Certain copper and ferrous alloys, including Hastalloy "C", monel and types 304 and 316 stainless steel also are resistant.

SPILL OR LEAK PROCEDURE

Wear rubber gloves, self-contained breathing apparatus, and protective clothing. Evacuate all downwind personnel not equipped with respiratory protection.

If a spill occurs, call the National Response Center 800-424-8802.

Remarks:

<u>ETHYL ACRYLATE</u>

Synonyms —Ethyl propenoate

United Nations Number.   1917
CHRIS Code . . . .   EAC

Formula—$CH_2CHCOOC_2H_5$

Boiling Point. . . . .   99 °C   211 °F
Freezing Point . . . . −39 °C   −103 °F

Appearance-Odor—Colorless liquid; pungent odor

Specific Gravity –0.93

Chemical Family—Acrylates

Applicable Bulk Regulations 46 CFR Subchapter   O

Vapor Pressure 20°C (68°F) (mmHg) 29.3
Reid Vapor Pressure (psia). 1.4
Vapor Pressure 46°C (115°F) (psia). 2.0
Vapor Density (Air = 1.0). 3.5
Solubility in Water. 1.5%

FIRE & EXPLOSION HAZARD DATA

Grade –C: Flammable liquid
Electrical Group –D

General—Ignited by heat, sparks or open flame. Fire may cause violent rupture of tank.

Flash Point (°F).   60
Flammable Limits . . . . 1.8% - 9.5% (calculated)
Autoignition Temp. (°F). . . . . Unavailable
Extinguishing Agents. . . . . CO_2, dry chemical, water fog, alcohol foam
Special Fire Procedures . . . . . . Keep tank cool with a water spray to prevent polymerization.

HEALTH HAZARD DATA

Health Hazard Ratings	Odor Threshold (ppm)	TLV (ppm)
3,2,3	.00047	25

General—Vapor irritating

Symptoms –Eye and throat irritation, shortness of breath, and convulsions.

*Short Exposure Tolerance –50 ppm for 15 minutes. 2000 ppm vapor killed rats in 4 hours with death attributable to severe pulmonary irritation.

Exposure Procedures–Vapor—remove victim to fresh air; if breathing stops, apply artificial respiration. Skin or eye contact—remove contaminated clothing and gently flush affected areas with water for 15 minutes. Get medical advice or attention.

REACTIVITY DATA

Stability –Will polymerize spontaneously if not inhibited.

Compatibility –Material: Not corrosive to the usual materials of construction.

Cargo: Group 14 of compatibility chart.

SPILL OR LEAK PROCEDURE

Wear rubber gloves, face shield, protective clothing. Have all-purpose canister mask available. Avoid contact with liquid. Secure ignition sources.

If a spill occurs, call the National Response Center 800-424-8802.

Remarks:

ETHYLENE OXIDE

Synonyms—1, 2-Epoxyethane, EO

United Nations Number. 1040
CHRIS Code . . . . EOX

Formula —C_2H_4O

Boiling Point. . . . . 11°C   51 °F
Freezing Point . . . . −111 °C   −168 °F

Appearance-Odor—Clear, colorless liquid; ether-like odor

Specific Gravity —0.88

Chemical Family—Alkylene oxides

Applicable Bulk Regulations 46 CFR Subchapter   O

Vapor Pressure 20°C (68°F) (mmHg) 1090
Reid Vapor Pressure (psia). 38.5
Vapor Pressure 46°C (115°F) (psia)   48.0
Vapor Density (Air = 1.0). 1.52
Solubility in Water. . . . . . . _____ Complete

FIRE & EXPLOSION HAZARD DATA

Grade—A: Flammable liquid
Electrical Group—B

General—Flammable—does not need oxygen for combustion. If local "hot spots" develop in the tank, the liquid in the tank may explode.

Flash Point (°F). . . . .   Below 0
Flammable Limits . . . .   2-100 %
Autoignition Temp. (°F).   804
Extinguishing Agents. . . . . . . CO_2, dry chemical, water fog
Special Fire Procedures . . . . . .   It is important to keep the temperature of storage tank low, use large amounts of water. Approach only after considering explosion danger. Keep firefighting personnel behind cover if practicable. If the water supply is inadequate or the tank shows signs of overheating, evacuate the area

---

HEALTH HAZARD DATA

Health Hazard Ratings	Odor Threshold (ppm)	TLV (ppm)
3,3,2	50	50

General—Moderate hazard, for both acute and chronic exposures. Volatility is high and pulmonary absorption is rapid.

Symptoms—Burning sensation in eyes, nose and throat; dizziness and headache.

*Short Exposure Tolerance—200 ppm for 30 minutes.

Exposure Procedures —Vapor—remove victim to fresh air, if breathing stops, apply artificial respiration. Skin or eye contact—remove contaminated clothing and gently flush affected areas with water for 15 minutes. Get medical attention immediately.

REACTIVITY DATA

Stability—Ethylene oxide's tendency to polymerize increases rapidly when the temperature goes above 30°C. It will decompose with explosive violence when the temperature reaches 571°C.

Compatibility—Material: EO may polymerize violently when in contact with highly active catalytic surfaces such as anhydrous iron, tin and aluminum chlorides, pure iron and aluminum oxides and alkali metal hydroxides. Do not use copper, silver or their alloys.
Cargo: Group 16 of compatibility chart.

SPILL OR LEAK PROCEDURE

Wear rubber gloves, large heavy face shield (if in doubt use body shield also) and self-contained breathing apparatus. Secure ignition sources. Avoid contact with liquid. Flush with large quantities of water. Notify local fire department.

If a spill occurs, call the National Response Center 800-424-8802.

Remarks

————— HYDROGEN (LIQUEFIED) —————

Synonyms—LH$_2$

United Nations Number. 1966
CHRIS Code . . . . HXX

Formula—H$_2$

Boiling Point. . . . . −253 °C   −423 °F
Freezing Point . . . . −259 °C   −435 °F

Appearance-Odor —Colorless liquid; odorless

Specific Gravity —0.07 at b.p.

Vapor Pressure 20°C (68°F) (mmHg) Very high
Reid Vapor Pressure (psia). . . . . . Very high
Vapor Pressure 46°C (115°F) (psia)   Very high
Vapor Density (Air = 1.0). 0.07
Solubility in Water. . . . . . . Negligible

Chemical Family –

Applicable Bulk Regulations 46 CFR Subchapter ——

FIRE & EXPLOSION HAZARD DATA

Grade –Liquefied flammable gas (I.FG)
Electrical Group—B

General—Will react violently with strong oxidizers. Will ignite easily with oxygen. Vapors form explosive or combustible mixtures with air over a wide range of concentrations.

Flash Point (°F). . . . .   Gas
Flammable Limits . . . .   4.0 - 75%
Autoignition Temp. (°F).   1075
Extinguishing Agents. . . . .   First stop flow of gas. CO$_2$, dry chemical, water
Special Fire Procedures . . . . . .   Source of hydrogen MUST be eliminated before fire is put out to prevent accumulation of explosive vapors. If the insulation fails on a liquid hydrogen tank exposed to fire, the tank will explode, evacuate fire fighters and have them take cover.

HEALTH HAZARD DATA

Health Hazard Ratings   Odor Threshold (ppm)   TLV (ppm)
Unavailable   Odorless   Unavailable

General—Not considered toxic. Avoid skin contact with liquid

Symptoms –Inhalation Drowsiness and high-pitched, squeaky voice. Skin contact Numbness and whitening of skin at the area of contact

Short Exposure Tolerance—Unavailable

Exposure Procedures—Remove victim to fresh air, if breathing stops, apply artificial respiration. In case of skin contact with liquid or cold gas, thaw frosted parts with cold water. DO NOT RUB Get medical attention immediately Avoid sparks and open flames

REACTIVITY DATA

Stability –Will ignite readily when exposed to spark source. Liquid hydrogen will flash into vapor at temperatures above −400°F resulting in a sudden and large increase in pressure if confined

Compatibility –Material Mild steel and most iron alloys become brittle at liquid hydrogen temperatures Aluminum and stainless steel (300 series) may be used

          Cargo   Not shipped in bulk

SPILL OR LEAK PROCEDURE

Secure all nearby ignition sources immediately. Isolate spill area and call local fire department and the Captain of the Port, U.S. Coast Guard. If the liquid does not catch fire, it will soon boil off and leave no residue

If a spill occurs, call the National Response Center 800-424-8802

Remarks: *Not allowed to be shipped in bulk

METHYL ALCOHOL

Synonyms —Acetone alcohol, carbinol, methanol, methyl
    hydroxide, wood alcohol

Formula –CH_3OH

Appearance–Odor–Colorless liquid; smells like wine or shellac
    thinner
Specific Gravity—0.79

Chemical Family—Alcohol

Applicable Bulk Regulations 46 CFR Subchapter ___D___

United Nations Number. 2030
CHRIS Code . . . . MAL

Boiling Point. . . . . 64 °C   148 °F
Freezing Point . . . . −98 °C   −144 °F
Vapor Pressure 20°C (68°F) (mmHg) 100
Reid Vapor Pressure (psia). 4.5
Vapor Pressure 46°C (115°F) (psia). 7.0
Vapor Density (Air = 1.0). 1.11
Solubility in Water. . . . . . _____ Complete

FIRE & EXPLOSION HAZARD DATA

Grade –C: Flammable liquid
Electrical Group –D

General —Methyl alcohol is a flammable liquid and at ordinary temperatures, gives off a vapor which is both toxic and, when
    mixed with air, explosive within certain limits.
Flash Point (°F). 61
Flammable Limits . . . . 5.5 - 36.5%
Autoignition Temp. (°F). 878
Extinguishing Agents. . . . . CO_2, dry chemical, alcohol foam, water fog
Special Fire Procedures . . . . . . Avoid breathing vapors. Provide body and respiratory protection for fire parties. Keep
    tanks cool with water spray. Water may not be effective unless large quantities are used.

HEALTH HAZARD DATA

Health Hazard Ratings	Odor Threshold (ppm)	TLV (ppm)
1,1,2	2000*	200

General —Vapor inhalation dangerous. May be absorbed through skin.

Symptoms —Dizziness, unconsciousness, and sighing respiration.

*Short Exposure Tolerance –1000 ppm for 1 hour has caused headache, eye irritation and fatigue.

Exposure Procedures—Remove victim to fresh air. Give artificial respiration if breathing stops. Skin or eye contact—
    remove contaminated clothing. Flush affected areas gently with water for 15 minutes. Get medical advice or attention.

REACTIVITY DATA

Stability –Stable. Can react vigorously with oxidizing materials.

Compatibility–Material: Compatible with most materials of construction.

      Cargo: Group 20 of compatibility chart.

SPILL OR LEAK PROCEDURE

Wear rubber gloves, protective clothing. Have all-purpose canister mask available. Avoid contact with liquid. Secure
ignition sources.

If a spill occurs, call the National Response Center 800-424-8802.

Remarks: *Exposure to potentially dangerous vapor concentrations can occur before the product can be detected by smell.

METHYL BROMIDE

Synonyms—Bromomethane, embafume, monobromomethane

United Nations Number. 1062
CHRIS Code . . . . MTB

Formula—CH_3Br

Boiling Point. . . . . 4.6°C   40.3°F
Freezing Point . . . . −92.8°C −135.0°F

Appearance-Odor—Colorless liquid; sweet, chloroform-like odor

Specific Gravity—1.73

Chemical Family—Halogenated Hydrocarbons

Applicable Bulk Regulations 46 CFR Subchapter   O

Vapor Pressure 20°C (68°F) (mmHg) 1420
Reid Vapor Pressure (psia). 45
Vapor Pressure 46°C (115°F) (psia). 60
Vapor Density (Air = 1.0). 3.27
Solubility in Water. 1.7%

FIRE & EXPLOSION HAZARD DATA

Grade—Depends on flash point
Electrical Group—D

General—Practically non-flammable. Fire and explosion hazard is slight.

Flash Point (°F). . . . . None listed
Flammable Limits . . . . 10 to 15%
Autoignition Temp. (°F). 998
Extinguishing Agents. . . . . . . Water spray, dry chemical
Special Fire Procedures . . . . . . This is a Class B poison. Cool tanks in vicinity of fire with a water spray. Leaking tanks
  must not be approached unless wearing full body and respiratory protection!

HEALTH HAZARD DATA

Health Hazard Ratings	Odor Threshold (ppm)	TLV (ppm)
3,3,4	Unavailable	4

General—Poisonous by inhalation. Effects may be delayed. Liquid causes burns; may be absorbed by clothing, particularly
  shoes, to cause delayed burns.

Symptoms—Double vision, nausea, dizziness, headache. Severe exposure results in convulsions, muscular tremors, and
  possibly death.

*Short Exposure Tolerance—20 ppm for 5 minutes.

Exposure Procedures—Remove victim to fresh air. Administer artificial respiration if unconscious. Oxygen administered
  by trained personnel is often helpful. Get medical attention immediately. NOTE—the effects of inhaling this material
  may be delayed.

REACTIVITY DATA

Stability—Forms aluminum alkyls in presence of aluminum. Aluminum alkyls are spontaneously ignitable materials.

Compatibility—Material: Not corrosive to most metals.

        Cargo: Group 36 of compatibility chart.

SPILL OR LEAK PROCEDURE

Wear rubber gloves, self-contained breathing apparatus, protective clothing. Avoid contact with liquid. Personnel without
respiratory protection must be kept upwind of spill.

If a spill occurs, call the National Response Center 800-424-8802.

Remarks: NOTE! Exposure to potentially dangerous vapor concentrations can occur before the product can be
            detected by smell.

NITROGEN DIOXIDE

Synonyms—Nitrogen peroxide, nitrogen tetroxide

Formula –NO$_2$ or N$_2$O$_4$

Appearance-Odor—Red-brown liquid (as shipped) with a
sharp-penetrating odor
Specific Gravity—1.45

Chemical Family—Unclassified

Applicable Bulk Regulations 46 CFR Subchapter ___*___

United Nations Number. 1067
CHRIS Code . . . . NOX

Boiling Point. . . . . 20 °C 68 °F
Freezing Point . . . . –11 °C 12 °F

Vapor Pressure 20°C (68°F) (mmHg) 760
Reid Vapor Pressure (psia). 30
Vapor Pressure 46°C (115°F) (psia). . . . 42
Vapor Density (Air = 1.0). 3.2
Solubility in Water. . . . . . . _____ Decomposes

FIRE & EXPLOSION HAZARD DATA

Grade—Not applicable
Electrical Group—Not applicable

General—Non-flammable but can support combustion under certain circumstances. May form explosive mixtures with
combustible materials. Reacts dangerously with many other cargoes.
Flash Point (°F). . . . .   Non-flammable
Flammable Limits . . . .   Non-flammable
Autoignition Temp. (°F). . . . .   Non-flammable
Extinguishing Agents. . . . .   Non-flammable
Special Fire Procedures . . . . . .   Shut off gas supply and cool tanks with water spray. Supply fire fighters with
breathing apparatus and protective clothing.

HEALTH HAZARD DATA

Health Hazard Ratings	Odor Threshold (ppm)	TLV (ppm)
4,4,4	5	5

General—Vapor causes severe irritation to skin and eyes. Vapor inhalation is very dangerous; may cause death due to lung
damage and asphyxia. Symptoms may be delayed.

Symptoms—Coughing, choking, headache, nausea, pains in chest and abdomen.

*Short Exposure Tolerance—25 ppm safe for a few minutes.

Exposure Procedures—Remove patient to fresh air. Keep at complete rest until seen by a physician. For eye or skin
contact, wash with copious amounts of water and refer to a physician.

REACTIVITY DATA

Stability—Highly reactive oxidizing agent that will react with organic materials. Decomposes into nitric oxide and oxygen
gas when heated. Dissolves in water to form acids.

Compatibility—Material: Copper and its alloys unsuitable.

Cargo: Not a bulk chemical.

SPILL OR LEAK PROCEDURE

Wear long rubber gloves, safety glasses or goggles, self-contained breathing apparatus, protective clothing. Residual
spillage will soon evaporate. Avoid contact with liquid. Secure ignition sources. If possible, allow gas to flow into a mixed
solution of caustic soda and slaked lime.

If a spill occurs, call the National Response Center 800-424-8802.

Remarks: *Bulk shipments not permitted.

OXYGEN (LIQUEFIED)

Synonyms—LOX

United Nations Number. 1073
CHRIS Code . . . . QXY

Formula—O_2

Appearance-Odor—Light-blue liquid; odorless

Specific Gravity—1.14 (at bp)

Chemical Family—

Applicable Bulk Regulations 46 CFR Subchapter ____*

Boiling Point. . . . . −183 °C   −297 °F
Freezing Point . . . . −227 °C   −376 °F

Vapor Pressure 20°C (68°F) (mmHg) Very high
Reid Vapor Pressure (psia). . . . . Very high
Vapor Pressure 46°C (115°F) (psia). Very high
Vapor Density (Air = 1.0). 1.1
Solubility in Water. . . . . . . _____ 4.5%

FIRE & EXPLOSION HAZARD DATA

Grade—Classified as nonflammable
Electrical Group—Not applicable

General—Oxygen does not burn but supports combustion vigorously. A combustible material onto which LOX has spilled
will burst into flame or explode if exposed to a spark source.
Flash Point (°F). . . . .   Non-flammable
Flammable Limits . . . .   Non-flammable
Autoignition Temp. (°F). . . . .   Non-flammable
Extinguishing Agents. . . . .   Use media suitable for substance which is burning.
Special Fire Procedures . . . . . .   If the insulation fails on a LOX tank exposed to fire, the tank will explode. Evacuate
firefighters to a safe distance and have them take cover.

HEALTH HAZARD DATA

Health Hazard Ratings	Odor Threshold (ppm)	TLV (ppm)
Unavailable	None	Unavailable

General—No hazard for gas. Liquid can cause severe "burns" and tissue damage on contact with skin.

Symptoms—Skin contact with liquid will freeze tissue.

*Short Exposure Tolerance—Unavailable

Exposure Procedures—Thaw frozen areas by immersing gently in cold water. DO NOT RUB. Get medical attention
without delay. AVOID SPARKS AND OPEN FLAME.

REACTIVITY DATA

Stability—LOX will flash into vapor at temperatures above −180°F. If unconfined, the vaopr will occupy about 860 times
the volume of the liquid. If confined, a sudden and large pressure increase will result.

Compatibility—Materials: LOX causes al, combustible materials to burn vigorously. A spark is not always needed to ignite
such a mixture.

SPILL OR LEAK PROCEDURE

Secure ignition sources, rope off the spill area and call the fire department. Oxygen will quickly boil off. Extreme precaution against sparks must be observed before re-entering the spill area because, unless the spill is in the open with a
good breeze blowing, the area will be oxygen-rich for a long time.

If a spill occurs, call the National Response Center 800-424-8802.

Remarks: *Not allowed to be shipped in bulk

-------------------- PROPANE --------------------

Synonyms—Dimethylmethane, propyl hydride

United Nations Number. 1978
CHRIS Code . . . . PRP

Formula—C_3H_8

Boiling Point. . . . . −42°C −44 °F
Freezing Point . . . . −187°C −305 °F

Appearance-Odor—Colorless gas or liquid; natural-gas odor

Specific Gravity—0.53 (liquid)

Chemical Family—Saturated hydrocarbon

Applicable Bulk Regulations 46 CFR Subchapter ___D___

Vapor Pressure 20°C (68°F) (mmHg) 6800
Reid Vapor Pressure (psia). 190
Vapor Pressure 46°C (115°F) (psia). 228
Vapor Density (Air = 1.0). 1.55
Solubility in Water. . . . . . . _____ Negligible

FIRE & EXPLOSION HAZARD DATA

Grade —Liquefied Flammable Gas (LFG)
Electrical Group—D

General—As with all gas fires, shutting off the fuel (gas) supply is the only effective procedure. Otherwise, putting out the
fire will permit the accumulation of an explosive concentration of vapor.

Flash Point (°F). . . . . Less than −64
Flammable Limits . . . . 2.2 - 9.5%
Autoignition Temp. (°F). 482
Extinguishing Agents. . . . . Stop flow of gas; CO_2, dry chemical, water fog
Special Fire Procedures . . . . . . Tanks exposed to fire should be kept cool with a continuous spray of water.

HEALTH HAZARD DATA

Health Hazard Ratings	Odor Threshold (ppm)	TLV (ppm)
0,0,0	5,000 - 20,000 ppm	1000

General —Liquid causes frostbite on skin contact. Cold vapor causes skin damage. Inhalation can lead to asphyxiation.

Symptoms—Headache, dizziness, drowsiness. Contact with the liquid will cause frostbite.

*Short Exposure Tolerance—A vapor concentration of 10,000 ppm for brief periods has been reported as producing no
symptoms.

Exposure Procedures—Remove victim to fresh air. Give artificial respiration if breathing stops. Get medical attention. If
liquid has spilled onto the skin, the areas touched will probably be frostbitten and should be handled gently. All cases
of frostbite should receive medical attention.

REACTIVITY DATA

Stability—Stable

Compatibility—Cargo: Group 31 of compatibility chart.

SPILL OR LEAK PROCEDURE

Wear rubber gloves, face shield, protective clothing. Have all-purpose canister mask available. Secure all possible
sources of ignition and call the fire department. The spilled liquid will boil away rapidly, leaving no residue.

If a spill occurs, call the National Response Center 800-424-8802.

Remarks: NOTE! Exposure to potentially dangerous vapor concentrations can occur before the product can be detected
by smell.

PROPYLENE

Synonyms —Methylethylene, propene

United Nations Number. 1077
CHRIS Code . . . . PPL

Formula—$CH_3CH : CH_2$

Boiling Point. . . . . −48°C   −53.8°F
Freezing Point . . . . −185°C   −301°F

Appearance-Odor —Colorless gas, liquid under pressure;
characteristic olefin (gassy) odor
Specific Gravity –0.52

Vapor Pressure 20°C (68°F) (mmHg) 7840
Reid Vapor Pressure (psia). 227.2
Vapor Pressure 46°C (115°F) (psia). 273.0

Chemical·Family—Olefin

Vapor Density (Air = 1.0). 1.48

Applicable Bulk Regulations 46 CFR. Subchapter   D

Solubility in Water. . . . . . 45 ml gas/100 ml water

FIRE & EXPLOSION HAZARD DATA

Grade—Liquefied Flammable Gas (LFG)
Electrical Group—D

General—As with all gas fires, the only effective method of extinguishing is to shut off the fuel supply. Otherwise a more
dangerous situation, the formation of an explosive mixture can result.
Flash Point (°F). . . . .   −162
Flammable Limits . . . .   2.0 - 11.0%
Autoignition Temp. (°F).   927
Extinguishing Agents. . . . .   Stop flow of gas; water fog
Special Fire Procedures . . . . . .   Tanks exposed to fire should be kept cool with a water spray.

HEALTH HAZARD DATA

Health Hazard Ratings   Odor Threshold (ppm)   TLV (ppm)
0,0,1   Unavailable   400

General—Absence of adequate warning indications such as strong odor or pronounced irritation of mucous membranes
of eyes and nose introduces possibility of exposure to concentrations productive of acute effects.

Symptoms—Dizziness, sleepiness

*Short Exposure Tolerance—Mixture of 6.4% propylene and 26% oxygen inhaled for 2¼ minutes produces mild intoxication,
drowsiness, tingling of the skin, and inability to concentrate.

Exposure Procedures—Remove victim to fresh air. Apply artificial respiration if breathing stops. Contact with liquid may
cause frostbite. Get medical attention.

REACTIVITY DATA

Stability—Stable at ordinary temperatures.

Compatibility—Materials: Noncorrosive, normal materials of construction may be used.

Cargo: Group 30 of compatibility chart.

SPILL OR LEAK PROCEDURE

Have all-purpose canister mask available. Shut off ignition sources. Call the fire department.
If product does not catch fire, it will soon boil off.

If a spill occurs, call the National Response Center 800-424-8802.

Remarks:

SODIUM HYDROSULFIDE
(45% Solution)

Synonyms—Sodium acid sulfide, sodium bisulfide

United Nations Number. . . . . Unassigned
CHRIS Code . . . . SHS

Formula—NaHS/Na$_2$S/H$_2$O

Appearance-Odor—Dark amber liquid with a rotten egg odor

Specific Gravity—1.26 to 1.28

Chemical Family—Caustics

Applicable Bulk Regulations 46 CFR Subchapter ___O___

Boiling Point. . . . approx. __140__ ^{0}C __284__ ^{0}F
Freezing Point . . . . __40__ ^{0}C __105__ ^{0}F

Vapor Pressure 20^{0}C (68^{0}F) (mmHg) __17.3__
Reid Vapor Pressure (psia). . . . . __0.95__
Vapor Pressure 46^{0}C (115^{0}F) (psia) . __1.51__
Vapor Density (Air = 1.0). . . . . __1.17__
Solubility in Water. . . . . . . _____ Complete

FIRE & EXPLOSION HAZARD DATA

Grade – C: Flammable liquid
Electrical Group—Unassigned

General—Moderate fire hazard due to hydrogen sulfide gas liberated when exposed to heat or flame.

Flash Point (^{0}F).   73
Flammable Limits . . . .   4.3 to 45.5%
Autoignition Temp. (^{0}F). . . . .   Unavailable
Extinguishing Agents. . . . .   Carbon dioxide
Special Fire Procedures . . . . . .   Unavailable

HEALTH HAZARD DATA

Health Hazard Ratings	Odor Threshold (ppm)	TLV (ppm)
Unavailable	Unavailable	Unavailable

General—Poisonous hydrogen sulfide may be evolved; this evolution increases with temperature. Solution itself is a skin irritant.

Symptoms—Rapid or irregular breathing, coughing, throat irritation, bluish color, dizziness, faintness, and weak irregular pulse. Skin contact will cause a caustic type burn.

*Short Exposure Tolerance—Unavailable

Exposure Procedures—Vapor—remove victim to fresh air. 100% oxygen inhalation is recommended. Skin—flush area with water. Eyes—flush with copious amounts of water. In all cases call a doctor.

REACTIVITY DATA

Stability –Stable. Solution is mildly alkaline.

Compatibility—Materials: Corrosive to steel above 150^{0}F. Avoid use of aluminum.
Cargo: Group 5 of compatibility chart.

SPILL OR LEAK PROCEDURE

Wear rubber gloves, boots, and goggles, and full skin protection. Avoid contact with liquid.

Is a spill occurs, call the National Response Center 800-424-8802.

Remarks:

STYRENE MONOMER (INHIBITED)

Synonyms—Cinnamine, cinnamol, phenylethylene, styrolene, styrol, vinyl benzene

United Nations Number. 2055

CHRIS Code . . . . STY

Formula—$C_6H_5CHCH_2$

Boiling Point. . . . . 145 °C   293 °F
Freezing Point . . . . −30 °C   −23 °F

Appearance-Odor—Colorless liquid; sweet odor when pure; sharp disagreeable odor when impure

Specific Gravity—0.92

Chemical Family—Monomer

Applicable Bulk Regulations 46 CFR Subchapter ___O___

Vapor Pressure 20°C (68°F) (mmHg) 6.0
Reid Vapor Pressure (psia). 0.27
Vapor Pressure 46°C (115°F) (psia). 0.4
Vapor Density (Air = 1.0). 3.6
Solubility in Water. . . . . . . _____ Negligible

FIRE & EXPLOSION HAZARD DATA

Grade—D: Combustible liquid
Electrical Group—D

General—Ignited by heat and open flame. Fire or contamination may cause violent rupture of tank.

Flash Point (°F).   100
Flammable Limits . . . .   1.1 - 6.1%
Autoignition Temp. (°F).   914
Extinguishing Agents. . . . . CO_2, dry chemical, water fog, foam
Special Fire Procedures . . . . . .   Provide body and respiratory protection for firefighting personnel. Tanks exposed to fire should be kept cool with a water spray.

HEALTH HAZARD DATA

Health Hazard Ratings	Odor Threshold (ppm)	TLV (ppm)
2,2,2	0.15	100

General—Vapor very irritating to eyes, moderately irritating to respiratory tract with moderate systemic effect. Liquid irritating to skin.

Symptoms—Weakness, dizziness, nausea, and sleepiness.

*Short Exposure Tolerance—10,000 ppm may be fatal in 30 to 60 minutes.

Exposure Procedures—Vapors—remove victim to fresh air; if breathing stops, apply artificial respiration. Skin or eye contact—remove contaminated clothing and gently flush affected areas with water for 15 minutes. Soap, if available, should be used on affected skin areas. Get medical attention.

REACTIVITY DATA

Stability —Will readily form peroxides which catalyze polymerization unless inhibited. Heat, light and strong acids also catalyze polymerization reaction.*

Compatibility —Material: Most materials of construction are suitable. Do not use copper or its alloys. Styrene can be polymerized at explosive rates by certain contaminants.

Cargo: Group 30 of compatibility chart.

SPILL OR LEAK PROCEDURE

Wear rubber gloves, face shield, protective clothing. Have all-purpose canister mask available. Avoid contact with liquid. Secure ignition sources.

If a spill occurs, call the National Response Center 800-424-8802.

Remarks.   *Even the inhibited product, when heated above 125°F, can polymerize with the generation of so much heat that ignition is possible.

TOLUENE

Synonyms—Methyl benzene, phenylmethane, toluol

Formula—$C_6H_5CH_3$

Appearance-Odor —Colorless liquid; benzene-like odor

Specific Gravity—0.87

Chemical Family—Aromatic hydrocarbon

Applicable Bulk Regulations 46 CFR Subchapter ___D___

United Nations Number	1294	
CHRIS Code	TOL	
Boiling Point	111 °C	231 °F
Freezing Point	-95 °C	-139 °F
Vapor Pressure 20°C (68° F) (mmHg)	28 (at 25°C)	
Reid Vapor Pressure (psia)	1.1	
Vapor Pressure 46°C (115° F) (psia)	1.5	
Vapor Density (Air = 1.0)	3.14	
Solubility in Water	Negligible	

FIRE & EXPLOSION HAZARD DATA

Grade—C: Flammable liquid
Electrical Group—D

General—Dangerous fire hazard when exposed to heat or flame; moderate explosion hazard when exposed to flame.

Flash Point (°F)   45
Flammable Limits . . . .   1.27 - 7.0%
Autoignition Temp. (°F)   1026
Extinguishing Agents . . . . CO_2, dry chemical, foam, water fog
Special Fire Procedures . . . . . .   Fight the same as a petroleum fire. The vapors are more toxic than those of petroleum and should be avoided. A fire should be fought in the same manner as any Grade C flammable petroleum product.

HEALTH HAZARD DATA

Health Hazard Ratings	Odor Threshold (ppm)	TLV (ppm)
1,1,2	0.17	100

General—Liquid slightly irritating. Vapor inhalation has moderate narcotic effect causing dizziness and headache, with severe fatigue and mental confusion.

Symptoms—Nausea, dizziness and headache. The victim may appear to be drunk

*Short Exposure Tolerance—Inhalation of 600 ppm for 30 minutes has caused severe fatigue, mental confusion, nausea, dizziness and headache.

Exposure Procedures —Ingestion—do NOT induce vomiting. Vapor—remove victim to fresh air; if breathing stops, apply artificial respiration. Skin or eye contact—remove contaminated clothing and gently flush affected areas with water for 15 minutes. Get medical advice or attention.

REACTIVITY DATA

Stability—Toluene is a stable compound.

Compatibility—Material: Rubber exposed to toluene will swell, soften, and deteriorate. Most metals are compatible with toluene.

Cargo: Group 32 of compatibility chart.

SPILL OR LEAK PROCEDURE

Wear plastic gloves, face shield, protective clothing. Have all-purpose canister mask available. Avoid contact with liquid. Secure ignition sources.

If a spill occurs, call the National Response Center 800-424-8802.

Remarks:

VINYL ACETATE (Inhibited)

Synonyms—VAM

United Nations Number. 1301
CHRIS Code . . . . VAM

Formula—$CH_3COOCH:CH_2$

Boiling Point. . . . . 73°C   163°F
Freezing Point . . . . −100°C −148°F

Appearance-Odor —Colorless liquid; sweet odor

Vapor Pressure 20°C (68°F) (mmHg) 90

Specific Gravity—0.94

Reid Vapor Pressure (psia). 3.7
Vapor Pressure 46°C (115°F) (psia). 5.8

Chemical Family—Monomer

Vapor Density (Air = 1.0). 2.97

Applicable Bulk Regulations 46 CFR Subchapter   O

Solubility in Water. 2%

FIRE & EXPLOSION HAZARD DATA

Grade—C: Flammable liquid
Electrical Group—D

General—On being heated, acrid vapors are given off. Ignited by heat, sparks or open flame. Fire may cause violent rupture of tank.

Flash Point (°F).   18
Flammable Limits . . . .   2.6 - 13.4%
Autoignition Temp. (°F).   801
Extinguishing Agents. . . . . CO_2, dry chemical, alcohol foam, water spray.
Special Fire Procedures . . . . . .   If fire parties must work in confined quarters, provide respiratory protection. Keep
  tank cool with a water spray.

HEALTH HAZARD DATA

Health Hazard Ratings	Odor Threshold (ppm)	TLV (ppm)
1,1,2	0.12	10

General—Liquid irritating to skin and eyes. Vapor inhalation causes slight narcotic effect.

Symptoms—Dizziness, drowsiness.

*Short Exposure Tolerance—Unavailable

Exposure Procedures—Vapor—remove victim to fresh air; if breathing stops, apply artificial respiration. Skin or eye contact—remove contaminated clothing and gently flush affected areas with water for 15 minutes. Get medical advice or attention.

REACTIVITY DATA

Stability—Polymerizes readily if not inhibited. Heat can start the reaction. Can react vigorously with oxidizing materials.

Compatibility—Material: Most of the usual materials of construction are suitable.

  Cargo: Group 13 of compatibility chart.

SPILL OR LEAK PROCEDURE

Wear rubber gloves, face shield, protective clothing. Have all-purpose canister mask available. Avoid contact with liquid. Secure ignition sources. Flush area with water spray.

If a spill occurs, call the National Response Center 800-424-8802.

Remarks:

VINYL CHLORIDE

Synonyms—Chloroethene, chloroethylene, VCL, VCM

Formula—CH$_2$CHCl

Appearance-Odor —Colorless liquid or gas; sweet odor

Specific Gravity—0.91

Chemical Family—Monomer

Applicable Bulk Regulations 46 CFR Subchapter ___O___

United Nations Number	1086	
CHRIS Code	VCM	
Boiling Point	−14 °C	7 °F
Freezing Point	154 °C	−245 °F
Vapor Pressure 20°C (68°F) (mmHg)	2580	
Reid Vapor Pressure (psia)	75	
Vapor Pressure 46°C (115°F) (psia)	95	
Vapor Density (Air = 1.0)	2.15	
Solubility in Water	Slight	

FIRE & EXPLOSION HAZARD DATA

Grade—Liquefied Flammable Gas (LFG)
Electrical Group—D

General — Dangerous fire hazard. Unless the flow of gas can be stopped, putting out a vinyl chloride fire will permit accumulation of an explosive vapor concentration with increased danger of reflash.

Flash Point (°F) . . . .   −108
Flammable Limits . . . .   3.6 - 33%
Autoignition Temp. (°F)   882
Extinguishing Agents . . . .   Stop flow of gas. CO$_2$, dry chemical, water fog
Special Fire Procedures . . . . . .   Cool tank with water spray. Heat decomposes vinyl chloride to form highly toxic phosgene gas. Heat can also cause vinyl chloride to polymerize with explosive force. Provide respiratory protection for fire-fighting personnel.

HEALTH HAZARD DATA

Health Hazard Ratings	Odor Threshold (ppm)	TLV (ppm)
2,1,2	260*	1

General—Vapor harmful. Liquid or cold gas may cause skin or eye injury similar to frostbite.

Symptoms—Dizziness and drowsiness. Frostbitten areas will look white.

*Short Exposure Tolerance—500 ppm for 5 minutes.

Exposure Procedures—Remove victim to fresh air. If breathing stops, apply artificial respiration. Do not rub frostbitten areas. In case of eye contact, flood eye gently with water for 15 minutes. Get medical attention.

REACTIVITY DATA

Stability—Polymerizes in presence of air, sunlight or heat.

Compatibility—Material: Steel is satisfactory. However, contact with copper or other acetylide-forming metals may form explosive compounds.

Cargo. Group 35 of compatibility chart.

SPILL OR LEAK PROCEDURE

Wear rubber gloves, self-contained breathing apparatus, protective clothing. Avoid contact with liquid. Secure ignition sources.

If a spill occurs, call the National Response Center 800-424-8802.

Remarks: *Odor threshold is not considered adequate warning to prevent exposure to possibly dangerous vapor concentrations.

— APPENDIX K —
SAMPLE ACCIDENT MANAGEMENT DECISION SCENARIO

1. INTRODUCTION

This appendix provides an example of an acciden management decision scenario prepared for the assessment of and recovery from a highway transportation accident involving the spill of a hazardous material. This scenario in its entirety is given in Chapter 3 to the Titan II Propellant Hazard Management Guide, 26 March 1982, Ogden Air Logistics Center pamphlet OO-ALCP 144-4. The complete scenario presents assumptions regarding availability and proper maintenance of equipment and gear needed when responding to a highway mishap involving an Aerozine-50 transport trailer/holding trailer. Alternate response actions are given for those situations which are extremely dangerous or present requirements beyond the limited availability of resources on-scene such as analytical and heavy equipment, neutralizing agents, personal protective clothing, etc. For purposes of this example accident management decision scenario two alternate actions are provided. For a complete listing of all alternate actions refer to Pamphlet OO-ALCP 144-4.

DECISION MATRIX 1 - ALTERNATE ACTION 1.0
SITUATION ASSESSMENT AND REACTION PLANNING

Condition	Actions/Considerations

Air Force involvement.

NOTE: The actions and considerations are given as guidance in assessing the seriousness of an mishap situation and for planning appropriate actions. A judgment of the hazards or potential hazards must be made on the situation.

1. Implement disaster reaction plan/responses based on the mishap situation. Specific requirements as well as reminders of potential needs are detailed below. This listing is not all-inclusive and each respective base OPLAN should be consulted.

2. Request backup resources if appropriate.

   a. Back-up PTS crew.
   b. Back-up firefighting and cooling water.
   c. Spill containment equipment, personnel, and techniques.
   d. Spill treatment materials, equipment, personnel, and techniques.
   e. Trailers or trucks for fuel transfer.

3. Identify additional resources which may be required.

   a. Emergency medical aid and/or facilities.
   b. Firefighting assistance: military, local civilian, government.
   c. Emergency response service agencies.
   d. Clean-up and disposal contractors.
   e. Potential disposal sites.

4. Notify environmental authorities, National Response Center as well as state and local authorities.

5. Estimate the fuel tank hole size then estimate and record fuel leak rate from Figures K-1a and K-1b _____ gpm.

NOTE: When hazardous conditions preclude direct reading of tank pressure gauges, assume worst case pressure values of 125 psig for transport trailer and 50 psig for holding trailer. Pressure relief valves will limit pressures to these values.

6. From Figure K-2 and Table K-1 estimate the water requirements for the three dilution ratios:

   a. Total water required for: reduction of flammable vapors (3:1) __ gallons.

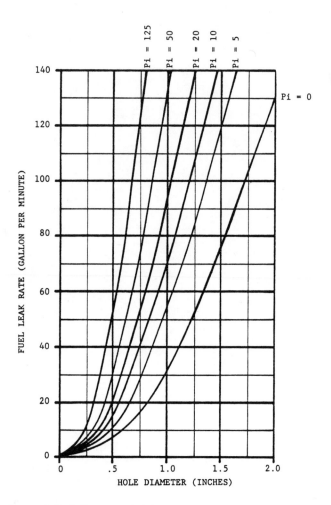

Pi = Internal Tank Pressure (psig)

FIGURE K-1a.   FUEL LEAK RATE VERSUS HOLE DIAMETER

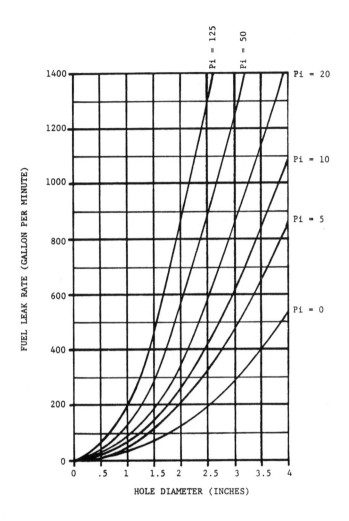

Pi = Internal Tank Pressure (psig)

FIGURE K-1b.   FUEL LEAK RATE VERSUS HOLE DIAMETER

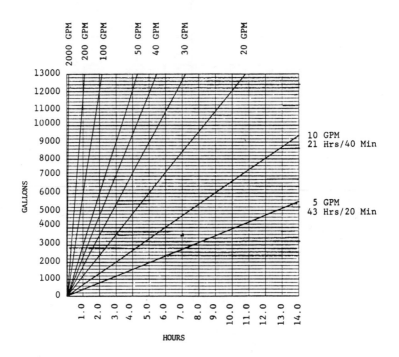

FIGURE K-2.   TANK CAPACITY DRAIN TIME AT VARIOUS FLOW RATES

TABLE K-1. FUEL AND DILUTED FUEL SPILL SIZE

Fuel Volume (Gallons)	Spill Size (Sq. Ft. per inch of Depth)	Total Spill Size With Dilution (Sq. Ft. per inch of Depth)	
		3:1	20:1
10	20	80	580
20	30	120	870
30	50	200	1,450
40	60	240	1,740
50	80	320	2,320
60	100	400	2,900
70	110	440	3,190
80	130	520	3,770
90	140	560	4,060
100	160	640	4,640
200	320	1,280	9,280
300	480	1,920	13,920
400	640	2,560	18,560
500	800	3,200	23,200
600	960	3,840	27,840
700	1,120	4,480	32,480
800	1,280	5,120	37,120
900	1,440	5,760	41,760
1,000	1,600	6,400	46,400
1,500	2,410	9,640	69,600
2,000	3,210	12,840	93,090
2,500	4,010	16,040	116,290
3,000	4,810	19,240	139,490
3,500	5,620	22,480	162,980
4,000	6,420	25,680	186,180
4,500	7,220	28,880	209,380
5,000	8,020	32,080	232,610

DECISION MATRIX 1 - ALTERNATE ACTION 1.0
SITUATION ASSESSMENT AND REACTION PLANNING (cont'd)

Condition	Actions/Considerations

Air Force involvement.

b.   Water required for dilution prior to neutralization (20:1) _____ gallons.

7.   Determine the total water rate available (pumper capacity) _____ gpm.

NOTE: At least 500 gpm of water may be available from a hydrant. Using another water source with a pump and a two-inch line would provide about 100 gpm.

8.   Estimate spill size with dilution for disposal purposes.

9.   Continue in decision matrix with continuous monitoring.

DECISION MATRIX 1 - ALTERNATE ACTION 1.0a
RISK ASSESSMENT
SITUATION ASSESSMENT AND REACTION PLANNING

Hazard	Assessment
Mishap.	1. In an mishap situation there may be insufficient information, materials, or equipment for an optimum reaction. There is a need for plans which give guidance on a broad range of mishap situations so that rational decisions can be made under emergency conditions. Since a mishap situation is dynamic, additional resources (materials, equipment, and personnel) should be anticipated and requested at the on-set of an mishap.
	2. Consideration should be given to safeguard civilian population, environment, property and other resources. These considerations may affect mitigating activities as well as treatment, cleanup and disposal needs.

DECISION MATRIX 1 - ALTERNATE ACTION 2.0
WATER NOT AVAILABLE OR INSUFFICIENT QUANTITY

Condition	Actions/Considerations

No water immediately available
or insufficient quantity

1. Immediately notify local/base fire
    department of situation.

WARNING

Do not approach mishap site without
sufficient water. With no water
immediately available, fuel vapors are
extremely hazardous to response
personnel. Any concentrations are toxic
by inhalation and skin absorption. High
concentrations are very explosive.

2. Remove all ignition sources.

NOTE: If some water is available apply fog
spray to tanker/trailer for cooling and to
suppress vapors.

3. Locate water source:

    a. Local hydrant
    b. River/stream
    c. Lake/pond
    d. Farm holding tanks
    e. Wells
    f. Swimming pools

4. Identify additional equipment needed to
    utilize water sources, pumps, hoses, fog
    nozzles.

5. Obtain water and monitor usage before
    proceeding.

6. Monitor water usage and go to Alternate
    Action 1.0, Formulate Reaction Plan.

DECISION MATRIX 1 - ALTERNATE ACTION 2.0
RISK ASSESSMENT
WATER NOT AVAILABLE OR INSUFFICIENT QUANTITY

Hazard	Assessment
No water immediately available or insufficient quantity.	1. With no water immediately available, high fuel vapor concentrations pose extreme problems to response personnel. The vapors are flammable and toxic by inhalation and skin absorption.
	2. The fuel is highly flammable and can easily be ignited by iron rust particles or any contaminant.
	3. Adequate water backup supplies are essential for vapor suppression which is of primary concern where response personnel are engaged in fuel spill, leak or fire situations.

— APPENDIX L —
TYPICAL EQUIPMENT AVAILABLE FOR OIL AND
HAZARDOUS MATERIAL SPILLS CONTAINMENT AND CLEANUP

VACUUM UNITS & ACCESSORIES
: 3500-Gallon Vacuum Inductor
Pump Trucks with Radio Equipment
1800-Gallon Vacuum Inductor Pump
Trucks with Radio Equipment
1500-Gallon Vacuum Skid Mounted Units
1500-Gallon Vacuum Skid Mounted Units with Steam
    Coils
1000-Gallon Vacuum Skid Mounted Units
Suction Hoses - 1 1/2", 2", 3", 4", 5", 6"
Manta Ray Skimmer Heads

OIL CONTAINMENT BOOM
: Booms - 4", & 6" with Trailers
Jon Boats with Motors - 14', 17'

BOATS
: Work Boats with Motors - 18', 20'
Ponton Boats - 30'

PORTABLE LIGHTING
: Generators - 1.5 KW, 3 KW, 5 KW, 10 KW, 12 KW,
    15 KW, 25 KW, 50 KW, 75 KW, 150 KW

TRUCKS
: Low Boys
Tractors and Box Trailers
Stake Trucks
Pollution Control Equipment Trucks
Tandem Dump Trucks
Transfer Vans
Equipment Vans
Tankers - 6,000-Gallon
Four-Wheel-Drive Vehicles "Radio Equipped"

HEAVY EQUIPMENT & TRAILERS
: Portable Welders
Front End Loaders, Tracks & Rubber Tires
Backhoes, Tracks & Rubber Tires
Dozers - 1 with Swamp Pads
Mobile Office Trailers
Crew Trailers with Galley & Sleeping Quarters
Portable Lab Trailers
Transfer Trailers

PUMPS
: High Pressure Wash Down Pump - 1 1/2"
Diesel Trash Pumps - 3", 4", 6"
Electric Trash Pumps - 2", 3"
Diaphragm Diesels - 3"
Gas Trash Pumps - 2", 3", 4"
Specialty Chemical Pumps

AUXILIARY PERSONNEL & EQUIPMENT
: Civil Engineers
Chemical Engineers
Chemists
Geologists
Disposal Facilities
Sorbent Materials - Complete Stock
Storatainers (Portable Storage Tanks)
Weed-Eaters
Communication Network - Base Stations,
Hand Held Units, Truck Mounted Units

AIRLIFT CAPABILITIES
: Cessna 310'S
Seneca II's
Navajo Chieftans
Grumman Mallards
Helicopters
Jet Service

PERSONNEL PROTECTION	Protective Clothing Acid Suits Chemical/Gas Suits Cooling Systems-Heat Exchangers Fire Entry Suits
BREATHING EQUIPMENT	Breathing Apparatuses Regulated Manifold Air Supply Systems Assorted Cannister Masks and Cartridges
TRANSFER	Chemical Handling Pumps, Hoses and Equipment Accessories Transfer Compressors with Dryers (Hydraulically Operated) Portable Steamers (up to 1,000,000 B.T.U.) Transfer Trucks and Trailers

LABORATORY
& MONITORING
EQUIPMENT
	Portable Field Labs
	Fixed Analytical Capabilities
	Explosion Meters (Combustible Gas/Oxygen
	   Monitoring Systems)
	pH Meters
	Air Sampling/Detection Equipment
	Spectrophotometers
	Computerized Gas Chromatographs
	   (Portable/Stationary)
	Field Laboratory Trailers
	Core Boring Equipment (Soil Sampling)

PORTABLE TREATMENT EQUIPMENT & SERVICES	Mobile Activated Carbon Filtration System Vertical Carbon Column Aeration and Retention Pools Flash Mixing and Flocculation Systems Groundwater Recovery Systems - Hydrostatic Injection Systems - Pneumatic Recovery Systems Mass Media Filters Ion Exchange Resin Systems In Situ Treatments (Biological and Chemical) Neutralizing Chemicals
ADDITIONAL EQUIPMENT	Explosion Proof Lighting Non Sparking Tools - Aluminum Bronze/Beryllium Copper Tank Patching Kits Power Entry Tools Air Blowers

GLOSSARY

AMBIENT CONDITIONS: Temperature and atmospheric pressure conditions of the surrounding environment. Reference point is 59°F and 14.7 psi (15°C and 760 mm Hg).

ANHYDROUS: Containing no water. Relative quantitative measure of water in a chemical compound below a certain limit.

BOILING POINT: The temperature at which the vapor pressure of the liquid equals atmospheric pressure. (Normal boiling point 760 mm or 14.7 psia.) Where an accurate normal boiling point is unavailable such as a hydrocarbon mixture (P-1, JP-fuels), the 10 percent point of a distillation performed in accordance with ASTM-D-86-62 may be used as the boiling point of the liquid.

BREACH: Puncture, tear, hole or rupture in a vessel that allows the contents to be released.

COMBUSTIBLE LIQUID: Any liquid that does not meet the definition of any other classification specified in 49 CFR section 173.115 and has a flash point at or above 100°F (37.8°C) and below 200°F (93.3°C) except any mixture having one component or more with a flash point at 200°F (93.3°C) or higher, that makes up at least 99 percent of the total volume of the mixture.

COMBUSTIBLE MATERIAL: A substance which will burn.

COMPATIBLE MATERIAL: Having no undesirable reaction or physical effect with or upon another material.

COMPRESSED GAS: Any material or mixture having in the container a pressure exceeding 40 psi absolute at 70°F (27.6 N/cm² at 21°C) or, regardless of the pressure at 70°F (21°C), having a pressure exceeding 104 psi absolute at 130°F (5,377 N/cm² at 54°C); or any liquid flammable material having a vapor pressure exceeding 40 psi absolute at 100°F (27.6 N/cm² at 38°C) as determined by ASTM Test D-323.

CONTAINER: Any vessel used to contain hazardous materials for transportation (e.g., tank car, tank truck, cylinder, drum, etc.).

CRITICAL PRESSURE: The pressure required to liquefy a gas at its critical temperature.

CRITICAL TEMPERATURE: The maximum temperature at which a gas can be liquefied. Above the critical temperature point the substance will remain in the gaseous state regardless of the pressure applied.

CRYOGENIC LIQUID: Any substance which must be cooled to a temperature of -238°F (-150°C) or lower in order to effect a change from gas to liquid.

DECONTAMINATING AGENT: An agent having a desirable controlled reaction rate or solvent action which is used to purge materials, components, systems or areas of residues or contaminants.

DEFLAGRATION: A rapid chemical reaction in which the rate of energy released causes the resulting pressure wave in the confinement of the reacting material prevents the release of pressure, deflagration may progress to a detonation where the pressure wave travels at supersonic velocity.

DENSITY: The ratio of mass to volume of a substance.

DETONATION: A chemical reaction in which the rate of energy released causes the resulting pressure wave in the surrounding medium to travel at supersonic velocities.

DIKE: An earth or concrete barrier surrounding a propellant tank and intended to contain a spill.

DUNNAGE: Pallets and spacers used in shipping, storage, and handling; frequently made of wood, although metal is preferred.

EMERGENCY-EXPOSURE LEVEL (EEL): The maximum concentration of a toxic gas which a normal person can endure for a specific period without lasting physiological effects. See pamphlet titled "Basis for Establishing Emergency Inhalation Exposure Limits Applicable to Military and Space Chemicals," 1964 Ed., Advisory Center on Toxicology, NAS/NRC, Publications Office, Washington, D.C. 20418, for a complete definition and the philosophy of hazards management.

EVAPORATION RATE: The ratio of the time required to evaporate a measured volume of one volatile material to the time required to evaporate the same volume of a reference solvent under identical test conditions (usually ethyl ether).

EXPLOSION: The sudden release of energy usually in the form of large volumes of gas which exert pressure on the surrounding medium. Depending on the rate at which energy is released, an explosion can be categorized as a deflagration, a detonation, or a rupture of a pressure vessel.

EXPLOSIVE LIMITS: The upper and lower limits of the vapor concentration of a material that will explode when ignited with an external energy source.

FIRE POINT (IGNITION TEMPERATURE): The lowest temperature at which a flame is continuously supported over a liquid surface upon exposure to an open flame.

FIREPROOF: Materials which will not burn when exposed to propellants or will not continue to burn after removal from contact with a hot flame ignition source.

FIRE RESISTANT: Materials which will resist burning when contacted by fuels or oxidizers, but after continuous contact and exposure to an ignition source, will eventually burn slowly.

FLAMMABLE: Materials which are easily ignited in air, oxygen, or other supporting atmosphere.

FLAMMABLE LIMITS: The upper and lower vapor concentration of fuel to air which will ignite in the presence of external ignition sources; often also referred to as the explosive range. Flammable limits in atmospheres other than air are also identified.

FLAMMABLE LIQUID: Any liquid having a flash point below 100°F (37.8°C), with the following exceptions: any mixture having one component or more with a flash point of 100°F (37.8°) or higher, that makes up at least 99 percent of the total volume of the mixture; or any liquid meeting one of the definitions specified in 49 CFR Section 173.300.

FLARE TYPE COMBUSTION: The combustion of a fuel and oxizider mixture as distinguished from combustion of only the fuel in air.

FLASH POINT: The lowest temperature at which a liquid surface may be momentarily ignited by open flame. It may be determined in either of two types of apparatus: "closed cup" where the fuel surface is enclosed, or "open cup" where the fuel surface is exposed to open air. Open cup flash points are higher than closed cup flash points. The open cup flash point values are usually followed by the letters "OC" to differentiate from closed cup values.

GALVANIC CORROSION: Corrosion due to an electrical current action on two dissimilar metals in the presence of an electrolyte.

HAZARD: A situation which may result in death or injury to personnel, or in damage to property. Includes effect of fire, flash, explosion, shock, concussion, fragmentation, corrosion and toxicity.

HYGROSCOPIC: The property of readily absorbing moisture from the atmosphere.

HYPERGOLIC MIXTURE: Instantaneous self-ignition of certain fuels and oxidizers upon contact with each other.

IGNITION TEMPERATURE: The lowest temperature at which combustion can be supported continuously on exposure to any ignition source.

INERT: Material which does not contain explosives, active chemicals or pyrotechnics, i.e., nonreactive as helium or nitrogen gas with a specified propellant.

IMPINGEMENT: An external source of fire that is applying heat and energy to the tanker. The tanker or its contents are not on fire.

LIQUEFIED GAS: Substance which is gaseous at room temperature and has been converted to a liquid under controlled pressure and temperature.

MISCIBLE: Liquids capable of being mixed.

OXIDIZER: A propellant, such as oxygen, nitric acid, fluorine, nitrogen tetroxide, and others which support combustion when in combination with a fuel.

PROTECTED: The term "protected" shall mean shock wave, spill, or fragment protection provided by terrain, effective barricades, net or other physical means to inhabited buildings within the hazardous area distances expected from the propellant facilities.

PYROPHORIC: Spontaneously ignitable in air.

RAILROAD: Any steam, electric, or other railway which carries passengers for hire or cargo in transport.

SOLVENT: That constituent of a solution which is present in a large amount.

SPECIFIC GRAVITY: The ratio of the mass of a given volume of liquid to the mass of an equal volume of water at a given temperature. At 75°F (24°C) the specific weight of water is 8.33 pounds per gallon (366 gm/cc).

THRESHOLD LIMIT VALUE: The average concentration of toxic gas to which most workers can be exposed during working hours (8 hours per day, 5 days a week) for prolonged periods without adversely affecting their health. (See also the complete definition "Threshold Limit Values for Chemical Substances and Physical Agents in the Work Environment" by the American Conference of Governmental Industrial Hygienists, 6500 Glenway Avenue, Building D-5, Cincinnati, Ohio 45211; (513) 661-7881).

TOXIC: Poisonous. A toxic material is one which will cause physiological damage to the human body. See Appendix A.

ULLAGE: The unfilled space in a tank or container, also known as "outage."

VAPOR VOLUME: The number of cubic feet of vapor at ambient temperature (say 75°F) which will be obtained by the evaporation of one gallon of solvent or toxic liquid. The number is useful for evaluation of the extent of a toxic exposure and is obtained by dividing the pounds per gallon by the molecular weight of the material and multiplying by 392 (to obtain the number of cubic feet for the number of pound-moles present).

ACRONYMS AND TERMS

AAR — Association of American Railroads

ADAPTS — Air Deliverable Antipollution Transfer System

AE — Acoustic Emission

AFCRL — Air Force Cambridge Research Laboratory

AFFF — Aqueous Film Forming Foam

AFRPL — Air Force Rocket Propulsion Laboratory

ASTM — American Society of Testing and Materials

BLEVE — Boiling Liquid Expanding Vapor Explosion

CAS — Chemical Abstract Service

CCC — Communications Command Center

CEQ — Council of Environmental Quality

CERCLA — Comprehensive Environmental Response Compensation and Liability Act

CFR — Code of Federal Regulations

CHEMTREC — Chemical Transportation Emergency Center

CHLOREP — Chlorine Emergency Plan

CHRIS — Chemical Hazards Response Information System

Cl_2 — Chlorine

CMA — Chemical Manufacturers Association

CO_2 — Carbon Dioxide

COTR — Contracting Officer's Technical Representative

CPU — Central Processing Unit

CWA — Clean Water Act

DDESB — Department of Defense Explosives Safety Board

DOC — Department of Commerce

DOD — Department of Defense

DOE — Department of Energy

DOI — Department of Interior

DOJ — Department of Justice

DOL — Department of Labor

DOS — Department of State

DOT — Department of Transportation

DTIC — Defense Technical Information Center

EMT — Emergency Medical Team

EO — Ethylene Oxide

EPA — Environmental Protection Agency

ER — Emergency Response

FEMA — Federal Emergency Management Agency

FRA — Federal Railroad Administration

GC/MS — Gas Chromotography/Mass Spectometry

HACS — Hazard Assessment Computer System

HM — Hazardous Materials

HZ — Hydrazine, Anhydrous

IATA — International Air Transport Association

ICGIH — International Conference Governmental Industrial Hygieniest

IR — Infrared

LEL — Lower Explosive Limit

LH_2 — Liquefied Hydrogen

LIDAR — Light Detection and Ranging

LNG — Liquefied Natural Gas

LO_2 — Liquefied Oxygen

LPG — Liquefied Petroleum Gas

MMH — Monomethylhydrazine

MSA — Mine Safety Appliances Co.

MTB	- Materials Transportation Bureau	OSC	- On-Scene Coordinator
NaOH	- Sodium Hydroxide	PEL	- Permissible Exposure Limit
NASA	- National Aeronautics and Space Administration	PPM	- Parts Per Million
		RCRA	- Resource Conservation and Recovery Act
NATES	- National Analysis of Trends in Emergency System	RRC	- Regional Response Center
N_2O_4	- Nitrogen Tetroxide (oxidizer)	RRT	- Regional Response Team
NDT	- Nondestructive Testing	SHELL R&D SPILLS	- Shell Vapor Dispersion Model
NEELS	- National Emergency Equipment Locator System	SOA	- State-of-the-Art
		SOP	- Standard Operating Procedure
NFPA	- National Fire Protection Association	SOSC	- State On-Scene Coordinator
NIOSH	- National Institute of Occupational Safety and Health	STCC	- Standard Transportation Commodity Code
		TEAP	- Transportation Emergency Assistance Plan
NO_2	- Nitrogen Dioxide		
NOAA	- National Oceanic and Atmospheric Administration	TLV	- Threshold Limit Value
		TNT	- Trinitrotoluene
NRC	- National Response Center		
NRT	- National Response Team	TTC	- Transportation Test Center
NTIS	- National Technical Information Service	UDMH	- Unsymmetrical Dimethylhydrazine
NTSB	- National Transportation Safety Board	UEL	- Upper Explosive Limit
		UN	- United Nations
OERR	- Office of Emergency and Remedial Response of EPA	USAF	- United States Air Force
OES	- Office of Emergency Services	USCG	- United States Coast Guard
OHMTADS	- Oil and Hazardous Materials Technical Assistance Data Systems	UV	- Ultraviolet
		VCM	- Vinyl Chloride Monomer

Other Noyes Publications

HAZARDOUS WASTE LEACHATE MANAGEMENT MANUAL

Alan J. Shuckrow   Andrew P. Pajak   C.J. Touhill

Touhill, Shuckrow and Associates, Inc.

Pollution Technology Review No. 92

This manual describes various management options available for controlling, treating and disposing of hazardous waste leachate. Leachate generated by water percolating through hazardous waste disposal sites could contain significant concentrations of toxic substances. Proper leachate management practices are essential in order to avoid contamination of surrounding soil, groundwater, and surface water.

There is little past experience in the area of hazardous waste leachate, therefore the manual draws heavily upon experience in related areas. Sufficient information is provided so that the user can readily identify potential treatment alternatives for a particular situation. Logical thought processes are developed for arriving at reasonable process trains for given leachates.

The manual starts with a discussion of factors influencing leachate generation, details leachate characteristics, and then identifies principal options for processing the leachates. Treatability data, by-product and cost information supplement processing descriptions. Other sections cover monitoring, safety, contingency plans and emergency provisions.

The condensed table of contents below lists **chapter titles and selected subtitles.**

ISBN 0-8155-0910-3 (1982)

379 pages

Other Noyes Publications

SPILL PREVENTION
AND FAIL-SAFE ENGINEERING
FOR PETROLEUM AND RELATED PRODUCTS

by

J.L. Goodier   **R.J. Siclari**   **P.A. Garrity**

Pacific Northwest Laboratory
Battelle Memorial Institute

Pollution Technology Review No. 100

Annual losses of petroleum and related products due to accidental spillage are tremendous. This spill prevention and fail-safe engineering manual was prepared to provide guideline information on spill prevention procedures for individuals who have the responsibility for maintaining a spill-free plant during the transportation, transfer, storage and processing of petroleum and related products.

An attempt has been made to cover every facet of spill prevention. Special emphasis is given to fail-safe engineering as an approach to preventing spills from the predominant cause—human failure. The book addresses state-of-the-art spill prevention practices and automation techniques that can reduce spills caused by human error. To emphasize the need for spill prevention measures, historic spills are briefly described, after which remedial action is defined in an appropriate section of the manual. The section on plant security goes into considerable depth, since few security guidelines have been provided for industrial facilities that transfer, store, and process petroleum and related products.

The condensed table of contents below lists **chapters and selected subtitles.**

ISBN 0-8155-0944-8(1983)

329 pages

REMEDIAL ACTION TECHNOLOGY FOR WASTE DISPOSAL SITES

by

P. Rogoshewski **H. Bryson** **K. Wagner**

JRB Associates, Inc.
for the U.S. Environmental Protection Agency

Pollution Technology Review No. 101

The remedial actions which can be applied to control, contain, treat, or remove contaminants from uncontrolled hazardous waste sites and the nature of contamination at waste disposal sites are described in this comprehensive handbook. Improper disposal of industrial, commercial, and municipal solid and hazardous wastes is one of the nation's most pressing environmental problems. The quantity of wastes generated and disposed of annually is tremendous and growing. Cases of improper waste management have resulted in contamination of local groundwater, surface water, land, air, and food and forage crops.

As a result of clean-up operations that have already been conducted, and in anticipation of site clean-up activities that will result from recent regulatory action, many technologies have and are being developed. Those technologies specifically designed for clean-up of waste disposal sites are called "remedial actions." Remedial actions include surface, groundwater, leachate and gas migration controls; direct treatment methods; techniques for contaminated water and sewer lines; and processes for contaminated sediment removal.

The book details available technologies and describes how they may be selected and applied for the clean-up of disposal sites, with particular emphasis on hazardous waste sites. Information on each remedial action includes a general description; applications; design, construction, and/or operating considerations; advantages and disadvantages; and installation and annual operating costs, with examples where possible. **Chapter titles and selected subtitles** are given below.

1. INTRODUCTION

2. APPLICATION OF REMEDIAL ACTIONS AT WASTE DISPOSAL SITES
Introduction
Environmental Contamination from Waste Disposal Sites
Selection of Remedial Action
Example Site

3. SURFACE CONTROLS
Surface Sealing
Grading
Revegetation
Surface Water Diversion and Collection

4. GROUNDWATER CONTROLS
Impermeable Barriers
Permeable Treatment Beds
Groundwater Pumping
Interceptor Trenches

5. LEACHATE COLLECTION AND TREATMENT
Subsurface Drains
Drainage Ditches
Liners
Leachate Treatment

6. GAS MIGRATION CONTROL
Pipe Vents
Trench Vents
Gas Barriers
Gas Collection Systems
Gas Treatment Systems
Gas Recovery

7. DIRECT WASTE TREATMENT METHODS
Excavation
Hydraulic Dredging
Land Disposal
Solidification
Encapsulation
In-Situ Treatment

8. CONTAMINATED WATER AND SEWER LINES
In-Situ Cleaning
Leak Detection and Repairs
Removal and Replacement
Costs
Monitoring

9. CONTAMINATED SEDIMENTS
Mechanical Dredging
Low-Turbidity Hydraulic Dredging
Dredge Spoil Management
Revegetation

APPENDIX A—Monitoring Systems
APPENDIX B—Wastewater Treatment Modules
APPENDIX C—Cost Indices

ISBN 0-8155-0947-2

500 pages

ACID RAIN INFORMATION BOOK
Second Edition

Edited by

David V. Bubenick
GCA/Technology Division

This second edition discusses the major aspects of the acid rain problem which exists today with much new information; it points out the areas of uncertainty and summarizes current and projected research by various government agencies and other concerned organizations. This edition is a revised and greatly enlarged version of the original *Acid Rain Information Book* published in 1982. The wealth of information published in the two years since the first edition was completed made this revision both necessary and desirable—in order to provide a more complete picture of the acid rain situation.

Several recently released studies place the responsibility for acid rain on one industrial source or another. This book does not intend to point a finger; rather it attempts to present, simply, acid rain information.

Acid rain, caused by the emission of sulfur and nitrogen oxides to the atmosphere and their subsequent transformation to sulfates and nitrates, is one of the most widely publicized and emotional environmental issues of the day. The potential consequences of increasingly widespread acid rain demand that this phenomenon be carefully evaluated.

The book is organized in a logical progression from sources of pollutants affecting acid rain formation to the atmospheric transport and transformation of these pollutants and finally to the deposition of acid rain, the effects of that deposition, monitoring and modeling procedures, and possible mitigative measures and regulatory options. This information is followed by a discussion of uncertainties in the understanding of acid rain and a description of current and proposed research.

A condensed table of contents listing **chapter titles and selected subtitles** is given below.

EXECUTIVE SUMMARY

1. INTRODUCTION
Acid Precipitation and Its Measurement
Discovery of the Phenomenon
Possible Effects
Federal Agency Interest and Involvement

Report Organization

2. SOURCES AFFECTING ACID RAIN FORMATION
Natural Sources
Anthropogenic Sources of SO_x and NO_x Emissions
Other Sources Affecting Acid Rain Information

3. ATMOSPHERIC TRANSPORT, TRANSFORMATIONS, AND DEPOSITION PROCESSES
Transport and Diffusion
Chemical Transformations During Transport
Neutralization of Acidity
Deposition Processes

4. MONITORING PROGRAMS AND RESULTS

5. REGIONAL TRANSPORT AND DEPOSITION MODELING
Event Simulation Models
Statistical Models
State-of-the-Art of Regional Modeling

6. ADVERSE AND BENEFICIAL EFFECTS OF ACID PRECIPITATION
Impacts of Acidic Precipitation on Aquatic Ecosystems
Impacts of Acidic Precipitation on Terrestrial Ecosystems
Effects of Acidic Precipitation on Animal and Human Health
Effects of Acidic Precipitation on Materials
Models to Determine Acceptable Loadings of Acidic Materials to the Ecosystem

7. REGULATORY ALTERNATIVES AND MITIGATIVE STRATEGIES

8. SUMMARY OF ISSUES, UNCERTAINTIES, AND FURTHER RESEARCH NEEDS

9. CURRENT AND PROPOSED RESEARCH ON ACID PRECIPITATION
Federal Research on Acid Precipitation
Non-Federal Research on Acid Precipitation

ISBN 0-8155-0967-7 (1984)

397 pages

Other Noyes Publications

COSTS OF REMEDIAL RESPONSE ACTIONS AT UNCONTROLLED HAZARDOUS WASTE SITES

by

H.L. Rishel   **T.M. Boston**   **C.J. Schmidt**

SCS Engineers

Pollution Technology Review No. 105

This book presents conceptual design cost estimates for remedial response actions at uncontrolled hazardous waste sites. Thirty-five unit operations, covering uncontrolled landfill or surface impoundment disposal sites, were costed in mid-1980 dollars for the Newark, New Jersey area; and upper and lower cost averages for the contiguous 48 states were also prepared.

The data in the book are based on a review of pertinent literature with subsequent conversion to a consistent computational framework such that costs of remedial response options can be readily compared.

Listed below is a condensed table of contents including **chapter titles and selected subtitles plus the 35 unit operations** covered in the book.

ISBN 0-8155-0969-3 (1984)

144 pages